Everyman's
Scientific Facts and Feats

Everyman's Scientific Facts and Feats

Magnus Pyke
Patrick Moore

J M Dent & Sons Ltd
London Melbourne Toronto

First published 1981
© Magnus Pyke and Patrick Moore 1981

This book is set in $11/13\frac{1}{2}$ Lasercomp Plantin
and printed in Great Britain at the Alden Press, Oxford
for J M Dent & Sons Ltd
Aldine House, 33 Welbeck Street, London W1M 8LX

British Library Cataloguing in Publication Data

Pyke, Magnus
    Everyman's scientific facts and feats.
    1. Science
    I. Title   II. Moore, Patrick
    500   Q158.5

ISBN 0-460-04540-7

Contents

Introduction by Magnus Pyke

Science affects almost all the things we do and the objects we use. The electric light, the telephone, the radio and the TV, all of which we use without thinking, have only become possible because of scientific discoveries made in a modern age that is only the twinkling of an eye in historical terms. Some of them, indeed, have only existed since I was a boy.

But science is also a way of thinking. Our ancestors were just as clever as we are but the way they thought about the things around them was different. It is interesting to know how they viewed chemistry and medicine, and what they thought about time, space and electricity, if only to see why it was they made so little progress so slowly and why we had to wait through the centuries of history for our own times before anyone could enjoy the benefit of nylon, or be safe from smallpox. Before our own times – that is before scientific thinking had reached its present state – nobody could possess a 'polaroid' camera, a quartz-crystal watch or a refrigerator, there were no communications satellites guiding jet aircraft making non-stop journeys from Los Angeles to London. The step-by-step advances of early scientists are worth studying if only to try to understand what kind of talent it is that enables a particular scientist here or another one there to make the intellectual leap that changes our understanding and gives us benefits never enjoyed before.

There are three good reasons why it is important to know the kinds of things which Patrick Moore and I have tried to describe in this book. Firstly, the information is useful. In a scientific world, it is important to understand what lies behind the processes by which silicon chips are assembled, chemical factories operated and photographic film made to produce a picture before one's very eyes – and in colour, too. The second reason is that it is delightful to know. The mechanism of the universe is as elegant and seemly as a lovely poem. There is a special kind of joy in finding that a complex biochemical mechanism, comprehensible only by the most advanced laboratory techniques, provides the knowledge to save a diabetic child who would otherwise have died. But it is just as satisfying to record the tremors of a vibration that comes to us from within a moment of the formation of the universe, 16,000,000,000 years ago.

The third reason why it is important for Everyman to know scientific facts and the feats they have made possible is that it allows us to give credit to the genius of those who have made the knowledge plain, saved us from famine and pestilence and given us the ability, if we choose to use it aright, to make this a good world to live in in the years to come.

Introduction by Patrick Moore

How can one explain the almost universal wish to 'find out'? I believe that it is inherent in human nature; were it not, we would probably still be living in a Stone Age. As things are, we have well and truly entered the Age of Science.

My own interest in such matters dates from the age of six, when I picked up a book about astronomy, read it through from cover to cover, and realized that I had been 'hooked'. Before I departed for the Royal Air Force, at the start of Hitler's war, I had spent a great deal of time in studying the Moon, and I was convinced that men would land there in the foreseeable future, though I admit that I erred on the pessimistic side, inasmuch as I could not believe that the first lunar voyage would take place much before the end of the century.

But so much has happened since then. The various branches of science have come together to a greater extent than ever before, and so much technical information is available that no ordinary person can hope to assimilate more than a fraction of it. Herein, in my view, lies the use of a book such as this. Inevitably we have not been able to cover every single application of science in modern life, but we have tried to give a helpful survey of what has been achieved in fields ranging from astronomy to transport, from medicine to the origin of life, from energy to communication. It has been a pleasure to collaborate with my colleague Magnus Pyke; and I hope that the result will please our readers as much as we have enjoyed writing it.

Acknowledgments

There are a number of people and organizations who helped us in the preparation of this book. First, we wish to express our thanks to our Research Editor, Petra Regent, and to the Research Assistants, Clive Dickinson, Ben Hamilton and Joseph Brundene. Next, we would like to thank all those, not otherwise credited in the text, who allowed us to reproduce the diagrams, tables, photographs and charts in the book. The drawing on p. 40, from Windsor Royal Library, is reproduced by gracious permission of Her Majesty the Queen. The picture on p. 274 is Crown copyright, Science Museum London; the picture on p. 152 is Crown copyright, reproduced with the permission of the Controller of Her Majesty's Stationery Office . In addition, thanks are due to the following for the illustrative material on the pages mentioned:

The Aker Group, Oslo: 123; The BBC Hulton Picture Library: 13, 50, 54, 128, 147, 149, 151, 154, 213, 216, 217, 235, 276, 280, 281; British Telecom: 285; Guy's Hospital (Paediatric Research Unit): 19; The John Topham Picture Library: 67, 69, 70, 71, 120, 131, 174, 175, 184, 190, 242, 253, 259, 264, 266, 282; NASA: 240; National Portrait Gallery: 219; Royal Greenwich Observatory, Herstmonceux: 236; The Science Museum, London: 92, 99, 215, 252, 274; The Wellcome Trustees of the Wellcome Institute for the History of Medicine: 48; and J M Dent & Sons Ltd for the diagrams, certain captions and other material taken from *Everyman's Encyclopaedia* (6th Edition, 1978); for three charts (pp. 57–8, 58–9 and 76–7) from *The Right Way to Eat* by Miriam Polunin (1978): and for three diagrams (pp. 195, 197 and 202) from *Earthshock* by Frank Fitch and Basil Booth (1979).

Much of the information contained in the lists that appear throughout our book is available in a range of existing reference books. Particular acknowledgment, however, is due to the following works from which tabular items were obtained: *The Book of Lists 2*, compiled by Irving Wallace, David Wallace, Amy Wallace and Sylvia Wallace (Hamish Hamilton and Morrow, 1980) for pp. 121 (bottom) and 124; *The Dunlop Book of Facts*, ed. Norris and Ross McWhirter (Dreghorn Publications, 1964), for pp. 47, 72–3, 73, 95, 127 (top), 199 and 288–9; *Energy Resources* by Andrew L Simon (Pergamon Press, Inc., 1975) for pp. 121 (top), 125, 127 (bottom) and 256; *Encyclopaedia Americana*, vol. 17 (Encyclopaedia Americana Corporation) for pp. 3 and 173 (top); Geographia Ltd for p. 227; *The Scribner-Bantam English Dictionary* (Charles Scribner's Sons, 1977) for pp. 177–8, 292–7; *The World Almanac and Book of Facts* (Newspaper Enterprise Association Inc., 1981) for pp. 25, 26, 112, 122 (bottom), 133 (bottom), 164, 168, 169, 173 (bottom), 189, 190, 191, 233–4, 261, 298–300.

List of Illustrations

1 Diagrams

2 Photographs and Prints

1

Life

Early Theories About Life and Death

Life today takes such varied forms that modern scientists are asking themselves how these forms are related and whether they had a common origin. Ideas about evolution have themselves changed radically over the centuries from what we would now regard as myth to modern scientific theories about the nature and origin of life. The Egyptians believed that life first came out of a 'primeval hillock' situated somewhere near the town of Hermopolis, which was the home of the gods. They also believed that life was created spontaneously each time there was an inundation of the Nile. Their idea about death was that the souls of the dead descended into the underworld where they were judged by the god Osiris, and in due course returned to the body. This is why they were so careful to mummify the bodies of important people so that they would be in good condition when they were needed again.

The Sumerians may not have had a very clear idea about where they came from, but they had melancholy views about where they were going to. 'The house where [the dead] sit in darkness, where dust is their food, clay their meat, they are clothed like birds with wings for garments. Over bolt and door, lie dust and silence.' Moving forward a thousand years or so to the India of 500 BC, we find the ideas of Buddhism in the conception of a 'cycle of lives'. A bad man who died might be reincarnated as a lower animal – a bull, for example, or a dog. A good man, on the other hand, could after death come back to life as an even better man until in the end he lost his own individuality in a universal 'self' or Nirvana. This was perfect peace.

Those who accepted the precepts of Islam believed, much like the Jews and Christians, that God created life, together with the heavens and the earth, in seven days. There was Adam in the Garden of Eden with all the animals, as well as Satan who encouraged Adam in wrong-doing. After death comes the Day of Judgment when the person on trial will be sent to Hell, remain in Purgatory or go to Paradise. The Greeks were more pragmatic than this and believed that the first animals arose from sea-slime and the first men from the bellies of fish. Aristotle extended this idea of 'spontaneous generation' by citing evidence to show that maggots were created spontaneously from bad meat, worms from decaying vegetables, and mice from sacks of grain. In *Georgics*, Virgil describes how a swarm of bees arose from the body of a calf. Lucretius, in *On the Nature of the Universe* says, 'Earth has won the name of Mother, since from earth have all things sprung. And even now, we see full many a breed of living creatures rise up out of the earth, begot by rains, and the genial warmth the sun doth shed.'

The theory of spontaneous generation lasted from times of antiquity right through until the nineteenth century. Even van Helmont (1577–1644), a distinguished scientist working in Brussels, who made substantial progress in the study of plant nutrition, could seriously write down the recipe for the creation of mice: thus 'If a dirty undergarment is squeezed into the mouth of a vessel containing wheat, within a few days a ferment drained from the garments and transformed by the smell of the grain encrusts the wheat itself with its own skin, and turns it into mice.'

It was Francesco Redi (1626–1697) who first reported convincing experimental evidence to show that life was not produced spontaneously but that a living creature could only appear after having been generated by its predecessors. In his treatise *Esperienze intorno alle generazioni degli insetti* (1668) he described a series of experiments showing that the white maggots in meat were simply the larvae of flies. He kept meat and fish in large vessels covered with the finest Neapolitan muslin and, for still more complete protection, covered the

Standard mortality and life expectancy data

Age	Deaths Per 1,000	Expectation of Life (Years)	Age	Deaths Per 1,000	Expectation of Life (Years)	Age	Deaths Per 1,000	Expectation of Life (Years)
0	7.08	68.30	34	2.40	37.60	67	38.04	11.73
1	1.76	67.78	35	2.51	36.69	68	41.68	11.17
2	1.52	66.90	36	2.64	35.78	69	45.61	10.64
3	1.46	66.00	37	2.80	34.88	70	49.79	10.12
4	1.40	65.10	38	3.01	33.97	71	54.15	9.63
5	1.35	64.19	39	3.25	33.07	72	58.65	9.15
6	1.30	63.27	40	3.53	32.18	73	63.26	8.69
7	1.26	62.35	41	3.84	31.29	74	68.12	8.24
8	1.23	61.43	42	4.17	30.41	75	73.37	7.81
9	1.21	60.51	43	4.53	29.54	76	79.18	7.39
10	1.21	59.58	44	4.92	28.67	77	85.70	6.98
11	1.23	58.65	45	5.35	27.81	78	93.06	6.59
12	1.26	57.72	46	5.83	26.95	79	101.19	6.21
13	1.32	56.80	47	6.36	26.11	80	109.98	5.85
14	1.39	55.87	48	6.95	25.27	81	119.35	5.51
15	1.46	54.95	49	7.60	24.45	82	129.17	5.19
16	1.54	54.03	50	8.32	23.63	83	139.38	4.89
17	1.62	53.11	51	9.11	22.82	84	150.01	4.60
18	1.69	52.19	52	9.96	22.03	85	161.14	4.32
19	1.74	51.28	53	10.89	21.25	86	172.82	4.06
20	1.79	50.37	54	11.90	20.47	87	185.13	3.80
21	1.83	49.46	55	13.00	19.71	88	198.25	3.55
22	1.86	48.55	56	14.21	18.97	89	212.46	3.31
23	1.89	47.64	57	15.54	18.23	90	228.14	3.06
24	1.91	46.73	58	17.00	17.51	91	245.77	2.82
25	1.93	45.82	59	18.59	16.81	92	265.93	2.58
26	1.96	44.90	60	20.34	16.12	93	289.30	2.33
27	1.99	43.99	61	22.24	15.44	94	316.66	2.07
28	2.03	43.08	62	24.31	14.78	95	351.24	1.80
29	2.08	42.16	63	26.57	14.14	96	400.56	1.51
30	2.13	41.25	64	29.04	13.51	97	488.42	1.18
31	2.19	40.34	65	31.75	12.90	98	668.15	.83
32	2.25	39.43	66	34.74	12.31	99	1,000.00	.50
33	2.32	38.51						

Source: Commissioners Standard Ordinary Mortality Table, issued by the US National Association of Insurance Commissioners.

vessels with frames on which muslin was stretched. Although plenty of flies settled on the muslin, no maggots appeared in the meat or fish. He described how flies laid their eggs on the muslin but only when these eggs fell on to the meat or fish did they develop into maggots. From this he concluded that decaying foods were only a nest for the development of insects, but without eggs no maggots would appear.

In spite of the clarity of Redi's experiments and regardless of the ridiculous nature of van Helmont's formula for creating mice, the difficulty of disbelieving what has been believed for centuries (no matter how silly the belief) made it necessary for Louis Pasteur in France, in 1862, nearly two hundred years later, to argue all over again the truth that life only comes from life. Following a brilliant series of experiments, the French Academy of Sciences awarded a prize to Pasteur for demonstrating the activity of micro-organisms in various infusions. He showed that micro-organisms were present in the air but that, if they were filtered out of the air, a broth which had been sterilized by heat and from which outside micro-organisms were prevented from gaining ingress, would remain sterile indefinitely.

The Origin of Life on Earth

For many millions of years, the earth was devoid of life. In order that life can proceed, two criteria must be fulfilled. The element carbon must be present in an available chemical state and amino acids, the essential structural components of living organisms, must be present. Amino acids are components of carbon, hydrogen, nitrogen, oxygen, and (for certain amino acids) sulphur. In the early years of the modern scientific age it was believed that organic compounds could only be produced by living creatures. It has since been shown that this is not so (see chapter 4). Biological compounds can be synthesized in the laboratory as readily as can inorganic compounds. Then in 1952 it was shown by Stanley Miller in the United States that if an electric discharge was passed through a mixture of water, hydrogen, methane and ammonia – all of which compounds could have been present in the earth's atmosphere in pre-biological times – the amino acids, glycine and alanine, could be detected in the resulting mixture. In 1959, it was found in Germany that similar results were obtained if the gas mixture was exposed to ultra-violet light rather than an electric discharge.

This evidence, that amino acids, essential for the process of life, can be formed by the sort of non-biological conditions likely to have been present during the early evolution of the earth, was soon reinforced. Sydney Fox, in America, found that many more than two amino acids could be produced under the conditions of what he called pan-synthesis. He also demonstrated that when such mixtures of amino acids were subjected to heat, quite large polypeptide units were formed, smaller than, but nevertheless similar to those of fully formed protein. In 1961, it was found that the presence of hydrogen cyanide among the starting gases led to the synthesis of so-called purines, components of nucleic acids, essential units controlling the replication of living cells. If the sugar, ribose, was present together with phosphate, adenosine triphosphate (ATP) could be produced. This compound plays a part in the release of the energy essential to the life process.

The hypothesis therefore is that the physical conditions existing in the primordial ocean, bathed in the light of the sun and subjected from time to time to the electrical energy of lightning, were such that amino acids and, from them, first polypeptides and then proteins, could over the millennia of geological time have begun to accumulate. In addition, the purines and pyrimidines, components of nucleic acids, could also have been synthesized. Following the experimental observations later made by Sydney Fox, it was clear that these diverse components could have coagulated into clumps which, as has also been shown, could develop the property of self-replication.

Over the millions of years elapsing, among the diverse forms of such elementary 'living' organisms, some could have evolved containing porphyrin rings, shown by Miller to be possible. These are the components of the pigment, chlorophyll, which possesses the property, when energized by light, of releasing oxygen from its bound form in carbon dioxide. By this means, oxygen could gradually build up as a component of the terrestrial atmosphere.

Although the length of time for this non-biological synthesis of amino acids and then of protein, of purines, pyrimidines and ribose and thence of nucleic acid, and of chlorophyll is very long, would it, one may ask, have been long enough? New observations now suggest that it may not have needed to be of such prolonged duration as was at first thought. In biological systems, besides such essential components as protein and nucleic acid, there is also another group of compounds characteristic to the life process. These are the enzymes. Enzymes are substances which facilitate a particular reaction without taking part in it themselves. It has now been shown by David White in California that certain short amino-acid chains serve as catalysts (the word used to describe in non-biological systems what would be called enzymes in biological ones) for the formation of more complex chains. But the process is more subtle than this.

White found that a pair of short amino-acid chains acted as a catalyst – or enzyme – which accelerated the formation on the one hand of nucleotides (which are fragments of nucleic acid) and, on the other hand, of peptides (which are fragments of protein). He also showed that a pair of short nucleotide chains catalysed the formation of peptide chains. Today, when one talks about the 'genetic code', what is meant is the way full-scale nucleic acid can control the assembly of an entire new creature. What White has shown at a very much more elementary level is that this short nucleotide chain has the 'code' for putting together two amino acids.

The curious 'naturalness' of the life process on earth is shown by the observation that when these enzyme reactions are carried out in the presence of the sort of clays that could have existed on the shores of the primordial seas, they happen even faster. This is because the particular peptides and nucleic acid fragments involved are brought closer together by being absorbed onto the clays. It now appears certain that zinc-bearing clays preferentially attract just those sugars, amino acids and nucleotides that are specifically present throughout the biological world in living cells.

The Classification of Living Things

Aristotle, born in a Greek colonial town on the shores of the Aegean, in 384 BC, set up a system of classification of animals that remained in use for nearly 2000 years. He described more than 500 species and arranged them on the basis that each was striving to attain such degree of perfection as it could. In this struggle, the species, man, must be ranged in the hierarchy as being at the top of the scale of perfection. Many of Aristotle's descriptions were remarkably shrewd. He realized that whales bore their young alive and classed them in the same category as mammals – not as fish. He also distinguished the cartilaginous fish from the bony fish. He rejected the principle of 'dichotomy', under which animals were placed in 'opposites', as in 'land and water animals' or 'winged and wingless animals', realizing that this could lead to the separation of animals which in fact had a great deal in common. For example, under the principle of dichotomy, wingless ants and winged ants would be in separate groups, while winged ants and birds would be in the same group. Aristotle also recognized that no animal had both tusks and horns, and no single-hooved animals had horns.

At about the same time that Aristotle was working out a rational classification for the diversity of animal creation known to him, Theophrastus was attempting to classify plants.

What made animal classification difficult was the fact that many animals which seemed to be related could not breed with each other, despite their external similarities. How were scholars to divide up animals when there were so many different criteria to choose from?

During the Renaissance, a great many new animals were discovered leading to an even greater need for putting them into some sort of logical order.

One of the most important steps forward was made by an Englishman, John Ray, in the seventeenth century. Although much of his work was concerned with plants, he also published a book that classified animals on a logical basis for the first time since Aristotle. His classification was mainly based on differences in hooves, toes and teeth. He even suggested – an advanced idea for his time – that fossils were the petrified remains of extinct creatures.

However, modern classification owes most to the Swedish naturalist, Carolus Linnaeus. In 1737, Linnaeus published a book called *Systema Naturae*. In this book he grouped species resembling one another into a *genus*, and put related *genera* into an order. Then he grouped similar orders into a class. An important aspect of his classification was his 'binomial nomenclature'. Each species was identified by being given a double name, which was made up of the name of the *genus* and of the species.

In 1800, the French naturalist, Georges Cuvier, added one more category to Linnaeus's system, that of the phylum. For example, animals which have haemoglobin in their blood, are vertebrates, and are four-legged fall into one phylum, while the insects, spiders and crustaceans are placed in another. Then in the nineteenth century, Jean Lamarck elaborated the system still further by subdividing the invertebrates, a group which up till then had been merely regarded as containing assorted 'worms', into the spiders and the insects, and established separate categories for the crustaceans and the echinoderms (a group including the starfish). His book, *Natural History of the Invertebrates*, was the foundation of modern invertebrate zoology.

The modern classification divides all living things into three kingdoms, the plant kingdom, the animal kingdom and the protista (which includes bacteria and other micro-organisms which cannot be fitted in anywhere else).

In the plant kingdom, there are two sub-kingdoms, the thallophyta, comprising plants which do not have stems, leaves or roots, such as algae and fungi, and the embryophyta, including the bryophyta (mosses) and the tracheophyta (plants with stems which circulate sap). The tracheophyta cover three main classes, the filicineae (the ferns, which reproduce with spores), the gymnospermae (cone-bearing trees), and the angiosperms (which include all plants which have their seeds enclosed in ovules). And so the classification continues.

In the animal kingdom there are 31 phyla. First come the protozoa, one-celled animals. Next are the porifera, animals consisting of a colony of single cells with a porous skeleton, such as the sponges. Because they are halfway between being independent cells and a complete colony, sponges can be strained through a cloth into separate cells, and then slowly grow together to form a sponge again. The first animals that are truly multi-celled are the coelenterata, with a hollow gut, and two layers of cells, the ectoderm (the outer skin) and the endoderm (the inner skin). The best-known animals in this phylum are the jellyfish and sea anemones. All the rest of the animals in all the other phyla have three layers of cells, an extra one, the mesoderm, lying between the first two. The mesoderm arises during embryonic development and, depending on how it is formed, divides up the animals into two super-phyla.

The annelid super-phylum includes the phylum of platyhelminthes which are the simplest phylum among the annelids. These include the tapeworm parasite, and also free-living flatworms, which have rudimentary muscles, reproductive organs, and the beginnings of excretory organs. The flatworms possess bilateral symmetry, being mirror images down the central line of their length. They also possess remarkable regenerative powers, being able to grow parts of their body which have been cut off. Another phylum is the nematoda (thread-worm). A member of this phylum is the hookworm. These creatures actually possess a bloodstream which bathes all their cells and carries oxygen to them. They also have a mouth, a gut and an anus.

The next two phyla have hard external 'skeletons' or, more precisely, shells. These two groups are the brachiopoda, which have calcium carbonate shells on the top and bottom, and the mollusca, whose soft bodies are enclosed in shells originating from their right and left sides. The most familiar of these are probably the clams and snails.

An important phylum in the annelid super-phylum is the annelida. These are segmented worms, each segment of which has its own nerves branching off the main nerve stem, blood vessels, excretory tubules, and muscles, and is almost like a separate organism. The most common of the annelids is the earthworm, *Lumbricus*. Many of the most successful species of the animal kingdom are segmented. For example, man possesses segmented vertebrae and ribs. The annelids are relatively soft and defenceless, but the phylum arthropoda (jointed-feet) has both segmentation and a skeleton. The skeleton is segmented, too, and jointed, so that it allows easy movement. The external skeleton is mainly made of chitin, a substance which is both strong and light. This phylum contains more species than all the other phyla together. The arthropoda includes lobsters, centipedes and insects.

The other super-phylum is the echinoderm (spiny skin), which includes the sea-urchins and starfish. The second phylum of the echinoderm super-phylum, the chordata, is the group to which man belongs. This phylum also embraces snakes, monkeys and frogs. Its key characteristic is the fact that these animals possess an internal skeleton, with a backbone and are, therefore, vertebrates. There is also a group of animals which has a half-backbone, called a notochord; this is really a rod of cartilage. Human beings possess a notochord when they are in embryonic form. Animals possessing notochords are classed together with those possessing backbones, as vertebrates.

The phylum chordata is divided into four sub-phyla, three of which consist of animals with a notochord and the fourth, the true vertebrates, with backbones.

The vertebrates fall into two super-classes, the pisces (fishes) and the tetrapoda (four-footed animals). The pisces super-class is made up of the agnatha class (fish which have skeletons, but no limbs or jaws, like the lamprey, possessing a sucker-type mouth), the chondrichthyes (cartilaginous fish, which have a skeleton of cartilage instead of bone, as do the sharks and rays), and the osteichthyes, or bony fishes.

The amphibians are the simplest of the tetrapods. Their best known representatives are the frogs and toads. The amphibians are characterized by having a water-living stage, during which they breathe with gills, followed by an adult stage when they possess four feet and breathe with lungs.

The reptilia (creeping animals) include the snakes, lizards, alligators and turtles. The reptiles breathe through their lungs from birth, and hatch their eggs on land.

The last two groups of the tetrapods are the aves (birds) and the mammalia (mammals). Both groups are warm-blooded and are capable of maintaining their body temperature at a steady level regardless of the temperature of the external environment. Birds, like reptiles, lay eggs, while mammals give birth to their young when they are nearly mature; sometimes they are able to fend for themselves at birth. For example, a calf or a foal is able to stand and walk within a few minutes of birth.

Mammals are divided into three sub-classes: the prototheria, the egg-laying mammals, such as the duck-billed platypus and the spiny anteater; the metatheria, where the young are not born in an egg but are only sufficiently developed to be able to crawl to their mother's nipple where they stay until they are able to fend for themselves – these are the marsupials, the most common examples being the kangaroo and opossum; lastly, there is the sub-class eutheria (which means 'true beasts'). The members of this sub-class have a placenta, a tissue barrier within the womb, which supplies blood, bringing food and oxygen to the growing embryo.

The placental mammals consist of twelve orders: Insectivora, which includes shrews and moles, which eat insects; the Chiroptera, the bats; the Carnivora, the meat-eating animals, such as the cat and dog families; the Rodentia ('gnawing') which includes the sloths and armadillos, and anteaters; the Lagomorpha, which includes rabbits and hares; the Artiodactyla (even-toes) which includes all hoofed animals with an even number of toes on each foot, i.e. cattle, sheep, deer and camels; the Perissodactyla, those animals with an odd number of toes on each foot, such as horses, zebras, tapirs and rhinoceroses; the Proboscidea (long nose), the elephants; the Odontocei (toothed whales), which includes the sperm whale; the Mysticeti (moustached whales) which includes the blue whale and other feeders which filter tiny, one-celled creatures through a 'sieve' in their mouths; and the Primates, which include lemurs, monkeys, apes and man. All the primates have hands that are used for grasping, with thumbs which can be opposed to their fingers. The digits have flattened nails, rather than claws. Their brains are quite large and good sight is a very important feature. Altogether there are nine primate families, insect-eating shrews, lemurs, three families of monkeys (which have tails) and the apes, which do not have tails. The last family, Hominidae, contains only one species, *Homo sapiens*.

Evolution

Just as the religions of the world taught the belief that man and all the diverse living creatures which surround him were brought into being by an act of creation, so, too, did it follow that those who believed in the truth of divine revelation were compelled to accept that each species of animal had always retained its characteristics just as they exist today. Gradually, however, as rational thinking about nature and the beginnings of science came to influence people's ideas about the nature of life and the diversity of living things, different views came into play.

In 1752, the French naturalist, Georges Buffon, in his extensive forty-four-volume work on natural history, recorded the fact that some animals possessed organs that appeared to serve no useful purpose. He suggested that over the generations changes might have occurred in the conformation of these animals causing particular structures to become redundant. This could imply that species might not be as immutable as had been supposed. Another series of observations which could be taken to challenge the notion of the perpetual fixity of animal species and the differences between them were the observations made by geologists of the fossil remains of living creatures from times long past.

It was in the seventeenth century that Nicholas Steno first argued that the lower strata of rocks were older than those laid down above them. In the eighteenth century, the Scottish geologist, James Hutton, developed further the idea of sedimentary rocks later compressed by other layers as geological ages proceeded. By the nineteenth century, the French anatomist, Georges Cuvier, made a classification of fossil creatures and observed that those found in the oldest rock strata were different from those discovered in later strata. Taken at its face value, this implied that some of the species present in earlier geological eras were different from those present on earth later on. Similarly, animal species which once existed, for example, the flying pterodactyl, which he discovered, had subsequently become extinct.

The findings of other geologists served to confirm these conclusions. William Smith working in England showed that the fossil creatures in certain rock strata were characteristic of the particular rock formation in which they were found. He concluded that the age of any particular stratum could therefore be fixed by the kinds of fossils found in it. And he noticed that the younger the strata were the closer was the similarity between the fossil animals and those

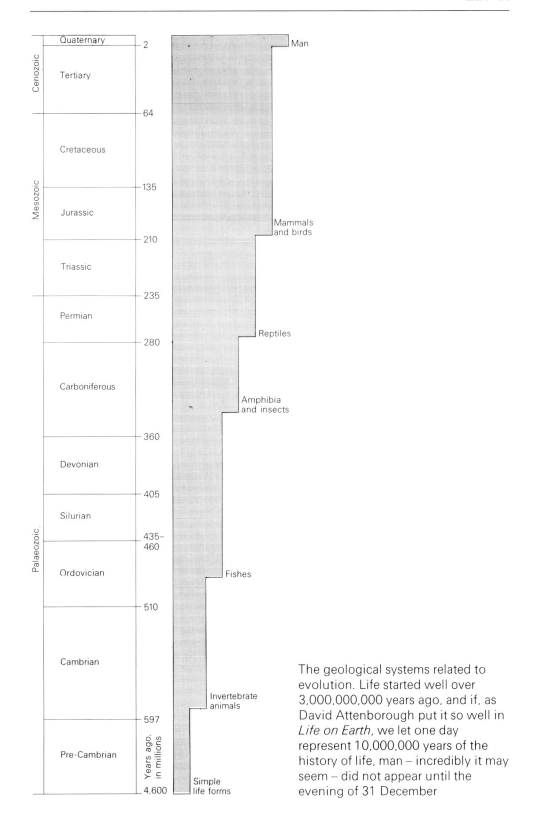

Cenozoic
Quaternary — 2
Tertiary
— 64

Mesozoic
Cretaceous
— 135
Jurassic
— 210
Triassic
— 235

Palaeozoic
Permian
— 280
Carboniferous
— 360
Devonian
— 405
Silurian
— 435–460
Ordovician
— 510
Cambrian
— 597
Pre-Cambrian
— 4,600

Years ago, in millions

Man
Mammals and birds
Reptiles
Amphibia and insects
Fishes
Invertebrate animals
Simple life forms

The geological systems related to evolution. Life started well over 3,000,000,000 years ago, and if, as David Attenborough put it so well in *Life on Earth*, we let one day represent 10,000,000 years of the history of life, man – incredibly it may seem – did not appear until the evening of 31 December

currently to be found alive. Charles Lyell, a Scottish scientist, collected even more supporting evidence from which he was able to compare the forms of certain living creatures with their fossil predecessors of 240,000,000 years before.

All this evidence laid the foundations for the theory of evolution, implying that animal species through which the diversity of life is exhibited may not have been immutably fixed since the time of the Flood (when they all walked out of the Ark) but have evolved from the simpler types of creatures whose fossil remains are to be found in the oldest rocks.

An early attempt to explain the mechanism by which animals could change from one form to another, and why some died out along the way, was that of the French naturalist, Jean Lamarck. In 1809 Lamarck published a book in which he argued that a changing environment caused creatures to acquire small changes which were then, he suggested, passed on to their offspring. He illustrated this idea with the example of the giraffe. Originally, he stated, the giraffe had a short neck, just like any other grazing animal, and reached up to the lowest branches of the trees to feed off leaves. Then, when the lower leaves were all gone, it had to stretch its neck higher and higher to reach new leaves. Eventually, its neck and legs became longer as a result of the continual stretching. It then passed these new characteristics on to its offspring, so that the baby giraffes were born with long necks. This was, no doubt, a pretty theory, indeed some of Rudyard Kipling's 'Just So Stories' depend on just such a hypothesis (he claimed that the elephant got its trunk because its nose became stretched when it tried to pull it out of a crocodile's jaws). Unfortunately, however, it was not supported by hard evidence. The theory of evolution had to await the closer reasoning and more accurate observation of Darwin and Wallace.

The test of time – ten prehistoric animals still in existence

Animal	Species	Age
Australian Lungfish	Fish	200 million years old
Coelacanth	Fish	400 million years old
Crocodile	Reptile	160–195 million years old
Duckbill Platypus	Aquatic Mammal	150 million years old
Horseshoe Crab	Crustacean	300 million years old
Okapi	African Mammal	30 million years old
Peripatus	Worm	500 million years old
Stephens Island Frog	Amphibian	170–275 million years old
Tuatara	Reptile	200 million years old
Turtle	Reptile	275 million years old

Charles Darwin, whose theory of
natural selection was the first step in
a century-old debate on the subject
of the evolution of life

In 1831, Charles Darwin, a young man, fond of field sports and from a reasonably well-to-do family, who had considered, on the one hand, studying for the church, on the other hand becoming a doctor, persuaded his father to allow him to join the British government's research ship as a naturalist. The voyage occupied five years during which Darwin collected an immense amount of information about the plants and animals he saw. He also had the opportunity to reflect about his observations and, having been impressed by Charles Lyell's ideas about the gradual evolution of fossil forms, he was struck by the possibility that living species might evolve from one form to another better suited to its environment. For example, he observed that in the Galapagos Islands, 650 miles from the coast of Ecuador, there were fourteen different species of finches. It occurred to him that originally one species must have colonized the islands from the mainland but that, gradually, as the birds dispersed to the various islands of the group, they had changed. In some areas their beaks had become adapted to catching insects where insects were the main source of food, in other areas they had adapted to eating seeds or fruit.

Gradually, he came to believe the different groups had diversified so much that they could no longer breed with each other, and became different species.

It was after he had returned to England and began to organize the large amount of information which he had collected that he was struck by the basic idea upon which his theory of evolution came to be established. This was the survival of the fittest. One day, when he was reading for pleasure Thomas Malthus' essay describing his ideas that if human population increased more rapidly than the food supply those least able to obtain subsistence would starve, Darwin realized that the same principle must be responsible for the origin of species. If certain members of a community of animals possessed a character-istic giving them an evolutionary advantage, no matter how small, that group would eventually supersede the rest of the community. For example, Lamarck's ideas about the giraffes' long necks could be looked at in a different light. If within a species of animals dependent for food on leaves plucked from trees certain animals were born with longer necks than the rest, these would obtain more food, would grow better and breed more successfully. Eventually, a species all with long necks – namely giraffes – would evolve to take the place of the shorter-necked predecessors.

Although Darwin was not able to put forward any suggestions as to how variations within a uniform community of creatures came about and what made them be inherited, he set to work to collect examples from the data which he had obtained during his voyage and from his general reading which supported this theory of 'natural selection'. In 1844, he began to write a book on the subject. Fourteen years later, he was still quietly at work on the book when Alfred Wallace, a keen traveller who had spent some time not in the Galapagos Islands but in the Malay Archipelago, asked for his advice on a paper he had written in which, without knowing it, he had put forward what was virtually the same theory of evolution and the origin of species. At Darwin's suggestion, Wallace generously agreed that a joint report should be made by the two of them to the Linnaean Society in 1858. In 1859 Darwin published *On the origin of species by means of natural selection or the Preservation of favoured races in the struggle for life*, now most commonly known as '*The Origin of Species*'.

The publication of Darwin's *Origin of Species* was a major step forward in the scientific understanding of the nature of life and its uniformity throughout the multitudinous species of living things. To start with, it implied that species were not immutable as had been asserted in biblical teaching. Furthermore, it also showed that man himself was part, together with the lower animals, of biological creation.

Genetics

The study of man's origins exerts to this day a great fascination over the minds of anthropologists. We know from the researches of the Leakey family – Louis, Mary and Richard – and from those of Don Johanson – that, from skulls and parts of skeletons that have been unearthed in Africa, mankind (or, perhaps, womankind, since one of the most spectacular finds has been of a female in her late 'twenties, called 'Lucy') is at least 3,500,000 years old. More important still, Lucy walked upright, even though she was less than four feet tall. Until Johanson's discovery of Lucy, it had been thought that man did not walk upright until he began to make tools; since Lucy was alive 1,000,000 years before the first tools were used, a radical shift in anthropological thinking has been necessary. And recently, close to Olduvai Gorge in Tanzania, Mary Leakey has unearthed the oldest human footprints in the world, made nearly 4,000,000 years ago. Controversy still rages over the nature of these ancient and upright creatures, and what actually made them get up from a four-footed posture and walk is still an unanswered question; at present the fossil evidence is remarkably scant for the period before Lucy.

Modern theories about the evolution of life generally are much concerned with the problem of whether living things evolved by a continuous process or by fits and starts, with some species making sudden jumps forward, others coming to catastrophic extinction. Various suggestions have been made as to the causes at work – climatic changes, supernova explosions, changes of the earth's magnetic field, the arrival of tektites or other material from space – but no single theory has become universally accepted.

Although the theory of evolution became widely accepted by the scientists of his time, Darwin's work presented certain difficulties. He was not able to suggest an explanation of why variants occurred in the first place or how such characteristics were inherited. In fact, the first step towards an understanding of heredity had already been made by Gregor Mendel, a monk working in what is now Czechoslovakia. But his results, published in 1865 in the *Transactions of the Brunn Natural History Society*, were unknown to Darwin. In this paper, however, Mendel had laid the foundations of the science of genetics.

Mendel used garden peas in his experiments into heredity. He had noticed that peas produced offspring with clear-cut differences. He started by crossing coloured peas with white peas, tall peas with dwarf peas, peas with yellow seeds with peas with green seeds, and peas with smooth seeds with peas with wrinkled seeds. The first generation of hybrids showed that white and coloured crossings produced only coloured flowers, that crosses of dwarf and tall peas produced only tall ones, that crosses of plants with wrinkled and smooth seeds produced only smooth seeds, and that yellow and green peas when crossed produced only yellow peas. In all these results, there was no 'blending' of colour or height or smoothness, each trait either occurred or it did not. Mendel called the traits which did appear 'dominant' and those which disappeared, 'recessive'.

Next he allowed each of the four varieties he had produced to self-pollinate. When he counted the numbers of plants produced showing the different characteristics which he had been studying, he found that the dominant trait appeared three times as frequently as the recessive trait. For example, in one trial, out of the 253 hybrid seedlings from the first cross between plants with round and wrinkled seeds, he obtained 7,324 seeds, of which 5,474 were round, and 1,850 were wrinkled, giving a ratio of approximately 3:1.

In an attempt to clarify his findings, Mendel represented the dominant character by a capital letter and the recessive by a small letter and set out his results thus:

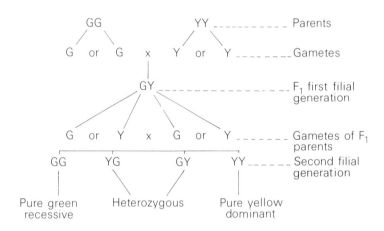

Next, in order to confirm that each characteristic was inherited independently, he made crosses using two different characteristics at the same time and found that the characteristics did indeed give every possible combination in the first generation of hybrids. In this trial, Mendel was lucky in the seven characteristics he chose to follow. It is now known that there are others which may be linked so that they do not show straightforward dominance and recessive behaviour.

Some years later, and quite independently of Mendel, Hugo den Vries in Holland, Carl Correns in Germany and Erich Tschermak in Austria also reached the conclusion that hereditary characteristics are inherited as discrete units and may be either dominant or recessive. When Mendel's paper came to the general notice of the scientific community, each of these workers gave immediate credit to Mendel for his pioneering discovery.

The problem now was: what was it in the pollen or the ovule of a plant or, for that matter, in the sperm or the egg of a higher animal, which carried the so-called 'gene' by which characteristics were transformed, either as dominant or recessive properties, from one generation to the next?

In 1839, two German scientists, Theodor Schwann and Matthias Schleiden, suggested that the cell is the basic unit of life in all living organisms.

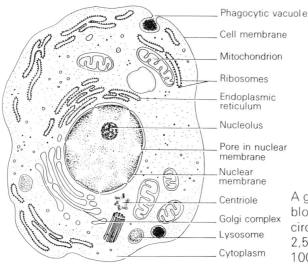

Phagocytic vacuole
Cell membrane
Mitochondrion
Ribosomes
Endoplasmic reticulum
Nucleolus
Pore in nuclear membrane
Nuclear membrane
Centriole
Golgi complex
Lysosome
Cytoplasm

A generalized animal cell. Human red blood cells are released into the circulation at the amazing rate of 2,500,000 per second, and last 100–120 days

The mechanism by which the division of plant cells was brought about was studied by Wilhelm Hofmeister in Heidelberg in the 1860s. Hofmeister observed through a microscope that before a cell divides, its nucleus first divides into two. He developed a process of staining by which he was able to see more clearly what was going on. Using this technique he was able to see that the nucleus contains in it certain string-like structures which, because they stained brightly, he called 'chromosomes'. It soon became apparent that before a plant or animal cell divides, these chromosomes were involved. Each different animal or plant species possesses a characteristic number of chromosomes. In 1882, Walther Flemming, a German scientist, first showed in detail what happened to the chromosomes when one living cell develops and becomes two. The process of cell division he called 'mitosis'.

In the process of mitosis, first a series of 'fibres' or 'asters' extends from one side of the cell to the other, to form a 'spindle'. The chromosomes arrange themselves along the spindles and each splits longwise almost as though it was being pulled apart by the spindles, so that it becomes two threads, where before there had been one. These two sets of chromosomes then move away from each other and the cell divides into two cells, both of which contain the same number of chromosomes as the original cell did in the beginning.

Mitosis is the means by which an ordinary cell (in a piece of skin knocked off one's knuckle, for example), can divide to produce a replica of itself. The process is, however, different when a cell is fertilized to produce a completely new progeny. The subdivision of such a fertilized cell is called 'meiosis'.

In 1875 Oscar Hertweg, a German scientist, showed that the nuclei of sperm and egg fuse to form one. These sex cells, or 'gametes', contain only half the number of chromosomes that normal cells contain. Thus, when the two nuclei fuse, a complete chromosome complement is formed. The way in which the chromosomes from the two nuclei combine, however, is not simple but provides opportunity for 'crossing over', whereby parts of the individual chromosomes may be, at random, fused with parts of chromosomes originating from the opposite nuclei.

By the beginning of the twentieth century, it was becoming obvious that the genes, which had been theoretically proposed to explain Mendel's observations, must in fact exist on the chromosomes. Detailed evidence supporting this proposition was provided by the work of Thomas Morgan in 1910.

Thomas Morgan, a researcher at Columbia University, used *Drosophila melanogaster*, a species of small black fruit-fly, which was a convenient creature for the study of genetics because it grew from egg to maturity in twelve days. It was also possible to work with hundreds of individuals at a time so that statistical conclusions could be drawn from the results. Morgan noticed that an albino mutation occurred in a few of the thousands of red-eyed flies he was breeding. When he crossed one of these white-eyed males with a red-eyed female, he obtained only a few white-eyed flies and those that he did obtain were all males. It seemed that a gene for white eyes was linked to sex. Morgan examined microscopically the chromosomes of the flies and found that all the males had one X-shaped chromosome and one Y-shaped chromosome, while all the females had two X-shaped chromosomes. These it seemed were the sex chromosomes and their presence could explain the results that he had obtained. If the gene for white eyes was only carried on an X chromosome, and red eyes were dominant to white eyes, then clearly, as the females had two X chromosomes, they would have to be homozygotic and carry two 'like' traits in order to show the outward sign of white eyes. The male, with only one X chromosome, needed only to have one recessive white-eyed gene for it to show, as he would not have a dominant red-eyed gene on the other Y chromosome. Morgan found that in fact there were many instances when *groups* of genes were inherited, rather than single genes. After studying thousands of flies, he was able to say that Drosophila's individual traits were linked to each other in four groups. He also knew that there were four pairs of chromosomes within the cells of Drosophila.

Nobody yet knew whereabouts on the threadlike chromosomes individual genes were situated. Morgan realized that the process of crossing-over which occurred at meiosis might provide an answer. If the genes were arranged in a

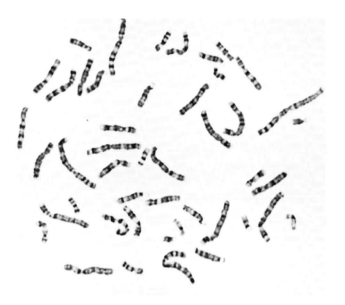

Human female chromosomes (×1,200). Using modern staining techniques, each pair of chromosomes is identified by the specific banding pattern.

row along the length of the chromosome, then when crossing-over occurred, it should be possible to trace the transfer of genes from one pair of chromosomes to another. This re-organization of genetic material was called 'recombination'. If two particular genes were at opposite ends of a chromosome, it would be more likely that one of them would be passed over. If the two genes were closer together, it was unlikely that the two genes would be separated. They would be either left together on the original chromosome, or transferred over together. If the experiment were repeated with many thousands of individuals, any chance errors would be eliminated, and the true distance would be revealed by the frequency or non-frequency of separation. From these results Morgan and his colleagues were able to 'map' 50 or so of the genes on the Drosophila chromosome.

Even so, these charts were not the actual indication of the physical position of the genes upon the chromosomes. In 1933, Theophilus Painter of Texas University pointed out that the study of the 'giant' chromosomes of Drosophila might help reveal the location of the genes. These 'giant' chromosomes existed in the salivary glands of the fly. It was possible actually to discern different banding patterns on different chromosomes, and after painstakingly correlating these banding patterns with particular genetic recombinations, it became possible finally to plot a particular gene on to a particular 'band' on the chromosome. In these maps, the order of the genes was the same as that of the previous 'statistical' maps, though sometimes the distribution and actual closeness of various genes was different. In 1934, H. Muller, who had worked with Morgan on the statistical mappings, and A. Prokofyeva, actually 'measured' the size of a gene in Drosophila – the maximum length was 1,250 ångströms (one ångström equals one hundred-millionth of a centimetre).

By 1940 it was rapidly becoming apparent that the actual definition of a gene required reappraisal. Sometimes a gene seemed actually to alter its influence upon a characteristic, depending upon which other genes it was next to (the 'position effect'); sometimes an X-ray could cause a mutation in a unit *smaller* than the measured size of a gene; it seemed that the 'gene' could operate as a smaller unit, that the current definition of a gene might be sub-divided, and that the mutation-sites *within* a gene might be mapped.

Deoxyribonucleic Acid (DNA)

At about this time, the attention of scientists turned away from genes as discrete structures believed to form parts of chromosomes. Instead, the idea took root that genes were part of a single chemical molecule, but a molecule of extraordinary size and complexity. This molecule was DNA. Deoxyribonucleic acid was identified as long ago as 1869 in the nucleus of pus cells, by a Swiss biochemist, Friedrich Miescher. In 1924 Robert Feulgen in Germany showed that DNA was present in the chromosomes of cells and that the bands on the chromosomes of Drosophila salivary glands were rich in DNA. The question arose as to whether DNA was the genetic material. It was soon established that every animal and plant species has in its cells a characteristic quantity of DNA in the same way that different species possess a characteristic number of chromosomes.

In 1928 Frederick Griffith was studying a bacterium which causes pneumonia, *Diplococcus pneumoniae*. There are two forms of this pneumococcus, smooth (S) which is virulent, and rough (R) which is harmless. Griffith found that after he had injected S pneumococcus into mice, he could later recover from the mice the R form. In the laboratory, S pneumococcus always bred true. What had occurred to 'transform' the S pneumococcus into R? In an attempt to find out, he injected mice with both S pneumococci rendered harmless by heating, and R pneumococci. The mice died of pneumonia and Griffith recovered from their tissues living virulent S pneumococci. It appeared that the DNA from the killed S pneumococci had caused a genetic change to take place in the harmless live R type and had converted them into virulent S type organisms.

Confirmation that it was the DNA component of killed bacterial cells which caused the transformation of the living cells into which it was brought in contact was provided by Oswald Avery and his colleagues at the Rockefeller Institute in America. They found that if the transforming agent was exposed to enzymes capable of destroying sugars, proteins and lipids, it retained its transforming capability. But when it was exposed to enzymes specific for DNA, it lost it. Rollin Hotchkiss, also working at the Rockefeller Institute, found that DNA obtained from pneumococci which had developed a resistance to the antibiotic, penicillin, conferred such resistance to penicillin to other pneumococci.

The question now arose: how did the chemical molecule of DNA transmit genetic information? The elucidation of the chemistry of DNA was one of the great scientific achievements of the 1950s and the further investigation of how it operates to control the development of complex animals of whom the diversity of living creatures is composed, is a continuing saga of current scientific achievement.

DNA – deoxyribonucleic acid – is a combination of repeating chains of four 'bases', adenine, thymine, guanine and cytosine, together with the sugar, deoxyribose, and a string of phosphate radicals. The kind of molecule it is was elucidated in a series of brilliant studies by numerous scientists of the first rank. Erwin Chargaff at Columbia University found that the proportions of adenine to thymine, and guanine to cytosine, were always equal. Adenine and guanine are both 'purines', which possess a double-ring formation, while cytosine and thymine are pyrimidines, with a single-ring formation. The sugar portion of each base-sugar combination is bonded to the next by a phosphate group, thus creating a sugar-phosphate backbone, running the length of the molecule.

In 1950, Maurice Wilkins and Rosalind Franklin, working at King's College, London, and using the technique of X-ray crystallography, found that the purine and pyrimidine bases in DNA formed a flat plane, and were located at a regular distance of 3.4 ångströms apart. They also observed a further regularity after every ten nucleotide bases showing that the DNA molecule was helical making a complete turn after every ten bases, this turn occupying a length of 34 ångströms along the molecule. They also deduced from density studies that each DNA molecule was composed of either two or three nucleotide chains.

The final details of the DNA molecule were discovered by Francis Crick and James Watson in 1953 working at Cambridge. Crick and Watson constructed a molecular model of DNA. They used the information that Wilkins had obtained, that the width of the DNA molecule was 20 ångströms. They knew that ten nucleotides fitted into every 34 ångströms of the molecule's length and were able to calculate the theoretical density of the molecule by adding up the weights of the individual atoms in it. Since this calculation of the density of a single helical chain was exactly half the true observed density, they deduced that DNA must consist of two chains. Knowing that Chargaff had found that the proportions of adenine and thymine and of guanine and cytosine were equal, they concluded that each purine might be paired with a pyrimidine, particularly since both base pairs measured 20 ångströms across which was the observed width of the DNA molecule. In their final model they arranged the base-pairs pointing inwards, forming the 'rungs' of a helical ladder, the two side struts being composed of phosphate and sugar. The paired bases were held together by hydrogen bonds, as Gulland had found. One side of the two-sided chain ran up the helix, while the other ran down. This brilliant interpretation was published in the British scientific journal *Nature* in 1953. It was immediately realized that this model not only accounted for all the findings made about the configuration of the molecule but also for its function. The double helix possesses a means for self-replication, something essential in genetic material which has to duplicate itself accurately every time a cell divides. Watson and Crick suggested that each nucleotide chain is the 'opposite' of the other. On one side, the sequence of bases could be A T G A T T C G G (where each letter is the initial of adenine, thymine, guanine and cytosine), when the other half would be: T A C T A A G C C. Watson and Crick suggested that the two chains might begin to 'unwind' at one end, rather as one might unravel twin-ply wool.

The discovery of the chemical structure of DNA was thus a tremendous advance in our understanding of how life reproduces itself. This molecule, in which two strands of a twisted sequence of four bases can separate, showed how like can generate like. The sequence in which the bases occurred along the length of the molecule, spelled out, like a complex puzzle-lock, the characteristics of the new cell and the new organism which was to reproduce the old. An immense amount of intricate work has been carried out, during the twenty years since the configuration of DNA has been understood, to elucidate the 'code' by which the bases lying along the backbone of the molecule direct the separate amino acids from which the protein of the new organism is to be composed. More and more of the 'code' is being understood, and some of it can already be manipulated. This lies behind what is being called 'genetic engineering'. A century ago, Pasteur studied the fermentation of starch by *Bacillus butylicus* yielding n-butyl alcohol and acetone. In the 1920s this process was used to produce acetone and n-butyl alcohol on an industrial scale. The organism had been bred to give increased yields before 'genetic engineering' had been thought of. Today 'genetic engineering' is being applied to try to get micro-organisms to produce, for example, insulin. The increased understanding of DNA – the chemical molecule of heredity – is a great achievement. The practical implications of this new scientific knowledge still remain to be determined.

These are early days but already progress is expected to be made in using genetic engineering in 'biotechnology', which could have wide applications in medicine, industry and so on. Today's scientists, with all their knowledge, have, however, still to outstrip what Pasteur did before the word 'biotechnology' was invented.

The Animating Principle – the Chemistry of Life

The difference between a living creature and a dead, non-living one, is that the living organism is a going concern. As long as life lasts, it calls for energy derived from some source of fuel to maintain the state of animation which is life itself. In a man, fuel must be consumed to keep the heart beating, pumping blood round the body. The lungs must inhale and exhale, the skeletal muscles maintain their due tension.

It was shortly after the discovery of oxygen and the elucidation of the nature of combustion, in which he played a significant part, that Antoine Lavoisier in 1780 solved the problem of the nature of life, in his celebrated aphorism, *La vie est une fonction chimique* – 'life is a chemical process'. Lavoisier's own experimental figures showed that under certain conditions the life process could be summarized, as can the process of keeping a motorcar going, as the combustion of carbon and hydrogen in the presence of oxygen thus producing carbon dioxide and water with the parallel release of energy, both as heat and mechanical work. This summary of the mechanism of life is, of course, an over-simplification. To start with, life processes cannot operate at the high temperature needed for combustion. It soon became apparent that they operate step by step and that each step is facilitated by a specific enzyme. Furthermore, there may be several parallel mechanisms by which the life force is made available.

A hundred years ago, Louis Pasteur observed that when yeasts were put to live on a nutrient medium mainly composed of sugar, they could get on perfectly well, although they were not equipped with the necessary enzymes to obtain *all* the energy there was in the sugar. Having broken down the chemical molecules of sugar through a number of stages as far as alcohol (the 2-carbon compound ethanol), the yeast could go no further. Pasteur found, however, that if he vigorously bubbled oxygen (as air) through the medium, the yeasts grew much better, used up all the sugar, breaking it down to carbon dioxide and water, and left no alcohol behind in the mixture. This phenomenon is called 'the Pasteur reaction' to this day. Indeed, it is used in industry. If people want to grow yeast (as in a bakers' yeast factory) they aerate the tanks in which they grow it. If they want alcohol (as in a brewery or a whisky distillery), they do not.

Human beings are not exactly like yeast, although there is a similarity. Under normal circumstances, we breathe and keep our 'fuel-combustion' system well aerated. The blood-sugar in our circulation is carried to the muscles where there is work to be done and there broken down through a quite complex series of changes into carbon dioxide and water which we expel in our breath. On the other hand, when there is need for a heavy output of energy, as in a 100-yard sprint – such energy can be released without breathing. The biochemical chain of reactions through which the energy is released does not get stuck at alcohol, as in a yeast cell, but at lactic acid. We can only tolerate a certain concentration of lactic acid in our muscles. If the level rises too high, for example, when one is holding up a heavy weight too long, one's arms begin to ache. The sprinter, having breasted the tape, throws himself down on the grass to pant and burn off the lactic acid through the alternative life-process chain.

There are two remarkable features about the biochemistry of the life-force. The first is that although there is a parallel between the overall chemistry of biological work and mechanical work, inasmuch as they both involve the combustion of carbohydrate (sugar in biology) and hydrocarbon (petrol in machines) mainly to carbon dioxide and water, whereas a motor car or railway locomotive is a heat engine, obtaining its power from the expansion of gases by heat, a living creature, getting its energy from the twitching of muscle fibres (the mechanism of which is not exactly understood), is primarily the only effective chemical engine in current use.

The second feature which illustrates the elegance of the life process is this. The whole of animal creation depends for its continuance on a constant supply of food capable of providing the fuel to operate the biological mechanism. I have so far referred to two chemical pathways through which energy may be made available to living cells. One is the fermentation mechanism, sometimes called the Embden, Myerhof, Parnas system, another is the Krebs Cycle, involving oxygen and offering not only the release of a pulse of energy but also, as a spin-off, allowing chemical units of the sugar intake to be used for body growth. The chemical configurations of the compounds involved in these interlocking systems moving from stage to stage are diverse. In the main, the 6-carbon unit of sugar splits into 3-carbon compounds and thence into 2-carbon compounds and so, finally, to 1-carbon compounds, ending as CO_2. But 4-carbon compounds also play a part.

It was during the course of studies into these mechanisms that Calvin, working in America, identified the 7-carbon compound, sedo-heptulose, in living tissues and worked out its place and function in the energy-release mechanism which keeps life going. What is remarkable about this is that sedo-heptulose was first identified in the leaves of the stone-crop, a plant belonging to the botanical family of *Sedum* (heptulose implies the presence of 7 carbon atoms). Much later, Calvin worked out the mechanism by which the energy of sunlight, trapped by the great tense molecule of chlorophyll, the green pigment in leaves, can, step by step, take the spent ashes of carbon dioxide and water in the atmosphere and, as it were, build them back up into the sugar we taste when we suck a stalk of grass. Following the consecutive stages through which this process of photosynthesis operates, upon which virtually the whole of life depends for food, Calvin found that at one point the chemical process passes through the stage of sedoheptulose.

Anyone possessing a sense of wonder must feel a thrill of delight at the thought that the linked chain of reactions by which photosynthesis builds up the world's food supply has a direct parallel with the chemistry of the energy-release system, the animating process, which is the chemistry of life.

Estimates and conjectures of the past and future population of the world

Year	World total	Population (millions)		Percentage	
		More developed region	Less developed region	More developed region	Less developed region
1970	3631	1090	2541	30·0	70·0
1750	791	201	590	25·7	74·3
1800	978	248	730	25·6	74·4
1850	1262	347	915	27·7	72·3
1900	1650	573	1077	34·7	65·3
1950	2486	858	1628	34·5	65·5
2000	6494	1454	5040	22·4	77·6
2050	(11,000)	(2000)	(9000)	(18·2)	(81·8)

The populations of the world's fifty largest urban areas

New York, N.Y. (est. 1977)	16,962,000
Mexico City, Mexico (est. 1978)	13,993,866
Tokyo, Japan (est. 1977)	11,695,150
Los Angeles-Long Beach, Cal. (est. 1977)	10,605,000
Shanghai, China (est. 1978)	10,000,000
Buenos Aires, Argentina (est. 1978)	9,749,000
Paris, France (census, 1975)	8,547,625
Peking, China (est. 1976)	8,000,000
Moscow, USSR (est. 1978)	7,909,000
Chicago, Ill. (est. 1977)	7,662,000
Sao Paulo, Brazil (est. 1975)	7,198,608
Calcutta, India (census, 1971)	7,031,382
Tientsin, China (est. 1978)	7,000,000
London, England (est. 1977)	6,970,100
Seoul, S. Korea (census, 1975)	6,879,464
Changaing, China (est. 1977)	6,000,000
Bombay, India (census, 1971)	5,970,575
Philadelphia, Pa. (est. 1977)	5,627,000
Cairo, Egypt (census, 1976)	5,084,463
Canton, China (est. 1977)	5,000,000
Rio de Janeiro, Brazil (est. 1975)	4,857,716
San Francisco-Oakland, Cal. (est. 1977)	4,693,000
Detroit, Mich. (est. 1977)	4,620,000
Hong Kong (est. 1978)	4,610,000
Jakarta, Indonesia (census, 1971)	4,576,009
Manila, Philippines (est. 1975)	4,500,000
Tehran, Iran (census, 1966)	4,496,159
Leningrad, USSR (est. 1978)	4,480,000
Shenyang, China (est. 1977)	4,400,000
Luta, China (est. 1977)	4,200,000
Bangkok, Thailand (est. 1975)	4,178,000
Boston, Mass. (est. 1977)	3,898,000
Istanbul, Turkey (est. 1975)	3,864,493
Santiago, Chile (est. 1978)	3,691,548
Delhi-New Delhi, India (census, 1971)	3,647,023
Madrid, Spain (est. 1974)	3,520,320
Wutan, China (est. 1977)	3,500,000
Karachi, Pakistan (census, 1972)	3,498,634
Lima, Peru (census, 1972)	3,302,523
Madras, India (census, 1971)	3,169,930
Berlin, E. and W. (both est. 1977)	3,038,224
Washington, D.C.-Md-Va (est. 1977)	3,033,000
Sydney, Australia (census, 1976)	3,021,982
Nanking, China (est. 1977)	3,000,000
Rome, Italy (est. 1977)	2,897,505
Cleveland, Oh. (est. 1977)	2,874,000
Bogota, Colombia (census, 1973)	2,855,065
Toronto, Ontario, Canada (census, 1976)	2,803,101
Montreal, Quebec, Canada (census, 1976)	2,802,485
Osaka, Japan (est. 1977)	2,723,752

The hundred most populated nations

(Estimates based on figures for mid-1979 unless stated otherwise)

		Population			Population
1	China	945,020,000	51	Uganda	13,220,000
2	India	650,980,000	52	Iraq	12,770,000
3	USSR	264,110,000	53	Ghana	11,320,000
4	USA	220,580,000	54	Chile	10,920,000
5	Indonesia	148,470,000	55	Hungary	10,700,000
6	Brazil	118,650,000	56	Mozambique	10,200,000
7	Japan	115,870,000	57	Portugal	9,870,000
8	Bangladesh	86,640,000	58	Belgium	9,850,000
9	Pakistan	79,840,000	59	Cuba	9,770,000
10	Nigeria	74,600,000	60	Greece	9,440,000
11	Mexico	69,380,000	61	Bulgaria	8,950,000
12	Germany, West	61,340,000	62	Cambodia	8,720,000
13	Italy	56,910,000	63	Madagascar	8,510,000
14	United Kingdom	55,880,000	64	Syria	8,350,000
15	France	53,480,000	65	Sweden	8,290,000
16	Vietnam	51,080,000	66	Cameroon	8,250,000
17	Philippines	46,580,000	67	Ecuador	8,150,000
18	Thailand	46,140,000	68	Saudi Arabia	8,110,000
19	Turkey	44,310,000	69	Ivory Coast	7,920,000
20	Egypt	40,980,000	70	Austria	7,510,000
21	Korea, South	37,600,000	71	Zimbabwe	7,140,000
22	Spain	37,180,000	72	Guatemala	7,050,000
23	Iran	36,940,000	73	Angola	6,900,000
24	Poland	35,230,000	74	Upper Volta	6,730,000
25	Burma	32,910,000	75	Mali	6,470,000
26	Ethiopia	30,420,000	76	Switzerland	6,330,000
27	South Africa	28,480,000	77	Tunisia	6,200,000
28	Zaire	27,870,000	78	Malawi	5,820,000
29	Argentina	26,730,000	79	Zambia	5,650,000
30	Colombia	26,360,000	80	Senegal	5,520,000
31	Canada	23,690,000	81	Bolivia	5,430,000
32	Yugoslavia	22,160,000	82	Dominican Republic	5,280,000
33	Rumania	22,050,000	83	Niger	5,150,000
34	Morocco	19,470,000	84	Denmark	5,120,000
35	Algeria	19,130,000	85	Haiti	4,920,000
36	Tanzania	17,980,000	86	Guinea	4,890,000
37	Sudan	17,890,000	87	Finland	4,760,000
38	Korea, North	17,490,000	88	Hong Kong	4,710,000
39	Peru	17,290,000	89	Rwanda	4,650,000
40	Taiwan	17,240,000	90	Chad	4,442,000
41	Germany, East	16,740,000	91	El Salvador	4,440,000
42	Afghanistan	15,490,000	92	Burundi	4,380,000
43	Kenya	15,320,000	93	Norway	4,070,000
44	Czechoslovakia	15,250,000	94	Israel	3,780,000
45	Sri Lanka	14,740,000	95	Laos	3,630,000
46	Australia	14,420,000	96	Honduras	3,560,000
47	Netherlands	14,030,000	97	Somalia	3,540,000
48	Nepal	13,710,000	98	Benin	3,470,000
49	Venezuela	13,520,000	99	Puerto Rico	3,410,000
50	Malaysia	13,300,000	100	Sierra Leone	3,380,000

The first four-legged amphibians were also the first animals to have voices.

The building materials used in the construction of the earliest human graves were the shoulder blades of prehistoric mammoths.

In ancient Egypt the symbol of life, the mind, and the creative spirit was the number 1.

In 1685 one person in twenty-three died in London, and 1685 was not reckoned to be a 'sickly year'.

Almost three-quarters of the babies born in London in the middle of the eighteenth century died before they reached the age of five.

Much of the human race lives more than 5,000 feet above sea-level.

The world's largest island, Greenland, is just under ten times the size of Great Britain, yet the population of Great Britain is over 980 times greater than the population of Greenland.

Almost 40 per cent of the Third World is under fifteen years old.

About one person in four on earth lives in China. By the year 2,000 some predictions anticipate that there will be 1,800,000,000 Chinese.

The likelihood of a mother giving birth to quadruplets is a chance of about 1 in 600,000.

2

Anatomy, Medicine & Disease

Early Theories

Even in the distant past, people struggled to stave off the affliction of disease. But all efforts were virtually ineffective until the modern age of science. No matter what doubts there may be of the scientific applications of the present age, there can only be gratitude for the blessings which they have brought in the prevention of pain and disease and the healing of the sick.

In the earliest times, disease was a catastrophe sent, it would seem, by the gods as a punishment of an individual or of an entire community. If, therefore, anything could be done to counter disease, it could only be achieved by a priest, a medicine man or a witch doctor who could communicate with the angry spirits. Charms and incantations could be used to protect the sick and steps taken to drive out the evil influences that made people ill. Prehistoric skulls have been found through which holes have been drilled to release the demon causing madness, an operation called trepanning.

The Sumerian civilization which evolved in the valleys of the Tigris and the Euphrates about 4000 BC, included a system of medicine in which plants and minerals were used as drugs. At the same time, however, the physicians believed that disease was basically a mystical phenomenon with a supernatural origin. They therefore based their treatment on the omens derived from consulting sheeps' livers and from the stars by which, they believed, human life and health were influenced.

A good deal of systematic information on human anatomy and disease began to accumulate from about 3000 BC in the civilizations that developed in Egypt, Mesopotamia, India and China. The Egyptians learned a good deal from their practice of embalming the dead. This involved opening the body and removing the visceral organs. At least they knew the position of the main organs, but their knowledge was limited because of the belief that dissection was an offence against the dead. Another factor hampering their search for anatomical information was the rule that if a surgeon operated on a patient who subsequently died, the surgeon's hand would be cut off. In those remote times, they had no understanding of the functions of the nerves, veins or arteries, and furthermore they believed that disease was caused by demons which sucked the marrow from their victims' bones or gnawed their intestines.

By about 1700 BC, medicine in Egypt was becoming systematized and surgeons had acquired considerable skill. For example, the Code of King Hammurabi stated:

> If a doctor has treated a nobleman for a severe wound with a bronze lancet, and has cured him, or if he has opened with a bronze lancet an abcess in the eye of a nobleman, and has cured him, he shall be paid ten shekels of silver.
>
> If the patient is a freeman, the doctor shall accept only five shekels of silver.
>
> If the doctor has treated a nobleman with a bronze lancet for a severe wound and has caused him to die, or if he has opened with a bronze lancet the

abcess of the eye of a nobleman, and has caused him to lose his sight, the doctor's hands shall be cut off.

The doctor in Egypt was part priest and part physician. All cures were believed to be the result of divine intervention acting through the drugs or treatment he prescribed. Only if the gods were willing could a man be cured, no matter what treatment was given. The Eberus Papyrus of 1550 BC consists of 110 pages of incantations and 700 lists of diseases and remedies. Most of these medicaments, however, were useless and in no way contributed to the welfare of the patient. A typical remedy was: 'For baldness . . . equal parts of the fats of lion, hippopotamus, crocodile, goose, serpent, and ibex; or . . . equal parts of cerebrospinal fluid and writing ink'. Other mixtures contained the excrement of lions, panthers, ostriches and gazelles, both crushed and live insects, and ravens' backbones. There were, however, certain effective drugs, including castor oil, opium and camphor.

Egyptian physicians believed the body to be a system of canals. In illness, these were choked with blood or some other substance which caused pain or sickness. Attempts were made to remove intestinal stoppages with enemas of ox-gall and fat administered through a cattle horn. 'Stoppages and inflammation of the blood' (whatever that was supposed to mean) were treated by bleeding or the application of leeches. It is curious to note that both bleeding and leeches remained part of medical practice until the nineteenth century, even though there was no solid evidence of any beneficial effect.

The Jewish medicine of the Old Testament was closely related to Egyptian and Babylonian practice. There was an emphasis on individual 'moral' reform, prayer and sacrifice as a means of averting ill health. The complicated Jewish dietary laws are often construed as possessing some medical basis, although the connection between 'clean' and 'unclean' foods and any specific malady is obscure, to say the least. Nevertheless, the passages in the Book of Leviticus concerned with leprosy, containing elaborate instructions on segregation, disinfection and the incineration of clothing, are common sense.

Anatomical knowledge was very imperfect in Jewish medicine. The Talmud gives the number of bones in the human body as 248 (there are, in fact, 206), with one bone, the 'Bone of Luz', being the indestructible nucleus from which the body would be raised at the resurrection. Blood was considered to be a miraculous 'vital' principle, the soul, as it were, permeating the whole body. Respiration was quite correctly likened to burning. Talmudic surgery included the suturing of wounds, bandaging, and the use of wine and oil both as a disinfectant and as a soothing ointment. It also, like Egyptian medicine, made use of leeching and of a sedative substance – probably opium – before an operation.

The Hindus excelled all other ancient peoples in operative surgery. Yet the earliest Sanskrit document, the *Rig Veda* from around 1500 BC, consisted largely of incantations for priest-doctors. Hindu medical books of a later date described symptoms of malaria, smallpox, dysentery, typhoid, cholera, the plague and leprosy. Yet for none of these maladies was there any cure. Much later, in the fifth century AD, sedatives began to be used during surgical operations, the cauterizing of haemorrhages, the treatment of fractures with splints, the delivery of babies by caesarian section, the excision of tumours, and the surgical treatment of cataract.

But Hindu knowledge of anatomy and physiology was lacking. The Hindus thought that vital processes were activated by air below the navel, that bile originated between the navel and the heart, and phlegm from above the heart. Health existed when there was a proper balance of the three primary substances. This irrational concept persisted into the Greek civilization as the theory of Four Humours, which lasted many hundreds of years in Europe, during which time no real medical progress was made.

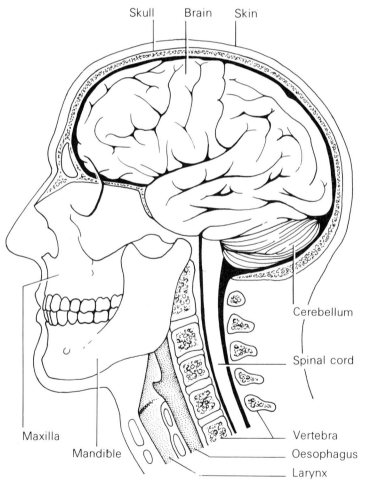

A sagittal section of the head showing the skull, the brain and spinal cord, and some of the associated structures. The soft, delicate brain is protected by being encased in the rigid, bony skull and by the shock-cushioning cerebrospinal fluid.

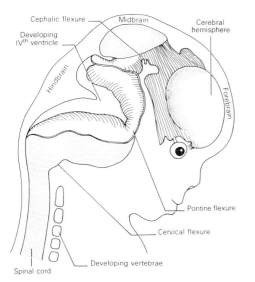

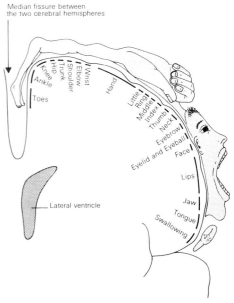

A profile view of the brain of a ten-week-old human embryo

C the areas of the cerebral cortex that control various parts of the body. The size of each area is related to the complexity of the functions it controls

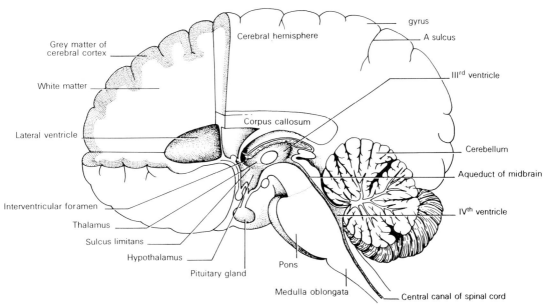

B median sagittal section of the adult brain

Ancient China was a country with a high degree of medical learning even though there was little anatomical knowledge. The Emperor Shen Nung first codified Chinese medicine around 3000 BC. His herbal, *Pen Tsao*, listed over 1000 drugs, some of which are still in use today. Acupuncture, the system of medicine based on the insertion of needles into various parts of the body, arose from attempts to drive demons from the sick. And, finally, it was believed that health was based on a balance between the forces of Yin and Yang (male and female) and the five elements (wood, metal, fire, water and earth). The Yin and Yang were associated with six different patterns of physiological function or malfunction, which could be revealed through six different states of the pulse.

With the growth of Greek medicine (500–400 BC), based on the medical knowledge of Egypt and Mesopotamia, the application of observation and reason rather than the use of unsubstantiated theory began to take hold. Hippocrates, who was born about 460 BC, formed a school of medical practice on the island of Kos in which the teaching was based on observation and practical experience in treating the sick and injured. In addition, Hippocrates drew up a code of ethics for doctors which has lasted to this day. This Hippocratic oath, which all physicians studying at the school at Kos had to take, ran as follows:

> I swear by Apollo the healer, by Aesculapius, by Health and all the powers of healing, and call to witness all the gods and goddesses that I may keep this Oath and Promise to the best of my ability and judgement.
>
> I will pay the same respect to my master in the science as to my parents and share my life with him and pay all my debts to him. I will regard his sons as my brothers and teach them the Science, if they desire to learn it, without fee or contract. I will hand on precepts, lectures and all other learning to my sons, to those of my master and to those pupils duly apprenticed and sworn and to none other.
>
> I will use my power to help the sick to the best of my ability and judgement; I will abstain from harming or wronging any man by it.
>
> I will not give a fatal draught to anyone if I am asked, nor will I suggest any such thing. Neither will I give a woman means to procure an abortion. I will be chaste and religious in my life and in my practice. I will not cut, even for the stone, but I will leave such procedures to the practitioners of that craft.
>
> Whenever I go into a house, I will go to help the sick and never with the intention of doing harm or injury. I will not abuse my position to indulge in sexual contacts with the bodies of women or of men, whether they be freemen or slaves.
>
> Whatever I see or hear, professionally or privately, which ought not to be divulged, I will keep secret and tell no one.
>
> If, therefore, I observe this Oath, and do not violate it, may I prosper both in my life and in my profession, earning good repute among all men for all time. If I transgress and forswear this Oath, may my lot be otherwise . . .

Hippocrates recorded many hundreds of detailed case notes, by which he could guide his treatment of new patients. He might not know the cause of any particular illness or have been able to record any method of cure. On the other hand, where successful treatment had been used once, it could be equally successful when used again. In a treatise, *The Science of Medicine*, Hippocrates defined medicine as 'the complete removal of the distress of the sick, the alleviation of the more violent diseases and the refusal to undertake to cure cases in which the disease has already won the mastery, knowing that everything is not possible to medicine . . .'

In stating that medicine could not cure all illnesses, Hippocrates for the first time adopted the rational stance of the doctors of the scientific age who were to follow him. Such men and women know that only when there is adequate knowledge of the nature of any particular disease condition can there be reasonable hope of successful treatment. Hippocrates collected all the information he could and consistently advocated a thorough examination of sputum, urine, stools and vomit, as well as the examination of swellings, difficulties in breathing and much else.

In contrast to his considerable knowledge of the medicine of his day, Hippocrates' knowledge of anatomy and physiology was scanty. It was believed by Greek doctors that the human body was made up of blood, phlegm, yellow bile and black bile. These were the 'four humours'. Hippocrates wrote, 'These are the things that make up its constitution and cause its pains and health. Health is primarily that state in which these constituent substances are in the correct proportion to each other, both in strength and in quantity, and are well mixed. Pain occurs when one of the substances presents either a deficiency or an excess, or is separated in the body and not mixed with the others.' The sort of evidence for this idea was, as he stated elsewhere, that the quantity of phlegm in the body

> increases in winter because it is that bodily substance most in keeping with the winter, seeing that it is the coldest. The following signs show that winter fills the body with phlegm: people spit and blow from their noses the most phlegmatic mucus in winter; swellings become white especially at that season and other diseases show phlegmatic signs. During the spring, although the phlegm remains strong in the body, the quantity of blood increases. Then, as the cold becomes less intense and the rainy season comes on, the wet and warm days increase further the quantity of blood. This part of the year is most in keeping with blood because it is wet and hot. That this is so, you can judge by these signs: it is in spring and summer that people are particularly liable to dysentery and these are the seasons, too, at which people are warmest and their complexions are ruddiest. The blood in the body reaches its lowest level in the autumn, because this is a dry season and the body is already beginning to cool. Black bile is strongest, and preponderates in the autumn. When winter sets in the bile is cooled and decreases while the phlegm increases again owing to the amount of rain and the length of the nights . . .

None of these statements – even when they possess a rational meaning – can be based on systematic evidence. It is a valuable lesson for a modern reader to reflect on the usefulness of the careful observations made by Hippocrates himself compared with the unsubstantiated theories which he accepted from the general beliefs of his times. These theories, though they lasted for centuries, were of no real help in healing the sick, whereas surgeons taught on the Hippocratic system performed successfully, dealt with fractures, and operated on piles, bladder and kidney stones, tumours, gangrenous wounds and hernias. They also learned to use clean bandages and sheets, fresh water and clean bronze surgical instruments.

But although in the age before science was applied to medicine there were, here and there, gifted men who made progress towards the understanding of the body and the diseases that afflict it, it was all painfully slow. Herophilus of Chalcedon in 300 BC had the insight to see that it was the brain and not the heart that controlled the emotions. Erasistratus at about the same time challenged the theory of the four humours and was the first physician to see the speed of the pulse as an indication of health. Yet he also propagated the mistaken belief that most diseases were caused by an over-production of blood by the heart, which led him to favour blood-letting and the use of leeches. His views on the flow of blood through veins and 'vital air' through arteries were confused, as was his understanding of the process of digestion. On the other hand, he correctly observed that water when drunk did not flow into the lungs but was blocked off by the epiglottis and diverted into the stomach.

Roman medicine, which superseded the Greek variety on the death of Cleopatra in 30 BC and the capitulation of Alexandria, was less rational and systematic. Much of it was based on magic and religious incantation and the use of fanciful mixtures. One alleged antidote for poison, for example, was a mixture of 63 ingredients including viper's flesh. Gradually rival schools of medicine grew up, some of which were based on Greek teaching. The methodists, founded by Asclepiades, asserted that all disease depended on the size of the pores and attempted to effect cures by altering their size by various means. The Empiricist school paid little attention to the causes of disease but concentrated on a miscellany of 'cures'.

One of the most influential physicians of this time was Claudius Galen. Galen, born in AD 129 in Asia Minor, professed to follow the teachings of Hippocrates. In fact he paid little attention to the making of accurate observations but dogmatically propounded his own theories which were mainly based on the theory of the four humours. To counter-balance an alleged 'imbalance' of the humours, he prescribed pepper to warm a cold patient, and cucumber seeds to cool a feverish one. Every treatment was designed to heat, cool, moisten or dry the body. He also originated the incorrect theory which was to last for nearly 2000 years that the presence of pus in a wound was a good sign and that pus was necessary to promote healing. Only when the scientific age arrived did it become apparent that pus is an indication of infection in a wound. Galen dissected apes and pigs, since the dissection of human bodies was forbidden by religious law. Unfortunately, he related his observations on these animals directly to the human anatomy. He consequently concluded that human beings have a five-lobed liver, a double bile-duct, a horned uterus, and a breast-bone with seven segments. He also believed that there were invisible pores between the left and right sides of the heart. Many of these mistaken conclusions remained unchallenged until the sixteenth century, when the ideas of modern scientific thinking arose.

Even though the outlook of the Romans hampered any sensible advances in medical understanding, their highly efficient administrative system and the competence of their engineers enabled them to establish remarkably high standards of public health and hygiene. Roman cities were paved and clean. Most important of all, underground sewers were built to prevent human excrement contaminating the drinking water. Mosquito-breeding marshes around Rome were drained and, to avoid the necessity of drinking the water of the Tiber, the Romans built splendid tiered aqueducts to carry fresh clean water into the towns from far out in the country. By the second century AD there were fourteen covered aqueducts carrying 300,000,000 gallons of drinking water to Rome every day. In addition, public baths were built for the ordinary citizen while many of the richer houses had water-flushed lavatories. Well-run military hospitals were also established providing, to be sure, only such herbal remedies as were available and the treatment of wounds with pitch or turpentine. Hospitals for the general public were established in AD 14. The lack of any real understanding of health and disease was demonstrated to some degree by the decline and final collapse of the Roman Empire in AD 476 which was brought about, not only by military, political and economic reverses, but also by the ravages of malaria, plague and smallpox.

During the Middle Ages, little progress was made in medicine. The Christian church was hostile to physicians. Suffering was considered to be good for the soul, or it might be a punishment for sin. The miraculous healing powers of Christ implied that disease was a visitation from God and His will alone could alter the course of disease. But although the linking of medicine to religion was an impediment to the progress of discovery, the succour of the sick was a virtuous act and hospitals were associated with convents and monasteries. As the centuries passed, the establishment of hospitals, as places of asylum for the sick, developed. A medical school was established in Salerno in Italy in the ninth century and in the twelfth century, when Arabian medicine had reached its peak, large hospitals were being built, the most important of which was completed in Damascus in 1160. A similar foundation was established in Cairo in 1276. Soon the doctors attached to these and other hospitals were expected to demonstrate their competence by passing examinations, and in due course medical schools were established at Montpellier, Bologna, Paris, Oxford, Cambridge, Naples, Padua, Heidelberg and Cologne.

Yet the amount of medical knowledge was limited. The Church remained opposed to surgery and, in spite of regulations insisting that doctors should study medicine for five years or more, knowledge of the cause and effective treatment of disease was simply not available for them to learn. The virtually complete incapacity of physicians to deal in these pre-scientific times with the major killing diseases was all too apparent in the fourteenth century. It was then that a major epidemic of plague devastated the human race.

The plague is believed to have originated in China around 1330, where it was reported that over 13,000,000 people had died. Superstitious reports, mostly circulated afterwards, claimed that as it crept across Egypt and Greece towards the centre of Europe, supernatural events occurred – Mount Etna erupted, France was invaded by swarms of locusts, there were earthquakes and bad harvests. When the disease struck, both the Church and the physicians were helpless. The people looked for any scapegoat they could find. Jews were persecuted, tortured and murdered, being accused of poisoning the wells. Dogs were killed by professional dog-hunters when the belief gained ground that they were responsible for spreading the disease. A meeting of physicians held in Paris in 1348 even reached the conclusion that cosmic influences had created a fatal damp mist which swamped the cities. It was not long before the doctors themselves were accused of spreading the plague and being in league with the grave-diggers and undertakers who profited from the spread of the disease. The term 'Black Death' was used to describe the appearance of the body after death, when haemorrhages under the skin gave the corpse a dark mottled colour. The symptoms of the plague were sudden shivering, headache, vomiting, pains in the abdomen and limbs followed by delirium. Then large and painful boils appeared on the joints. Death usually occurred in five days.

The virulence of the plague was catastrophic. The disease followed the trade routes from China. Although it was not known at the time, the black rat was the carrier of the infection. Consequently outbreaks were started at the ports in India, Egypt and North Africa. It was supposed to have reached Sicily with a Genoese crew who had been besieged by a Tartar army whose troops were infected. From Sicily, the Black Death spread all over Italy. People fleeing from ports as the disease broke out spread the infection. So fast did its ravages extend that it soon reached the Baltic, Iceland, Greenland and Russia.

Later estimates suggest that a quarter of the entire population of the earth at that time (about 60,000,000 people) died from the plague. Poland and the Pyrenees were least affected. It is now thought that this was partly due to large local populations of brown rats, which prevented an influx of black rat plague carriers. Fourteen thousand people died in Basle, 40,000 in Vienna, 50,000 in Paris, and 100,000 in London.

Social life, trade and war all came to a standstill during the worst of the plague years. But gradually conditions improved, trade revived and Europe, together with the rest of the world, moved out of the terrible years of pestilence towards a revival in learning of all sorts, including medicine.

The Renaissance, originating in fourteenth-century Italy, reinstated the curiosity of the Greeks, their urge to question everything, to break away, if need be, from the deadening dogma of religion. Artists, freeing themselves from the obscurantism about the human body, studied its anatomy and made accurate drawings of what they saw. Leonardo da Vinci and Albrecht Durer made exact drawings of human dissections for the first time and were able to illustrate the structure of the muscles, the lungs, the heart with its valves, the viscera and the brain.

Leonardo, surely a true man of science, wrote in his notebook, commenting on the exact drawings he had made:

> You who say that it is better to watch an anatomical demonstration than to see these drawings, you would be right if it were possible to observe all the details shown in such drawings in single figure in which with all your cleverness you will not see or acquire knowledge of more than some few veins, while in order to obtain a true and complete knowledge of these, I have dissected more than ten human bodies, destroying all the various members and removing the minutest particles of the flesh which surrounded these veins, without causing any effusion of blood other than the imperceptible bleeding of the capillary veins. And as one single body did not suffice for so long a time, it was necessary to proceed by stages with so many bodies as would render my knowledge complete; this I repeated twice in order to discover the differences. And though you should have a love for such things you may perhaps be deterred by fear of passing the night hours in the company of these corpses, quartered and flayed and horrible to behold. [These were the bodies of criminals that people such as Leonardo were allowed to dissect] And if this does not deter you, then perhaps you may lack the skill in drawing, essential for such representation . . .

Of the tongue Leonardo wrote

> . . . No organ needs so great a number of muscles as the tongue – of these 24 were already known apart from the others that I have discovered; and of all the members moved by voluntary action this exceeds all the rest in the number of its movements . . . The present task is to discover in what way these 24 muscles are divided or apportioned in the service of the tongue in its necessary movements which are many and varied; and in addition it has to be seen in what manner the nerves descend to it from the base of the brain, and how they pass into this tongue distributing themselves and breaking into ramifications. . . . Moreover you should show whence these muscles have their origin, that is some in the vertebrae of the neck . . . some in the maxilla, and some on the trachea . . . And similarly how the veins nourish them and how the nerves give them sensation . . .

The Renaissance, by which new ideas were gradually edging medicine towards, if not science, at least a serious look at the facts as they existed, brought progress. Printing, developed by Gutenberg in Germany in 1455, inevitably led to a freer exchange of ideas. It followed that over the subsequent 300 years

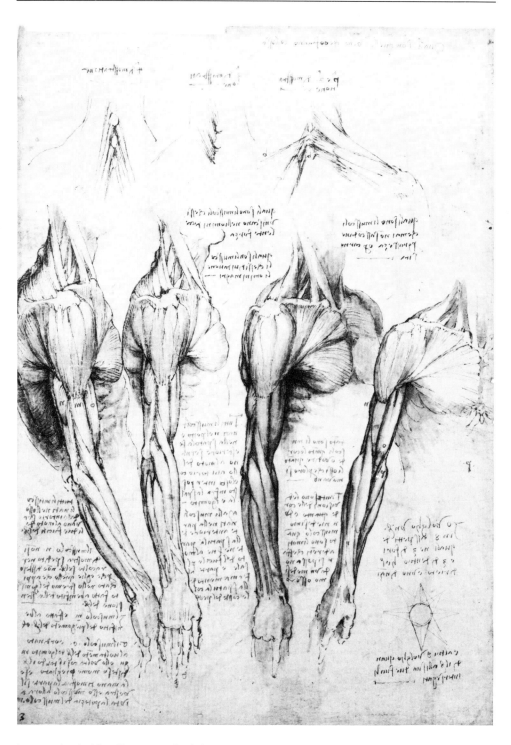

Leonardo da Vinci's anatomical drawings were remarkably detailed and accurate. This is his Four Sequential Studies of the Superficial Anatomy of the Arm, Shoulder and Breast (c. 1510–11)

much more about the structure and mechanism of the human body was established. New medical thinkers appeared. Paracelsus, Professor of Medicine at the University of Basle, modified the theory of the four humours in asserting that the human body was composed of three basic elements, sulphur, mercury and salt. Even though this was nonsense and none of his other mystical ideas made any practical contribution to medicine, his teaching did introduce the idea of chemical analysis into medical practice.

The greatest anatomist of his time was Andreas Vesalius (1514–64) who abandoned Galenic medicine and undertook himself to study the human body regardless of the still continuing public objection to dissections. Vesalius had to acquire his corpses from the gallows under cover of darkness. By patient work and careful dissection he firmly established a solid knowledge of human anatomy. When, as Professor of Surgery and Anatomy at Padua University, he was dissecting a monkey, he observed a bony projection on one vertebra which Galen had described as being present in human beings, showing that Galen's descriptions had been based on the dissection of animals and not of human bodies. In 1543 Vesalius published *De Corporis Humani Fabrica* (on the structure of the human body) containing over 300 beautiful and remarkably accurate woodcut illustrations of his findings.

Vesalius finally discredited the ideas of the 'bone of Luz', the five-lobed liver, the seven-segmented sternum, the double bile-duct and the horned uterus. He showed the presence of valves in the veins (although he did not appreciate their function in what much later was discovered to be the circulation of the blood). He also pointed out that the Bible was incorrect in claiming that man had one less rib than woman, and he was contemptuous of the manner in which anatomy was taught in the medical schools of his day. 'The instruction is very bad, days are lost dealing with silly questions, and in the confusion the student learns less than a butcher could teach the professor.'

Ambroise Paré, another Renaissance man, was an army surgeon at the time when surgery was still regarded as work only fit for barbers. He possessed both anatomical knowledge and surgical skill. One of his most important innovations was to replace the barbarous practice of pouring boiling oil into gunshot wounds and he stopped bleeding by cauterizing the arteries by applying soothing ointments to the wounds and tying off the arteries to prevent bleeding. His skill in making artificial limbs and gold and silver artificial eyes also contributed to the improvement of the status of surgery. In 1540 King Henry VIII established the official 'City Livery Company of Barber-Surgeons' with a seven-year apprenticeship.

It was in 1628 that William Harvey made a discovery which represented a major advance in the understanding of the mechanism of the body in line with the growth of knowledge of its structure. Harvey observed that in the arteries the blood always flowed away from the heart, and that in the veins it always flowed towards it. The valves in both arteries and veins prevented the blood from flowing in the reverse direction. He calculated that two ounces of blood passed into the arteries with every heartbeat. Normally a man's heart beats 72 times a minute. This implies that 270 lbs of blood pass into the arteries each half hour. Harvey reasoned that only the circulation of the blood round the body could account for such a large quantity of blood. In his treatise, *De Motu Cordis*, he argued that the heart, acting as a pump, sent the blood into the arteries and then received it back again through the veins. On its way it passed through the lungs for purification. Harvey could not discover how the link between the circulatory system and the lungs worked. The tiny capillaries were too small to be seen at all easily by the naked eye. It was not until 1661, 33 years later, that Malphighi, making use of the newly-developed microscope, was able to observe the capillaries linking the arteries to the veins.

The seventeenth century was the beginning of the modern age of science. The Royal Society of London was founded in 1662. In Italy Galileo had made his fundamental discoveries in astronomy and by doing so brought science into direct collision with religious dogmatism. While observations continued to be made in medicine, the conclusion which needed to be drawn before real control of disease could be achieved still eluded those working in the field. In 1665, when the plague again struck London, little could be done. Again, it was mainly the poor who suffered. Living in crowded dwellings in the city, they died as in the days of the Black Death. Although it was now known that the plague was carried by rats and fleas, remedies to contain the disease were largely ineffective. Observations of other diseases, however, were beginning to bring

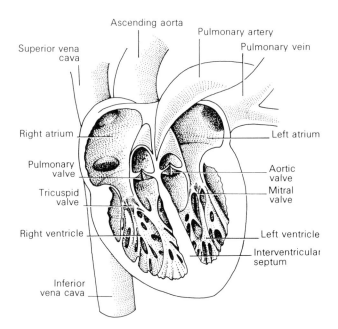

Ascending aorta
Pulmonary artery
Pulmonary vein
Superior vena cava
Right atrium
Left atrium
Pulmonary valve
Aortic valve
Tricuspid valve
Mitral valve
Right ventricle
Left ventricle
Interventricular septum
Inferior vena cava

The adult human heart showing the four chambers. It is about the size of a closed fist, though of course it varies according to a person's weight, age, sex and health. It is estimated to beat over 100,000 times a day and 2,000,000,000 times in an average lifetime. The muscle power generated per day is enough to lift four large cars to a height of over twelve feet.

practical results. The precise studies of Thomas Sydenham, a general practitioner, led him to the discovery that iron was an effective remedy for certain types of anaemia and that cinchona bark (the active principle of which is quinine) could be used in the treatment of malaria ('the ague').

By the beginning of the eighteenth century a further advance towards scientific medicine was taken by the adoption of post-mortem dissection to

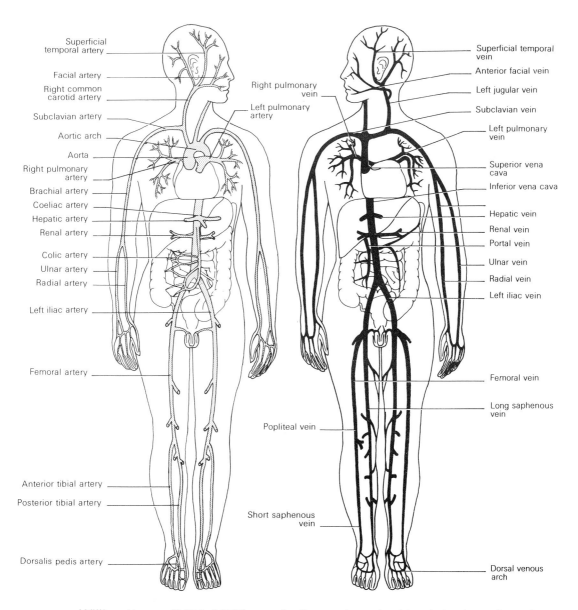

William Harvey (1578–1657) was the first to show that blood circulates through the blood-vessels of the body. *Left*, the major arteries; *right*, the major veins

enable physicians to investigate directly the damage caused by a particular disease on the functions of the various organs of the body. The leading doctor to introduce this important area of study in 1701 was Hermann Boerhaave, Professor of Medicine at Leyden. Medical students flocked to his lectures from all over Europe and introduced post-mortem examinations when they returned to their own medical schools.

By 1741 Edinburgh had also become a productive centre of medical learning, as also had Glasgow, and it was in Scotland that William Smellie introduced the serious study of obstetrics into the medical curriculum where previously it had been ignored. John Hunter, trained in Glasgow, significantly improved the practice of surgery by taking advantage of the information acquired in post-mortem studies, and this was in spite of the lack of both anaesthetics and antiseptics.

In 1700, Bernardino Ramazzini, a professor from Padua, published the first book on occupational and industrial diseases, covering the respiratory diseases of miners and stonemasons, lead poisoning of potters and printers and the eye diseases of blacksmiths.

There were also some limited advances in military medicine. In the eighteenth century, soldiers lived in filthy barracks often supplied with contaminated water. They were, in consequence, ready victims to cholera and typhus. John Pringle, a pupil of Boerhaave, realizing that dirt could be the cause of some of the occupational diseases of the army, made strenuous efforts to create military hospitals with good sanitation and drainage and a clean water supply. He wrote a book on the subject, *Observations on the Diseases of the Army*, in which he listed a number of necessary improvements.

The Navy of the day had its own medical problems. Naval vessels setting out on long voyages carrying ample supplies of salt beef, biscuit and pork often had to abandon their journey because half the crew became ill with a disease which caused their teeth and gums to bleed and old-healed wounds to break open. The men gradually became weaker until they died. This was scurvy. A Scottish doctor, James Lind, serving with the Navy, conducted a series of trials on sailors who were suffering from scurvy. To one he gave cider, to another nutmeg, to another sea water, to another vinegar, to another elixir of vitriol and garlic mustard, and to another lemons. He found that the cider caused some minor improvement, while the lemons produced a rapid and complete cure. Lind published a report of this admirably designed scientific experiment in *A Treatise on Scurvy* in 1753. In this he showed that fresh lemons would prevent scurvy, not only cure it. Captain Cook, acting on Lind's conclusions in his voyage to the South Pacific between 1768 and 1771, introduced sauerkraut and fresh fruit and vegetables into his sailors' diets. Even though his ship, the *Endeavour*, sailed over 30,000 miles during a voyage lasting two years, not one person died of scurvy. Acting on Lind's conclusions, the Admiralty introduced lemons into Naval rations. Later, limes were substituted as being cheaper.

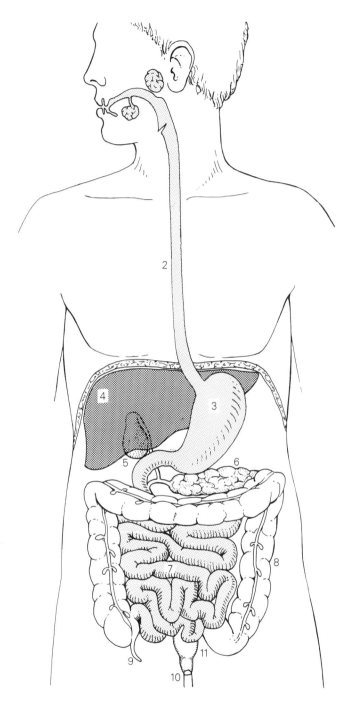

1 Salivary glands 2 Oesophagus 3 Stomach 4 Liver 5 Gall bladder
6 Pancreas 7 Small intestine 8 Large intestine 9 Appendix 10 Anus
11 Rectum

The human digestive system

British sailors, indeed, became known as 'limies'. But before long scurvy again appeared on board ship. The reason for this was that, although limes do contain vitamin C, the active agent preventive of scurvy, the amount of vitamin C in limes is less than that in lemons.

A similar innovation, based on scientific observation but on only partial scientific knowledge, was also introduced in the eighteenth century. In 1718, Lady Mary Wortley Montagu described the oriental process of vaccination against smallpox, when she returned to England from Turkey, where her husband had been British Ambassador. A small cut was made in the arm and a piece of thread which had been soaked in the fluid from a smallpox pustule was drawn through the incision. This method of vaccination was sometimes successful. On other occasions, however, it could be disastrous, giving the patient the smallpox it was intended to prevent and killing him.

The next step was made in 1796 by the Gloucestershire doctor, Edward Jenner. He observed that dairy maids who suffered from the trivial condition of cowpox, causing merely a mild eruption on their hands, appeared to be totally immune to smallpox. Jenner carried out the bold experiment of infecting an eight-year-old boy, James Phipps, with pus from the hand of Sarah Nelmes, a dairymaid, suffering from cowpox. After two months, he inoculated the boy with pus from a smallpox patient. The boy did not contract the disease. It appeared that the previous infection with cowpox had rendered him as immune as if he had had smallpox and recovered.

Vaccination against smallpox was made compulsory in England in 1853. As a result of this national vaccination programme, smallpox cases fell throughout the nineteenth century. It was largely due to what was in the beginning an only partly-understood application of the scientific approach to medicine that by 1979 it was possible for the World Health Organization to announce that the last case of smallpox had been eradicated from the world.

New equipment and new techniques were entering medicine. Previously, doctors had tested temperature by placing their hand on the patient's forehead and taking his pulse with their fingers. Sir John Floyer of Lichfield developed a portable pulse-watch. A rather cumbersome thermometer had been initially designed by Sanctorius in the early seventeenth century. In 1740 a mercury thermometer using the newly invented Fahrenheit scale became available in England. In 1761, Leopold Auenbrugger, a Viennese doctor, suggested that percussion on the human chest could reveal whether the cavities of the lung were congested with fluid. This was the same technique as that used for testing the fullness of wine barrels. The auscultation technique of pressing one's ear to the patient's chest to listen to the regularity of the heartbeat or to the state of the lungs, had been used for a long time. The stethoscope, invented by René Laënnec in Paris, improved the clarity and loudness of the heartbeat sounds.

During the eighteenth century, many great hospitals had been founded, including Guy's, St George's, the Middlesex, the London Hospital and the

Westminster Hospital. St Bartholomew's, St Thomas's and the Bethlehem Hospital for the insane ('Bedlam') were re-endowed as secular rather than religious institutions. After the Dissolution of the Monasteries in the sixteenth century, thirty-seven hospitals were founded in the provinces of England and nine in Scotland. In the existing state of ignorance and lacking scientific knowledge about the nature of disease, these hospitals, founded with such good intentions, were feared and avoided. The chance of getting out of a hospital alive after major surgery was small. More commonly, people's surgical wounds became infected even if they had withstood the hideous shock of suffering a major operation without an anaesthetic. On being admitted to St Bartholomew's hospital, patients were asked to deposit 19 shillings and 6d as a burial fee, which would be returned if they recovered.

Human height from birth to age 18

Age in Years	Boys	Girls	Age in Years	Boys	Girls
Birth	28.6%	30.9%	7	69.0%	75.0%
$\frac{1}{4}$	33.9%	36.0%	8	72.0%	77.5%
$\frac{1}{2}$	37.7%	39.8%	9	75.0%	80.7%
$\frac{3}{4}$	40.1%	42.2%	10	78.0%	84.4%
1	42.2%	44.7%	11	81.1%	88.4%
$1\frac{1}{2}$	45.6%	48.8%	12	84.2%	92.9%
2	49.5%	52.8%	13	87.3%	96.5%
$2\frac{1}{2}$	51.6%	54.8%	14	91.5%	98.3%
3	53.8%	57.0%	15	96.1%	99.1%
4	58.0%	61.8%	16	98·3%	99.6%
5	61.8%	62.2%	17	99.3%	100.0%
6	65.2%	70.3%	18	99.8%	100.0%

The number of bones in the body

Skull	22
The Ears	6
Vertebrae	26
Vertebral Ribs	24
Sternum	4
Pectoral Girdle	4
Upper Extremity (arms)—2 × 30	60
Hip Bones	2
Lower Extremity (legs)—2 × 29	58
	206

Micro-organisms, the Cause of Infectious Disease

Louis Pasteur, who subsequently became Professor of Chemistry at Lille University in 1855, was as a young man asked to investigate why wine will, from time to time, turn sour. Scrutinizing the 'sick' wine through his microscope, he observed in it certain tiny micro-organisms, smaller than and different from the ordinary yeast. He conceived the idea that it was these 'germs' that turned the wine sour, and he demonstrated that this was so. Taking the same idea further, he not only suggested that other similar organisms could be the cause of sickness in animals and people, but also succeeded in isolating the organisms responsible for anthrax in sheep and cholera in chickens and getting them to grow in his laboratory in nutrient broth. When he injected these cultures into healthy animals they developed the disease. But when an old culture of chicken cholera was injected into healthy birds, they only became mildly ill, this process conferring immunity. Not only had Pasteur demonstrated the cause of these diseases, but also the method of circumventing the damage they could do.

One of his more dramatic achievements was with rabies, caused by the bite of a rabid animal. He injected a boy bitten by a mad dog with a weakened preparation made from an infected animal and gradually increased the virulence of the injections. The boy lived.

Louis Pasteur (1822–95), whose great discoveries in relating micro-organisms to disease led to the science of bacteriology

Pasteur's conception of infectious disease being due to a particular micro-organism, which could be said to be the beginning of the science of bacteriology, bore rich fruit. His work was continued by Robert Koch, who later became head of the Berlin University School of Bacteriology. Koch developed special plates of jelly culture medium allowing single bacterial cells to grow into colonies readily visible to the naked eye. In 1882 he isolated the micro-organism responsible for tuberculosis and in 1884 he isolated that causing cholera.

Building further on what Pasteur had done, Koch discovered that the blood of an animal which had been infected with diphtheria and recovered, contained a substance that combatted subsequent infection by diphtheria. The blood of animals which had died of diphtheria did not possess this anti-diphtheria activity. It appeared that an animal which had recovered from a disease had produced in its blood a specific substance which was antagonistic to diphtheria germs. This 'anti-toxin' could be injected into another animal when it would confer immunity to the animal receiving it. Here we see the beginning of the idea of immunization as a protection against disease. By 1906, among the variety of protective procedures available, a vaccine had been produced to counter tuberculosis, called BCG.

The application of scientific thinking pioneered by Pasteur opened the way to the control of many of the micro-organisms which cause disease. There was, however, another form of infection which caused equivalent widespread suffering and death. Even in the latter part of the nineteenth century, something of the order of 90 per cent of patients undergoing surgery in London hospitals died of sepsis after their operations. This infection was spread by the hands of the surgeons, moving from one patient to the next, by the frock coats of the surgeons, by general dirt in the hospitals and by soiled bandages and unclean instruments.

A major source of death among new-born babies and, more particularly, their mothers, was puerperal fever. No sensible woman who could avoid it would ever opt to have her baby in hospital. In 1874, Philip Semmelweiss, a Hungarian working at a maternity hospital in Vienna, instituted a system whereby all students and surgeons coming into the wards must rigorously wash their hands in a calcium chloride solution before touching a patient. Within two years, the mortality in the hospital had fallen by 90 per cent. But in spite of these impressive results, the medical fraternity of Vienna, who felt themselves criticized by the methods he had adopted, resisted his innovations during his lifetime.

In 1865, Joseph Lister, Professor of Surgery at Glasgow University, had read about Pasteur's researches relating micro-organisms to disease. He realized at once that similar micro-organisms must be responsible for the infection of wounds after surgical operations. It seemed to him that a way to destroy such micro-organisms as might otherwise infect wounds would be to treat the entire environment with antiseptic. With this in mind he applied carbolic acid to the surfaces of wounds, to dressings which he had previously boiled, and to his surgical instruments. He further devised a spray which sent a fine mist of carbolic acid into the air above the patient, to kill micro-organisms in the atmosphere of the theatre during the operation. By this means he achieved substantially sterile conditions and was able to perform ambitious operations, penetrating deeper into the body where it was paramount that infection should not occur.

Joseph Lister (1827–1912), the first medical man to be raised to the peerage (1897), for his work in antiseptic surgery

By the use of these techniques, surgeons found that they could reduce the mortality rate among the patients. Other improvements were the development in Germany of a sterilizer to render instruments germ-free and the introduction, in America, of rubber gloves to avoid possible infection from the surgeon's hands, which can never be rendered entirely sterile. In 1899, gauze face masks were first worn, to prevent the surgeon's breath spreading germs on to the patient. Lister himself devised dressings which were not only themselves sterile but which were so made as to prevent germs from outside infecting the wound.

The results of these changes were immediate. Surgeons were now able to operate on the abdomen and the internal viscera, the kidneys, liver, stomach, intestines, bladder and appendix. New techniques were developed for suturing wounds and conducting increasingly delicate operations. Such were the advances made possible by a sound scientific understanding of what was required.

Tropical diseases presented a rather special problem for medical research. The three great killers were malaria, yellow fever and sleeping sickness. In 1880 a French army medical officer, Alfonse Laveran, found the parasite which causes malaria and established that it did its damage by destroying the red blood cells of its patient. Patrick Manson, an English doctor who had spent many years in China, was convinced that malaria was carried by a particular species of blood-sucking mosquito. He was able to arrange for some hundreds of different species of mosquito to be examined and in 1897 Ross, an army doctor in India, found traces of the malaria parasite in female Anopheles mosquitoes. Before long, Manson was able to show that people who could protect themselves against being bitten by mosquitoes did not catch malaria. Clearly, if mosquitoes could be exterminated or their numbers reduced, the incidence of malaria would be reduced. Initially, steps were taken to drain ponds and marshes where mosquitoes were known to breed. Later, when these steps were supported by the use of new and more effective insecticides developed by chemical research, dramatic improvement in public health was achieved.

The insecticidal properties of the organochlorine compound, DDT, was discovered by Paul Müller in 1939. It was used to control mosquitoes during World War Two in North Africa, the Middle East and South-East Asia and, later on, in India. The World Health Organisation estimated that DDT, in only its first eight years of use, prevented about 100,000,000 illnesses and 5,000,000 deaths.

As distinct from the prevention of malaria, treatment has also received scientific attention. Quinine has been used since the seventeenth century, when it had been found that the Peruvians had traditionally employed cinchona bark in which quinine is the active agent. During World War One, the Germans manufactured the first artificial drug for the treatment of malaria, 'mepacrine'. Later, improved modifications were developed, notably daraprim and maloprim, which only need to be taken once a week.

Of the other two great tropical diseases, yellow fever was, like malaria, also found to be linked to another mosquito, Stegomyia. Great efforts were made in Cuba to control this insect – and with some success. Again, the building of the Panama Canal could hardly be achieved until in 1904 the yellow-fever mosquito had been suppressed by the draining of infected swamps. In a previous attempt to build the canal, in 1880, the French labourers had died in their thousands of yellow fever.

Sleeping sickness, a disease beginning with high fever, followed by wasting, lethargy and death, was a scourge in many parts of Africa. Only when David Bruce, a British Army doctor, discovered at the beginning of the present century that it was caused by a parasite transmitted by the tsetse fly was it possible to cope with the disease by destroying the breeding grounds of the fly.

Public Health

The scientific basis upon which effective steps have been made possible to improve the public health has been primarily the discoveries initiated by Pasteur showing that infectious diseases are caused by specific micro-organisms. Secondary considerations include (a) the provision of money to make medical treatment widely available to every member of the community and (b) continuing research into other causes of illness such as diet, toxic hazards and body malfunctioning leading to diabetes, heart disease and cancer. Nevertheless, by far the most important piece of scientific knowledge has been that of microbiological infection and, in particular, the crucial significance of keeping sewage separate from drinking water. Public health is best served by the provision of lavatories, sewers and clean piped drinking water. It is good science to concentrate on these. Without them typhoid fever, dysentery and scarlet fever will occur, as well as the epidemics of cholera, which became a terrifying blight on nineteenth-century Europe.

In the 1830s a cholera epidemic struck Europe during which thousands of people died. Medical treatment to control the severe diarrhoea with the consequent dehydration that occurs was unavailable, nor was the nature of the causative organism known in those pre-Pasteur days. But by the time of the next epidemic in 1848, the relationship between cholera and unsatisfactory sewage and water supply had begun to emerge. In 1842, Edwin Chadwick published his *Report on the Sanitary Condition of the Labouring Population of Great Britain*. Among other matters he calculated what the cost would be of providing every citizen with a well-drained street and a house with a private tap and lavatory linked to a sewage disposal system. A subsequent Royal Commission showed that only two out of every hundred towns had an adequate sewage system, and only twelve had a satisfactory water supply.

By 1849, the connection between contaminated drinking water and cholera became even more apparent. It was then that Dr John Snow observed that the people who used one particular pump caught cholera, while people living in the next street, but using another pump, did not. In his report, *On the Mode of Communication of Cholera*, he argued that many water supplies, including some piped sources, had become contaminated by cholera-infected excreta. He showed that the susceptibility of various sections of the community to cholera depended to a predominant degree on what they drank. In the 1866 epidemic, records were kept of the sources from which cholera patients obtained their drinking water. The results confirmed Snow's hypothesis. In 1884, Robert Koch, working in Germany, isolated the cholera bacillus. The Sanitary Act of 1866 and the Public Health Act of 1875 were the beginnings of the application of scientific principles to such mundane matters as the substitution of glazed earthenware sewage pipes in place of wood-lined or brick-lined tunnels which brought about the improvement in public health we enjoy today where, in our happy industrial communities, few people have ever seen a case of typhoid fever, let alone cholera.

While the institution of a proper water supply and sewage-disposal system is the cornerstone of any rationally based public health system, the provision of general medical care for the public can do much. Nevertheless, any national health system making available doctors and hospitals for those who are sick can only achieve what scientific knowledge allows. The virtual extinction of tuberculosis, the effective treatment of diabetes and pernicious anaemia and the control of poliomyelitis were only possible, no matter how comprehensive a national health service there may have been, when scientific understanding was available to bring them about.

Effective Drugs at Last

Before the age of science there were few effective drugs available to the physician. Most of these were of vegetable origin. There were morphine, strychnine, digitalis, quinine from cinchona bark and – probably as popular as any – alcohol. It is interesting to note – and should be understood by every modern citizen claiming to be well-informed about scientific facts and feats – that virtually all the drugs used today have been produced since 1900 and most of them since 1930.

Salvarsan for the cure of syphilis   In 1907, Paul Ehrlich, at that time working in Frankfurt in Germany, found that if he injected the chemical dye, trypan red, into the blood of animals infected with trypanosomes, it was taken up by those organisms and killed them. This led him to his famous research to find a chemical compound (a 'magic bullet') which would search out and kill a particular disease organism. He concentrated on syphilis, the terrible venereal disease which, because of his scientific genius, was first brought under control. In 1910, when he was testing the 606th chemical, he found that he had succeeded. The modified chemical structure which he had developed was called Salvarsan.

Sulphanilamides to resist pneumonia   In 1933, Gerhard Domagk, also in Germany, found that another red dye, made from sulphanilamide, killed bacteria. It was quickly shown in France that the bacteriocidal effect was due to the sulphanilamide itself in the more complex dye which Domagk had made and called Prontosil. Chemists all over the world experimented with modifications of the sulphanilamide molecule and before long a battery of so-called 'sulpha drugs' became available for the treatment of a variety of infections. Perhaps the most dramatic cures were achieved in the previously highly lethal condition of pneumonia. Before the sulpha drugs were available, 20 to 40 per cent of pneumonia patients died. After the drugs had been developed, the mortality rate fell to less than 10 per cent.

Antibiotics, the conquest of tuberculosis and much else   In 1928, the Scottish bacteriologist, Alexander Fleming, working in St Mary's Hospital in London, made the brilliant observation that a patch of mould by which one of his culture plates of staphylococci had become contaminated exuded a substance which checked the growth of the bacteria. He called this unknown inhibiting substance 'penicillin'. It took ten years before even crude penicillin could be isolated and found to be spectacularly effective against streptococcal infection in mice – and in people. Other antibiotics were isolated, notably streptomycin. Together they revolutionized the treatment of virtually all diseases due to bacterial infection. Scarlet fever, streptococcal sore throat, pneumonia, meningitis, plague, blood poisoning, syphilis, tuberculosis and Rocky Mountain spotted fever all became curable. We who live in this same generation of scientific advance should remember that before the discovery and isolation of antibiotics, many of these diseases meant serious illness or death.

Sir Alexander Fleming (1881–1955), discoverer of penicillin in 1928

Controlling blood pressure   As the infectious diseases that used to kill young and old indiscriminately come under control, people live longer and the average age at which they die rises. It follows, therefore, that the diseases of later life assume more and more importance. Among these is high blood-pressure (hypertension). The discovery of a valuable agent for reducing blood pressure was in some ways a remarkable achievement. The plant, Rauwolfia, had been used traditionally in India to treat a variety of conditions but it was only in 1931 that two Indian scientists isolated the active alkaloids in it. Later the chemical structure of reserpine, the effective compound, was isolated in Switzerland and worked on in America. Even more recently, other drugs capable of reducing blood pressure have been prepared.

Steroids in medical practice and as contraceptives   In modern medicine, steroid drugs have been found of great value in the control of inflammation, in the treatment of shock and in wasting conditions where there is need to rebuild the tissues. They possess what amounts to a life-saving function for patients suffering from Addison's Disease. This malady, first described by Thomas Addison in 1855, involves progressive weakness, low blood pressure and continuous loss of weight. When treated with appropriate steroid drugs and attention is paid to their intake of minerals, patients can be restored to a virtually normal life instead of dying, as they were often destined to do before these drugs were available. In the 1920s, cortisone was first isolated from the adrenal glands of farm animals and found to possess potent activity but it was only after quite large amounts had been prepared that it was found to possess what appeared to be anti-rheumatic activity. When more was known of its chemistry, it became possible to produce it in bulk by a semi-synthetic process using a species of Mexican yam as starting material.

Although not directly related to medicine and disease, the use of steroid drugs as oral contraceptives was first achieved in the 1960s, and has had profound social effects on communities in many lands. It was estimated that in the United States alone, by the 1970s, there were, 9,000,000 women dependent on steroids taken orally to avoid becoming pregnant.

Drugs to change the mind   It is now recognized that little can be done to cure patients suffering from severe illnesses of the mind such as schizophrenia or manic-depression. Within the last twenty years, however, it has been realized that drugs can be produced that will influence the mood of those taking them. It was noted, for example, that reserpine, used to reduce blood pressure, affected the mood of those taking it. Then in France, the compound, chlorpromazine, was synthesized for use in the anaesthetic mixture employed in anaesthesia. It could, however, also be effective in improving the condition of sufferers from certain mental disorders. There followed intense research activity, during which more than 1200 compounds were synthesized. Among these was a range of so-called 'tranquillisers'. Today, it has been estimated that more of the tranquilliser, valium, is consumed than of aspirin. The net effect of these agents on health and disease is, however, hard to estimate. Another series of chemical compounds has been synthesized as 'anti-depressants'.

Big pain and little pain   Morphia has throughout the ages been the sovereign reliever of pain. Unfortunately, it is habit-forming. At a lower – but still useful – level of effectiveness comes aspirin. This substance is a salicylate, in fact acetyl-salicylic acid. Salicylates form the basis of a number of traditional herbal remedies. Aspirin was introduced into medicine by Hermann Dreser in 1893 and has ever since eased the lot of millions. A different chemical compound giving similar effects while being less abrasive to the patient's stomach is paracetamol. But when morphine was first successfully synthesized in 1952 in the laboratories of the University of Rochester in America, chemists in a number of centres were able to prepare a series of compounds containing part of the morphine molecule. Pentazocine and cyclazocine were two derivatives possessing analgesic (pain-killing) activity but with less addictive danger than morphine. Many more compounds with tailored, pain-controlling effectiveness are being continuously produced.

Control of diabetes   Diabetes is a disease in which the system by which healthy people are able to maintain a uniform concentration of sugar (glucose) in their bloodstream, becomes deranged. In healthy people, after a meal, when sugar floods into the blood it is quickly withdrawn and stored either in the liver or the muscles. After exercise and no food, sugar is mobilized from these stores to maintain a constant blood level. People with diabetes cannot do this: the pancreas is unable to produce sufficient insulin, the substance which activates the sugar-control mechanism. In the early 1920s, through the brilliant researches of Banting and Best in Toronto, Canada, insulin became available to provide diabetics, many of whom would otherwise have died, with an effective treatment. An observation made in France in 1942 that some of the sulpha drugs caused hypoglycaemia (fall in blood sugar) led to the development of tolbutamide, a sulpha derivative, for the treatment of diabetes. Another compound, chlorpropamide, has been found to possess longer-acting effect. These compounds have now acquired wide usage.

Pernicious anaemia and a millionth of a gram of cyanocobalamin   Pernicious anaemia is a disease afflicting more blue-eyed, fair-haired Scandinavians and Irish than dark-haired, brown-eyed Italians and Africans. The patients find their hair going grey, their tongues red and smooth and a crippling paralysis coming over them. In the end, their skin becomes yellowish, their bowels disordered – and they die. In 1926, George Whipple who had noticed that liver usually cured anaemia in dogs, tried it on human patients with pernicious anaemia – and they immediately improved. The dying came back to life and the count of red cells in their blood began to increase towards normal numbers. For twenty years, until 1946, patients, if they wanted to stay well, had to eat pounds of liver every day until they were nauseated. In the latter part of this period, to be sure, they could inject themselves with liver extract. Then in 1948, it was discovered that merely by taking some few millionths of a gram of a newly-discovered vitamin B12 (cyanocobalamin) their pernicious anaemia was controlled.

Minerals we eat and why we need them

Mineral	Amount needed daily Best food sources	Results of deficiency – and who's at risk
Calcium	500mg. Milk and other dairy foods, green vegetables	Deficiency leads to retarded bone growth, spasms, nervous excitability, kidney failure, congestive heart disease, loss of muscle power. At risk: pregnant and breastfeeding women, those taking cortisone and other steroid drugs. Main cause of deficiency: is poor absorption, rather than poor supply.
Chromium	Not known	Trace element: little known, but deficiency leads to bloodshot eyes, poor vision, poor growth, upsets body's ability to turn food into energy, and is linked with heart trouble. At risk: low levels are noted in heart patients. Also diabetics and pregnant women. Cause of deficiency: very difficult to absorb more than 3% of amount eaten in food.
Cobalt	Not known	Trace element: few facts known, but proved to be essential in 1948, when shown that 4% of vital vitamin B12 is cobalt. Total amount in body: about 2mg.
Copper	Estimated at 2mg. Many foods	Deficiency leads to general weakness, impaired breathing, grey hair, lack of fertility, heart defects, digestive disturbances and anaemia. Also to degeneration of nerve sheath endings. At risk: those eating low protein diets, or being fed long-term intravenously. Cause of deficiency: not known, except that other minerals can interfere with its availability to body.
Fluorine	Not known	Trace element: function not known in man, though recently proved essential for rat growth. No deficiency symptoms known.
Iodine	Drinking water, tea, particularly China 150mcgs. Sea food and kelp	Unique in being an essential part of some hormones. Deficiency leads to whole action of body slowing down, and enlarged thyroid gland (goitre). At risk: people living in low iodine, inland areas where soils are naturally lacking in this mineral, usually limestone areas (e.g. Derbyshire) or mountainous ones (Alps, Himalayas).
Iron	18mg for women and boys; 10mg for men Liver, beef, whole grains, dried apricots, molasses and treacle	Lack leads to anaemia, sore mouth, cracked lips, poor memory, constant fatigue, depression, reduced resistance to infection. At risk: women of childbearing age, because of menstruation; people with rheumatism and arthritis; in kidney, heart and many infectious diseases. Main cause of deficiency: absorption is poor in the absence of enough vitamin C, too little digestive acids in stomach, too much fatty food.
Magnesium	300–400mg. Cereals and vegetables	Deficiency leads to mental confusion and delirium, convulsions, mental depression, spasms, and changes in heart beat. Lack accelerates ageing, and is seen in those who have died of heart attack. At risk: heavy drinkers, those with high blood pressure, patients after operations, pregnant women. Cause of deficiency: poor supply from processed food, stress, eating too much sugar.
Manganese	Not known Beans and peas, nuts, tea, coffee	Little understood, but essential for activating enzyme systems. Deficiency leads to impaired growth, loss of sexual interest, poor fertility, uncoordinated muscle movements. At risk: pregnant women, rheumatoid arthritic patients, individuals with inborn inability to use it. Some cattle have been found deficient due to soil deficiencies. Cause of deficiency: not known.

Mineral	Amount needed daily Best food sources	Results of deficiency – and who's at risk
Molybdenum	Not known Not known, apart from water.	Trace element, accepted as necessary for man but poorly understood as yet. More concentrated in hard water, so could be linked with lower heart disease frequency in hard water areas.
Nickel	Not known	Trace element found in liver and pancreas, but role not known. Chemically similar to cobalt.
Phosphorus	0.8–1.4gms. Almost all foods	Present in large amounts in body, mostly in bones like calcium. Also involved in many body functions, including use of B vitamins. Dietary deficiency is unlikely because it is so widespread, but can occur if diet consists mainly of processed and refined foods. Usually found in foods with calcium.
Potassium	None fixed In many foods especially vegetables	With sodium, balances body's water stores, so is *vital* to blood pressure, kidney health. *At risk:* anyone taking diuretic drugs, cortisone and steroid drugs, or regularly taking strong laxatives. *Cause of deficiency:* rarely lack of supply, but often drugs.
Selenium	Not known Not known	Trace element recently realized to be vital to function of vitamin E – but how is not understood. Selenium reduces or prevents the effects of vitamin E deficiency in animals, lack may be linked with muscular dystrophy. *At risk:* new born children, particularly if premature; anyone lacking vitamin E.
Silicon	Not known	Trace element, recently reported to be essential to rats, but not yet accepted as essential to man.
Sodium	None fixed Almost all foods	With potassium controls body's water balance. Excess rather than deficiency is problem in Western diet, and is linked with high blood pressure. Too much very bad for people on steroid drugs.
Strontium	Not known Same foods as calcium	Like calcium and magnesium it is stored in bone. No knowledge of role, if any, but present in everyone's bones.
Sulphur	Not fixed In all proteins	Present in all living matter, but role not fully understood. Deficiency not known. Two known B vitamins, thiamin and biotin, contain sulphur.
Tin	Not known	Trace element, see silicon.
Vanadium	Not known	Trace element, recently reported that *deficiency leads to* impaired growth in rats, poor feather growth in chickens. Very little known, but limited trials suggest that a high blood cholesterol level means a low vanadium level in both diet and tissues.
Zinc	10–15mg. Oysters, nuts gm=grams mg=milligrams mcg=micrograms	*Deficiency leads to* decrease in growth in young, fatigue, congenital abnormalities in babies, defects in sexual organ development, hair loss and skin blistering and breaking. Wounds will not heal normally. *At risk:* low zinc levels are found in those with high blood pressure, arterial heart disease, women who are pregnant or taking contraceptive pills, heavy drinkers, suffers from TB, and anaemia. *Cause of deficiency:* inborn in a few people; otherwise not understood.

The essential vitamins and why we need them

Vitamin	Best food sources	Function	Deficiency signs	Minimum daily need
A **retinol**	Fish liver oil, oily fish, liver, kidney, dairy foods, margarine, green vegetables, yellow fruit	Essential for growth, health of eyes, structure and health of skin	Night blindness, cararrhal and bronchial infections, skin complaints	Children under 13: 1200iu (=360mcg). Adults: 2500iu (=750mcg)
B1 **thiamin**	Yeast, wheat germ, meat, soya beans, bread, green vegetables	Essential for growth, release of energy from carbohydrates, health of nerves, muscles	Neurological disorders, skin and hair and digestive disorders, beri beri	Children under 13: 0.8mg Adults: 1–1.2mg
B2 **riboflavin**	Yeast, wheat germ, meat, soya beans, eggs, vegetables milk, liver	Essential for growth, health of skin, mouth, eyes, general well-being	Dry hair and skin, mouth sores, lack of stamina	Children under 13: 0.8mg Adults: 1.7mg

Vitamin	Best food sources	Function	Deficiency signs	Minimum daily need
pantothenic acid	Yeast, liver, wholemeal bread, brown rice, eggs	Health of skin and hair, including hair growth. Needed for all tissue growth	Dry skin and hair	Children under 13: 2.5mg Adults: 5–10mg
B6 pyridoxine	Yeast, wheat germ, meat, fish, wholemeal products, milk, green vegetables	Essential for body's use of protein, health of skin, nerves and muscle	Irritability, depression, skin eruptions, insomnia, muscle cramps	2mg. Women taking oral contraceptives need much more
B12 cyanocobala-min	Liver and meat, spinach, eggs, lettuce	Health of nerves and skin, body's use of protein, growth	Anaemia, tiredness, skin disorders	Children under 13: 0.5–1mcg Adults: 1–5mcg
biotin (B group)	Liver, kidney, vegetables, nuts	Probably essential for healthy skin, nerves and muscles	Falling hair, eczema	Children under 13: 0.25mcg Adults: 1mcg
choline and inositol (B group)	Eggs, liver, yeast, offal	Both essential for functioning of liver, prevent build-up of fats in body	Liver disorders, reduced alcohol tolerance	Children under 13: 2.5mg Adults: 10mg of each
folic acid (B group)	Offal meats, green vegetables, yeast	Essential for all growth, healthy blood	Anaemia, weakness, depression, diarrhoea	0.5mg
niacin nicotinic acid (B group)	Fish, poultry, yeast, peanuts	Essential for growth, health of skin, digestion of carbohydrates, nervous system	Skin disorders, nervous and intestinal upset, headaches, insomnia, pellagra	Children under 13: 5–16mg Adults: 18mg
C ascorbic acid	Fruit and vegetables	Essential to health of cells, blood vessels, gums and teeth, healing of wounds	Sore gums, slow healing, painful joints, scurvy	15mg is minimum
D calciferol	Fish liver oils, sunshine on skin, oily fish, butter and margarine, eggs	Formation of bones and teeth	Retarded growth, crooked bones (rickets), tooth decay, weak muscles	Children under 13: 250iu (=10mcg) Adults: 100iu (= 2.5mcg)
E tocopherol	Vegetable oils, wheat germ, wholemeal bread, egg yolks, green vegetables, nuts	Known to be essential, but function not fully understood. Needed for fertility and muscle health by animals	In animals, muscular disorders, infertility and nervous disorders	Not certain but estimate at 10iu (=10mg)
K phytomenadione	Green vegetables, soya beans, liver, oils	Essential for blood clotting	Prolonged bleeding from cuts or sores	About 100mcg

Modern Medical Machinery

The advance in scientific understanding of the structure and chemistry of the body which has led, within little more than a single generation – our own generation, let us not forget – to greater progress in medicine than has occurred in the whole of history, has been matched by parallel progress in machines and techniques which science now makes available to the physician.

Open heart surgery   The discovery of anaesthetics and the understanding of the importance of asepsis (the need to keep operations free from invading micro-organisms from the operating theatre and the air in it, from the surgeon's breath and hands and from his instruments) enabled surgeons to carry out more radical operations than had before seemed possible. First came such life-saving procedures as appendectomy. To have one's appendix out seems simple to us whereas, before Lister's time, it could be a sentence of death. A major step forward in surgery was, however, made possible by the development of machines in which the heart and lungs could be by-passed. The equipment made provision for pumping the blood with a mechanical pump, through a system in which it could be aerated and from there back through the patient's body while the operation, which might be prolonged over a period of several hours, was in progress.

'EMI' body scanner   The discovery in 1895, by Wilhelm Röntgen, at that time professor of physics at Würzburg, of X-rays represented a major contribution of science to medicine. X-rays enabled surgeons to locate the exact position of foreign bodies, for example gun shot, in the tissues of their patients and hence know precisely where to operate. More than that, doctors were soon able to detect pathological states by, for example, feeding a patient a liquid 'barium meal' opaque to X-rays, and by the shadows of the organs themselves. Now, by the use of a complex and sophisticated piece of equipment – the 'body scanner' – the structure of the brain and of other organs can be 'viewed' in three dimensions. The equipment is designed to take X-ray pictures of a series of fine 'slices' of the organ under examination and can then combine the information derived from all the 'slices' to produce a complete 3-dimensional picture of its entire interior structure. From this the physician can hope to identify damage or disease.

Electro-encephalogram (EEG) and the activity of the brain   Although nerves, which carry messages from different parts of the body to the brain, back again from the brain to the muscles, and from one part of the brain to another, do not work like wires carrying electricity, when they operate they do produce electric signals. An electro-encephalogram is a quite complex piece of equipment designed to give a continuous record of these signals derived from electrodes fastened to the patient's scalp. Different traces are recorded from electrodes attached to different parts of the scalp. Changes in the traces recorded also appear when the patient's eyes are closed, when he is asleep and, during sleep, when he is dreaming. Of greater interest for the physician is the fact that a characteristic spike occurs in the trace produced by patients with epilepsy. This machine is of value in the diagnosis and treatment of malfunction of the brain.

Electrocardiogram (ECG) and the beating of the heart Each time the muscles of the different quarters of the heart rhythmically contract and relax, a change in the polarisation of the potassium ions inside the muscle fibres and the sodium ions outside occurs. These changes can be recorded as electrical pulses by an electrocardiogram. The complete trace produced by this sophisticated piece of scientific equipment tells a doctor, in considerable detail, whether a patient's heart is healthy or, if not, in what respect it is at fault. Modern machines can be constructed to monitor a sick man's heart and automatically switch on a pacemaker should the need arise.

In a healthy person, a subtle physiological system in the heart initiates the process of polarisation and depolarisation of the heart muscles whereby a steady heart-beat is maintained. In certain types of heart-failure, this automatic system is disturbed. Within recent years, a small electrical device has been developed, powered by a nickel-cadmium battery designed to last for from three to five years which delivers a pulse at regular intervals of time. The electrode from this machine is lodged in the right ventricle of the heart and the machine itself with its battery is embedded in the chest under the skin. Recently a more subtle pacemaker has been developed called the 'ventricular-inhibited demand-pulse generator'. This possesses a sensing circuit capable of detecting the natural pulsation of the ventricle of the heart. The sensing circuit only brings the electrical pacemaker into operation when the natural function fails.

Dialysis machines It was Claude Bernard, the greatest of all French physiologists who, in the middle of the nineteenth century, discovered the importance of there being at all times a stable concentration of all the various chemical components of the bloodstream. This stability is maintained to an astonishing degree by the kidneys. If a man drinks a lot of water which, on being absorbed, would dilute the bloodstream, the kidneys allow exactly the right amount to be excreted as urine, but no more. Kidney failure, whereby the stability not only of the concentration of water but of other compounds and particularly of urea, derived from the breakdown of such protein as is used as fuel, is a serious condition. Machines have recently been developed in which the blood of a patient with kidney failure can be pumped across a semi-permeable membrane through which urea can penetrate and is then reintroduced into the patient's body. Clearly, it is of vital importance that during this procedure complete sterility is maintained to avoid the possibility of the blood being infected or contaminated during dialysis. Again we have an example of science – the knowledge that urea in the blood must be removed and that this can be done by dialysis – underlying the construction of a machine by which patients can live and without which they would die.

Micro-surgery and tissue transplants   Let us finish this chapter with an example, if not of a machine, then of the use of sophisticated modern equipment to do something, in combination with newly-discovered drugs and techniques, without which the end in view could not be attained. Patients with kidney disease can be kept alive and in good health by dialysis. And for this they are grateful. Nevertheless, it is a hardship for them to know that their life hangs on a session, once or twice each week, during which their blood must flow through a machine. To save them from this, surgeons have succeeded in transplanting into their bodies a healthy kidney, sacrificed for their good by a courageous donor, or bequeathed by some unselfish and far-sighted person who later became victim to an accidental death. The first kidney transplant was done in 1961 and within five years, 600 patients had thus benefited. Today, other organs have been successfully transplanted including the heart.

The technical achievement of connecting a complex organ to a patient's body calls for the use of newly-developed techniques of micro-surgery whereby, not one surgeon, but a team of surgeons are enabled to see through a microscope what they are doing as they work. The tools and sutures they use need to be correspondingly small so that they can join together blood vessels, muscle fibres and nerves.

And supporting their technical virtuosity, the surgeons also need to possess the scientific understanding of 'rejection'. The human body, like that of other animals, possesses a biochemical defence mechanism which causes it to reject any foreign substance which may gain access to its tissues. This mechanism can reject a transplant. Recent discoveries have been made which show that certain drugs together with certain types of irradiation will overcome the 'immune response' through which rejection is brought about, making successful transplants possible.

At the beginning of this fruitful modern period of the application of science to medicine and disease, good came to the community on a grand scale. Drains, lavatories and clean piped water may seem simple consequences to arise from the science of Pasteur but their introduction did away with cholera, typhoid and dysentery. In the middle period, DDT killed the mosquitoes which carried the malaria and millions benefited, and streptomycin did away with tuberculosis from which my father died at an age younger than I [MP] am now. Today, while dramatic procedures save the few in need of a new heart or kidney or liver, other scientists, their feats still to be achieved, strive to understand the cancer process and the secrets of heart failure. Science has indeed done much in the history of medicine, but there is more still to do.

In the earliest blood transfusions the blood used came from animals.

An abracadabra was originally a charm used to cure hay fever.

3,986 people in London officially died of dropsy caused by alcohol in the years 1657–1665.

Even before the Great Plague of 1665 over 75,000 Londoners had died of the disease in the previous sixty years. Indeed between 1603 and 1665 only four years out of the sixty-two had been completely free from plague.

Among his many observations, Charles Darwin noticed that lice which had emigrated from Hawaiian islanders to English sailors died within a week.

The novelist, Arnold Bennett, died in Paris in 1931 from typhoid, which he contracted after drinking a glass of water to prove that Parisian water was perfectly safe to drink.

One male death in ten in Great Britain in 1976 was the result of lung cancer.

Victims of the disease, bulimia, can spend as long as twelve hours a day eating. In the case of Matthew Daking, the twelve-year-old boy consumed 384 lb 2 oz of food in only six days.

You can use blackberries to make a wine, a hair-dye, a medicine for treating whooping cough and a refreshing drink for patients with a high temperature.

It is estimated that medical students increase their vocabularies by as many as 10,000 words during their studies.

The human nervous system is the product of millions of years of evolution. It is comprised of over 10,000,000,000 nerve cells.

3

Food & Agriculture

Farming

It is generally assumed that prehistoric people picked up a living as best they could by eating what wild plants they found to be edible and hunting such animals as they were able to catch. These early communities, however, appeared quite soon to have hit on the idea of farming. Neolithic settlements show evidence that seeds of grain were sown and that domestic animals were kept. Predynastic tombs in Egypt, early Sumerian houses in Mesopotamia dating back to 3500 BC and lake dwellings in Switzerland have yielded grain of comparatively advanced type implying that even then agriculture was by no means new. There is other evidence to show that different types of wheat were being cultivated in different centres even in prehistoric times: soft wheats in Afghanistan, durum wheats in North Africa and the primitive form, einkorn, in Asia Minor. Historical writers of classical Greece and Rome write of agriculture as having been practised for centuries. Pliny described elaborate systems for farming wheat, beans and olives together with the use of advanced stock-breeding systems. Indeed, Roman agriculture, disseminated across those areas of Europe, Asia and Africa which came under the civilizing influence of the Empire, although it was disrupted by the later barbarian incursions, was not improved until the introduction of the scientific ideas of the nineteenth century culminating in the major advances of today.

In medieval times, the land in England was farmed communally. While the lord of the manor might have his special rights, and tenants could lay claim to particular areas of the strips into which the land was divided, after the harvest was taken in, everybody's livestock was let loose to wander at will. This system was highly inefficient. Fertilizers had not been invented and crop yields were low. A farmer could only expect to get back four times his weight of seed oats, five times his seed wheat, six times his seed beans, seven times his seed rye and eight times his seed barley. Returns of meat and milk were equally unsatisfactory since, everybody's livestock wandering together, the systematic improvement of the breed was impossible. It was not until the enclosure of the land, beginning in Tudor times, was virtually complete by the middle of the nineteenth century, that major improvements in agriculture and food production were achieved.

Before the application of science to agriculture revolutionized the situation, virtually within the present century, a number of important innovations had been made. Sir Richard Weston (1591–1652) introduced turnips and sown grasses, including clover, which enabled farmers to keep their cattle through the winter. Not only did this increase the production of meat but the extra amounts of manure thus available added fertility to the soil. In 1845, Thomas Scroggy invented a machine for moulding cylindrical tiles which enabled farmers to drain heavy wet soil. But perhaps the man whose influence was most effective in bringing agriculture into the scientific age was John Bennet Lawes who, together with a young chemist, Joseph Gilbert, organized a series of systematic trials on his farm at Rothamsted which have been continued to this day. In 1843, Lawes and Gilbert studied the effect on crop yields of applying fertilizers of various chemical composition. Among these was superphosphate which they manufactured themselves.

By 1850 the manufacture of artificial fertilizers was in full swing and by 1870 the general standard of wheat production had been raised from its medieval level of about 10 bushels per acre up to 30 bushels per acre.

The spread of scientific knowledge about farming, and in particular about the value of artificial fertilizers able to contribute nitrogen, phosphorus and potash, led to an enormous increase in the world's food supplies during the latter part of the nineteenth century and the early part of the twentieth. At this time the wide acres of the prairies of Canada and the United States were being opened up successfully while further tracts of arable land were being brought into production in Australia. Yet the great expansion of wheat production which allowed the world population to grow and be fed was due mainly to the science of biology, as exemplified in genetics, rather than to the science of chemistry. It also owed much to innovations in engineering from which came the reaper and binder, to be followed later on by the combine harvester. These came into existence following the invention of such implements as the horse-hoe in the eighteenth century.

Science in the aid of agriculture – four combine harvesters move across part of the greatest grain-producing area of the world, mid-western America

Biological science enabled plant breeders to produce new wheat varieties capable of growing in the vast cold and arid areas of Canada where no crops could be produced before. The early pioneers in Canada, before the work of Darwin on evolution had been established and while Mendel and his system of genetics were still to be accepted, were yet seized with the restless ideas of experimentation upon which science is based. In the 1840s a few ears of corn were observed to thrive better than their neighbours. From this observation, a strain of wheat, Red Fife, was cultivated. Charles Sanders, studying Red Fife, separated another, even stronger-growing seedling. This was later called Marquis. The two varieties – Red Fife and Marquis – proved to be well suited to prairie conditions and enabled wheat to be grown farther northward and westward than had previously been possible. Then, in 1916, when immense fields covering almost the whole area of the plains of Manitoba, Alberta and Saskatchewan were sown with Marquis, there came an epidemic of a fungus disease, stem rust. In one year, 100,000,000 bushels of wheat were lost. And after the outbreak of 1916, there followed others. In 1927, 90,000,000 bushels were lost; in 1935, the loss was 87,000,000 bushels. In the eleven years from 1925 to 1935, the total loss of wheat due to stem rust in Manitoba and Saskatchewan was nearly 4,000,000,000 bushels.

The successes of chemistry in the development of artificial fertilizers and the consequent improvement in the production of food have already been referred to. The further progress made in the development of fungicides, insecticides and herbicides, is touched on below. But in the 1930s no chemical check to the ravages of rust diseases could be found. The control of rust was, nevertheless, achieved. In 1924, a strain of wheat called Ceres, resistant to stem rust, was developed by plant geneticists in the United States, and for a decade until 1935 was successfully grown as the chief immune wheat in Canada. Then, a strain of the fungus, *P. graminis*, which could attack Ceres wheat, spread across the fields and the crops again succumbed. Almost immediately, another wheat strain was developed in the laboratory under the name of Thatcher, resistant to the infection, stem rust. Later, Canadian geneticists produced a cross-breed variety of wheat, called Regent, resistant to both stem rust *and* leaf rust.

The ability of biological scientists to use genetics to produce cereal strains resistant to the attacks of fungus diseases have been signal successes in the development of agriculture in supplying food. These advances making use of biology have been linked with parallel progress in chemistry leading to the development of superphosphate by Lawes followed by what was probably of even greater importance, namely the Haber process for the fixation of nitrogen from the atmosphere.

Plants have a need for nitrogen from the soil to enable them to grow. The nitrogen must, however, be in an available form, for example, as ammonia or ammonium compounds. For most crops, the nitrogen of which about 80 per cent of the atmosphere is composed, cannot be utilized. Certain plant species, of

The harvest from the sea

which the legumes, comprising peas and beans and clover, are the best known, by virtue of micro-organisms which grow in association with their roots, *can* use nitrogen from the air. This not only enables them to dispense with nitrogenous fertilizer but also contributes nitrogen available to subsequent crops to the soil on which they are grown.

Before World War One broke out in 1914, Fritz Haber in Germany had succeeded in working out a process whereby nitrogen gas and hydrogen, raised to a temperature of $555\,^\circ$C and a pressure of 200 atmospheres, combined to form ammonia. In collaboration with Karl Bosch, he developed a large-scale process capable of producing not only ammonia but ammonium sulphate, ammonium nitrate or ammonium phosphate, all of which are excellent fertilizers.

The combination of chemical advances leading to the manufacture of artificial fertilizers and biological research leading to the development of improved strains of crop varieties is strikingly demonstrated in the work of Borlaug in the 1970s. The production of improved strains of cereals suited to culture in such places as Canada and Australia and later resistant to fungal

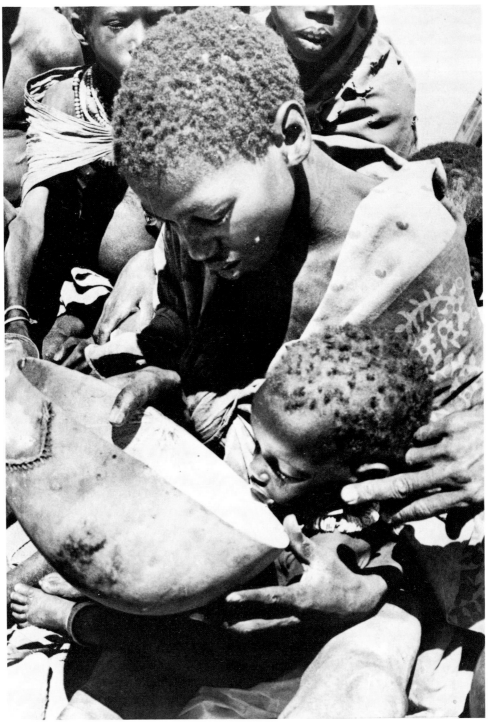

Famine is one of the worst disasters to befall mankind. Here a Ugandan mother helps her baby to eat at a Save the Children feeding centre in the famine-stricken Karamoja region of Uganda in 1980

Drought in Third World countries frequently leads to widespread famine. Here a villager in New Delhi in 1979 examines dried stalks from his farm – all that was left of his summer rice crop which was destroyed in India's worst drought in 25 years.

attack, was achieved with only a general understanding of plant genetics. Borlaug and his colleagues, however, succeeded in producing strains of wheat and rice capable of yielding greatly increased crops of grain by having been bred to devote less of their energies to producing stalk. At the same time these improved short-stalked varieties (produced by the application of biology) responded readily to the appropriate application of artificial fertilizers (produced by the application of chemistry).

The co-operative effects of scientific plant-breeding on the one hand – this patient exercise in applied biology – and chemistry on the other, have also been exemplified in the development of new chemical insecticides even if, beside the enormous importance of the fertilizer industry, these other contributions of chemistry may seem small. The first important discovery in this field was made in 1858 when it was found that, by spraying grapevines with carbon disulphide, phylloxera, or root-aphis, which was devastating the vineyards of Europe, could be controlled. Then, in 1860, Paris Green (the pigment, aceto-arsenite) was used to kill leaf-eating insects. It is interesting to note that Paris Green was still in use to kill Colorado potato beetles when I [MP] was a student in Canada in 1930. Next came lead arsenite, of which 20,000 tons or more a year were used to combat the gipsy moth in America.

In 1944 a major advance occurred in the development of DDT (dichloro-diphenyl-dichloro-ethylene) as an insecticide. This is discussed on page 114.

The dramatic improvement in the yield of cereals due to the application of genetics leading to the development of more productive strains also took place when genetics were applied to the production of meat, milk and poultry. The jungle fowl, laying one or two clutches of eggs a year, was taken from the Indian forests and converted into a monosexual marvel laying 300 eggs a year. Likewise the cow, once content to produce milk for its own calf and a little over, was bred and nourished to produce milk by the ton.

By thus applying science to agriculture, the productivity of the land was increased to a remarkable degree. By the early 1970s, in Ireland, where 12 kilos of nitrogen were used per hectare of land, the agricultural output per hectare was costed at £60. In Great Britain, where, on average, 60 kilos of nitrogen was applied, £200 worth of food was harvested. In Belgium, where 110 kilos of nitrogen were employed, the value of the crops was £410 per hectare, while in Holland where the farmers used 170 kilos of nitrogen, the value of a hectare's worth of crops averaged £590.

Common vegetables – their scientific names and origins

Common name	Scientific name	Geographical origin	Date first described or known
Asparagus	*Asparagus officinalis*	Eastern Mediterranean	*c.* 200 B.C.
Beetroot	*Beta vulgaris*	Mediterranean Area	2nd century B.C.
Broad Bean	*Vicia faba*	—	prehistoric
Broccoli	*Brassica oleracea* (variety *Italica*)	Eastern Mediterranean	1st century A.D.
Brussels Sprouts	*Brassica oleracea* (variety *Gemmifera*)	Northern Europe	1587
Cabbage	*Brassica oleracea* (variety *Capitata*)	Eastern Mediterranean lands and Asia Minor	*c.* 600 B.C.
Carrot	*Daucus carota*	Afghanistan	*c.* 500 B.C.
Cauliflower	*Brassica oleracea* (variety *Botrytis*)	Eastern Mediterranean	6th century B.C.
Celery	*Apium graveolens*	Caucasus	*c.* 850 B.C.
Chive	*Allium schoenoprasum*	Eastern Mediterranean	*c.* 100 B.C.
Cucumber	*Cucumis sativus*	Northern India	2nd century B.C.
Endive	*Cichorium endivia*	Eastern Mediterranean lands and Asia Minor	B.C.
Garden Pea	*Pisum sativum*	Central Asia	3000–2000 B.C.
Garlic	*Allium sativum*	Middle Asia	*c.* 900 B.C. (Homer)
Gherkin	*Cucurnis anguria*	Northern India	2nd century B.C.
Globe Artichoke	*Cynara scolymus*	Western and Central Mediterranean	*c.* 500 B.C.
Kale	*Brassica oleracea* (variety *Acephala*)	Eastern Mediterranean lands and Asia Minor	*c.* 500 B.C.
Leek	*Allium porrum*	Middle Asia	*c.* 1000 B.C.
Lettuce	*Lactuca sativa*	Iran	6th century B.C.

Common name	Scientific name	Geographical origin	Date first described or known
Marrow	Cucurbita pepo	America?	16th–17th century
Muskmelon	Cucumis melo	Iran and Transcaucasia	c. 2400 B.C.
Onion	Allium cepa	Middle Asia	c. 2400 B.C.
Parsnip	Pastinaca sativa	Caucasus	1st century B.C.
Pepper	Capsicium frutescens	Peru	1493
Potato	Solanum tuberosum	Southern Chile	c. 1530
Radish	Raphanus sativus	China and Middle Asia	c. 3000 B.C.
Runner Bean	Phaseolus vulgaris	Central America	c. 1500
Soybean	Soja max	China	c. 2850 B.C.
Spinach	Spinacia oleracea	Iran	A.D.647
Swede	Brassica napobrassica	Europe	1620
Sweet Corn	Zea mays (variety Saccharata)	Andes	c. 1801
Tomato	Lycopersicon esculentum	Bolivia–Ecuador–Peru area	1554
Turnip	Brassica rapa	Greece	c. 400 B.C.

Common fruits – their scientific names and origins

Common name	Scientific name	Geographical origin	Date first described or known
Apple	Malus pumila	Southwestern Asia	4th century B.C.
Apricot	Prunus armeniaca	Central and western China	B.C.
Avocado (Pear)	Persea americana	Mexico and Central America	c. 1825
Banana	Musa sapientum	Southern Asia	c. 1st cent. A.D.
Cherry	Prunus avium	Europe (near Dardanelles)	300 B.C.
Date	Phoenix dactylifera	unknown	B.C.
Fig	Ficus carica	Syria westward to the Canary islands	c. 2000 B.C.
Grape	Vitus vinifera	around Caspian and Black Seas	c. 4000 B.C.
Grapefruit	Citrus grandis	Malay Archipelago and neighbouring islands	c. 1693
Lemon	Citrus limon	Northern Burma	11th–13th centuries
Lime	Citrus aurantifolia	Northern Burma	11th–13th centuries
Mandarin (Orange)	Citrus reticulata	China	220 B.C.
Mango	Mangifera indica	Southeastern Asia	c. 16th century
Olive	Olea europaea	Syria to Greece	B.C.
Orange	Citrus sinensis	China	2200 B.C.
Papaya	Carica papaya	West Indian Islands or Mexican mainland	14th–15th–centuries
Peach	Prunus persica	? China	c. 2000 B.C.
Pear	Erwinia amylovora	Western Asia	c. 10th century B.C.
Pineapple	Ananas comosus	Guadeloupe	c. 1493
Plum	Prunus domestica	Western Asia	c. 1500
Quince	Cydonia oblonga	Northern Iran	B.C.
Rhubarb	Rheum rhaponticum	Eastern Mediterranean lands and Asia Minor	2700 B.C.
Water Melon	Citrullus vulgaris	Central Africa	c. 2000 B.C.

Food Processing

The traditional methods of processing foods are based on scientific principles just as are the newer methods of food technology. Virtually every article of diet needs to be processed before it is eaten. While a number of the traditional methods which originated before there was any scientific understanding of the principles upon which they were based are still used, the growth of scientific understanding and the development of modern technological processes have given modern generations certain advantages not possessed by their ancestors.

Milling and baking   The importance of cereals, wheat and rye in the West and rice in the East, lies in the fact that the plants store starch in their seeds to feed the new seedling during its early stages of growth before leaves develop capable of trapping the energy of sunlight. They therefore form an excellent source of energy for the people who eat them. But just as the seeds must be separated from the straw and the husk, so also must the endosperm of the seed, containing the store of starch, be separated from the tough outer layers of the grain. After threshing, therefore, must come the process of milling. From early times this was done by grinding up the grain between mill stones. The flour thus produced tended to be coarse and was of a brownish off-white colour even if it was carefully sifted. Furthermore, it tended to become mouldy and sour if kept for any extended length of time. In the nineteenth century, the modern milling process was developed. The grain is initially passed through fluted 'break' rolls which crack the seeds open. Sieves then separate the little lumps of flour, now called semolina, from the coarse 'wheat feed'. When the semolina is passed between pairs of smooth rollers it is reduced to fine white flour, which is then separated from any admixture of outer structures of the grain by sieving. This system permits the whitest flour to be milled or flour containing any desired proportion of wheat fraction other than starch to be produced.

The next operations, making dough and baking it, are ancient procedures which remained virtually unchanged until the present day. They are required because, even when flour has been separated from the rest of the grain, the starch granules of which it is mainly composed cannot readily be digested. The heat of the oven operating on the dough bursts the starch granules and renders them digestible. Yeast incorporated in the dough produces carbon dioxide gas as part of its life process (just as we do). The bubbles of gas expand in the heat of the oven and give the dough an open porous structure, stretching the fibres of the protein, gluten. Eventually, the temperature rises to a point at which the protein becomes 'denatured' and fixed in the honeycomb structure of a well-risen loaf.

Sugar refining   Sugar only became readily available within comparatively modern times when science was being applied to technical processes. Sugar cane contains from 14 to 17 per cent of sugar; sugar beet about 18 per cent. To extract the sugar, cane is cut up and the bits pressed between rollers; the sugar from beet is extracted with hot water. The syrups thus obtained are concentrated by a highly efficient process of multiple evaporation, and the crude sugar crystals separated on a battery of centrifuges and washed in hot water. They are then subjected to a series of purification processes using first lime and subsequently bone charcoal. The final white sugar crystals are virtually pure sucrose.

Meat processing The high quality of tender fresh meat obtainable in a technically competent community depends on the application of a few basic scientific principles. To start with, the farmer, by selecting the appropriate breed of animal, and the use of properly selected diet and handling, can alter the conformation of his animals to produce beef, mutton and pork of the desired quality. A second important point is to ensure that the animals are relaxed and rested immediately before they are killed. If they have struggled or are otherwise exhausted on coming to slaughter, the level of glycogen in their muscles will be reduced and will not be sufficient to provide the degree of acidity required for good-quality meat.

The quality of meat that has been transported long distances, usually by ship, can be maintained only if the appropriate level of refrigeration is employed and if the required level of carbon-dioxide gas is kept in the atmosphere of the store.

Milk, butter, margarine and cheese production Science has performed several notable feats in providing well-run societies with a uniform supply of reliable milk. In nineteenth-century England, a slang expression for milk was 'sky blue'. This implied that the milk had been watered. Only when accurate laboratory techniques were developed was it possible to monitor its composition.

Of even greater importance was the campaign which only reached its successful conclusion in the 1940s to ensure a safe milk supply uncontaminated by the bacilli of bovine tuberculosis. It was Louis Pasteur in the 1870s who demonstrated that the bacteria in food could be destroyed by raising the temperature high enough to kill them without necessarily damaging the quality of the food. The harmful bacteria in milk can be killed by raising the temperature to 65 °C and keeping it at that temperature for 30 minutes, or by heating the milk to 72 °C for 15 seconds. Recently, the UHT process (ultra high temperature) has been developed whereby milk is heated to 132 °C for one second, after which it is immediately cooled. Milk treated thus can be kept without refrigeration for some weeks without suffering deterioration.

Butter is a product made from milk fat (butter fat as it is called). Naturally-occurring, acid-forming bacteria sour cream which, by being subjected to the appropriate mechanical agitation of churning, is converted from a watery suspension of fat globules (cream) into a suspension of water globules in fat (butter). Margarine, invented by Hypollite Mèges Mouriès in 1870, is a comparable preparation using some other vegetable or animal fats rather than butter fat alone.

Butter was originally produced as a milk product which could be kept longer than milk itself. Cheese was developed in the distant past as an even more durable milk product. Whereas the fat from milk is the main ingredient in butter, in cheese the principal component is the protein, casein. Again, however, the manufacture of cheese depends on the use of a bacterial culture producing acid which, at an appropriate degree of acidity, the so-called iso-electric point, causes the protein to curdle. By appropriate treatment of the curd, liquid whey runs out and the curd, carrying with it more or less fat, depending on the type of cheese desired, hardens into the finished cheese.

Changes in our food since 1800

1800   Main foods for most people were bread, cheese, beer, meat, fish, root vegetables and cabbage family. Expensive but growing in popularity were tea, sugar and coffee which were all imported and subject to heavy taxes which made them luxury foods. There was only homegrown fruit, vegetables and meat. Flour was the main commodity; it was sieved wholemeal, so it retained all nutrients except some bran. No preserving methods except drying, salting or cheesemaking for milk.

1810   Bottling as a method of food preservation was invented by Nicholas Appert, a Parisian confectioner, who won the prize Napoleon had offered in 1795 for the person who devised a successful food preserving method.

1812   Tinned canisters were used instead of bottles by a London firm, Donkin, Hall and Gamble. Very expensive as each tin was hand made: mainly used for naval expeditions.
Grocers multiplied to supply growing urban communities. They sold a very limited range, almost all basic foods: tea, coffee, chocolate, spices, sugar, rice, sago, semolina, dried fruit, nuts and a few more. There were virtually no branded, ready-made foods in shops.

1831   First commercial biscuit factory was started by Jonathan Dodgson Carr, son of a Kendal grocer.

1830s   Potatoes joined staple foods. Railways started up on a countrywide scale, but were not used extensively for food transport because the travel cost made the food uncompetitive with local supplies.

1841   First commercial jam factory was set up in Soho by Messrs. Crosse and Blackwell. Before this, jam was made at home or bought from local shops. Commercial manufacture only became practical because of lower sugar prices as taxes were cut in '36 and '44.

1845   More reductions in sugar tax followed over next 10 years. Railway transport continued to develop.

1864   Tax on sugar and tea removed, resulting in big jump in consumption of both, and of sugar-based foods such as jam, chocolate and sweets.

1866   Solid chocolate first sold, made by John Cadbury and his brother.

1869   Margarine first experimentally made by Mège-Mouriès in France.

Sugar consumption about 6lbs per year. Bread and flour about 370lbs per year, or about 1lb per day. Fat intake under 1oz per day.

Low intake of fruit and vegetables, but what was eaten was locally grown and usually fresh. More bulk of food eaten but only slightly more calories, in spite of much higher calorie use for most people.

If calorie intake was high enough, diet provided enough nutrients except for iodine-deficient areas and sometimes vitamin D shortage, producing rickets.

Arrival of railways first step in move to centralized food production, rather than local. New need was for food that could travel without spoiling.

Sugar consumption jumped to about 17lbs per person per year in 1844; rose to 34lbs by 1854, 42lbs by 1864 with removal of tax.

More fruit and vegetables eaten, but otherwise trend moved towards processed foods with losses of vitamins and minerals. Branded foods began to appear in shops. Tea consumption soared from 1833 level of $1\frac{1}{4}$lbs per head a year to $3\frac{1}{4}$lbs by 1863. Potatoes important: about 300lbs per person a year.

1870s	Tinned meat technique developed to bring meat from Australia cheaply. It cost the equivalent of about $2\frac{1}{2}$p per lb bones, about a third of UK meat price.
	Roller mills introduced for grinding wheat. They quickly replaced most stonegrinding mills because they were faster and made whiter flour, really white instead of sieved wholemeal.
1880	Refrigerated shipping developed for meat, butter, lard and bacon imports, so these foods became much cheaper as supply improved. Tinned food became generally available. More preservative chemicals used.
1890	Refined breakfast cereals (Cornflakes) invented by Dr Kellogg at Battle Creek sanitarium, Michigan.
1900	Sugar prices continued to be low, so that sugar and fat became cheap foods after centuries of being costly.
1920	Spray drying and roller drying developed to produce 'instant' powdered foods such as milk and coffee. Vacuum drying applied to vegetables. Lorries arrived in force.
1930	Frozen food became commercially successful. For the first time, the seasons became much less important in food supply.
1940s	First period when almost every westerner had not only enough to eat, but a choice of food. Food processing industry developed fast as trend began to produce foods in large-scale plants, from where it was distributed countrywide. This brought the need for food to be durable under storage and transport: the need for food to keep longer than it would naturally encouraged the growth of the additive industry.
1950s on	Convenience foods became more and more important, following the sharp decline in domestic service, equally sharp rise in number of working women. Additive industry produced hundreds of new compounds and new uses to make food keep longer, look more uniform or attractive.

Cheaper fat and protein encouraged switch from potatoes, bread and flour. Bread intake down to 280lbs a year. New roller-milled flour was without wheat germ oil, bran and many vitamins and minerals. Cut in fibre intake from bran because of milling method, and because of falling bread intake. Fat intake still restricted by poverty, meat about 4oz per day. Sugar intake up to 85lbs per person per year. Tea consumption still rising. Switch to processed foods, encouraged by better transport.

Sharp drops in potato, bread and flour intakes, replaced by sugar, fat, as incomes rose. Bread and flour down to about 150lbs per person a year (up during war years to 240–250lbs), sugar topped 110lbs (under rationing, 70–80lbs), fat over 50lbs (30–40lbs during rationing). Potatoes down to 190lbs (up to 280 during war). Bread and flour intake down to about 110lbs per year, still dropping. Potatoes down to under 200lbs. Sugar: about 126lbs (about $5\frac{1}{2}$oz per day). Fat: about 114lbs (5oz per day). Meat up to 135lbs (about 6oz a day) – and protein from eggs has trebled.

Net results

1 Sugar up 20 times.
2 Fat up at least 5 times.
3 Protein up slightly.
4 Fibre or roughage down by about half:
   cereal fibre reduced to negligible amount,
   but fibre from vegetable and fruit up.
5 Almost all food is processed, with changes in its basic properties.
6 To help centralized production, use of additives has soared.

Canning The principles upon which canning is based are (i) to pack food in an impervious container. This is usually a steel box lined with tin. A glass bottle can also be used or, now that polymers are being made capable of withstanding high temperatures, a plastic pouch or other container. When the food has been thus packed it must (ii) be heated to a temperature sufficient to kill all the micro-organisms which could do harm to those who ate the food, or make the food go bad.

Nicholas Appert invented the process in 1806 on empirical grounds, that is to say, he did not understand the principles on which it is based because Pasteur had not then discovered bacteria. It is, therefore, not surprising that, in 1845, canned food supplied to the British navy was the cause of a serious outbreak of food poisoning. The heating to which the cans were subjected was not sufficient to raise the temperature at the centre to a level lethal to the micro-organisms there. Since that time, however, millions of cans containing a great diversity of foods have been successfully processed.

Freezing The freezing of food by which the quality and diversity of the modern diet is enhanced was made possible by the principles developed by Nicholas Carnot early in the nineteenth century, who demonstrated theoretically how heat could be pumped by a machine as if it were a fluid. Today, heat is removed from food by three main processes. *Immersion freezing* requires the articles to be frozen to be plunged into a bath of some very cold liquid. *Cryogenic freezing* is a modification of this process in which liquid nitrogen at the exceedingly low temperature of $-196°C$ is sprayed on to the food. *Multiplate freezing* involves the use of a cabinet with a number of hollow shelves which supply the freezing surface. The food is put between the shelves which are then made to press upon it. *Convection or blast freezing* is done by exposing food to a strong blast of refrigerated air. A variation of this method is *fluidized bed freezing* in which a blast of cold air is blown upwards through a bed of peas, or whatever the food may be, in such a way that they bounce up and down in the air flow and the entire mass behaves as if it were a liquid.

Dehydration Drying has been used since times of antiquity as a means of preserving food. Early processes not only involved losses in nutritional value – whether in converting grass into hay or fresh fish into red herring – but also a serious deterioration in dietetic quality. Perhaps the most sucessful modern dehydration technique to be developed has been *spray drying*. In this process, milk, liquid egg, or whatever product is to be dried, is converted into a fine spray and allowed to fall from the top of a tall vessel shaped as an inverted cone. As it falls it encounters an upward draught of warm air so adjusted that when the spray reaches the bottom of the vessel, it has been converted into a fine dry powder. *Roller drying* is also used on a large scale. This involves the deposition of a sheet of liquid on to a large horizontal heated roller. The liquid dries as the roller turns carrying the product – milk, soup or whatever it may be – towards a fixed knife which scrapes the now dry material off the roller. *Accelerated freeze drying* is an advanced modification of the drying technique. The food to be dried is frozen. It is then put into a modified cabinet capable of subjecting the product to a high vacuum. Then, when the temperature is raised, the water, which is in the form of ice, is sucked off as vapour without being converted into water at all. This process is expensive to operate but (for example, with coffee) it gives a dried product of very good quality.

A Varied Wholesome Diet

The application of science and technology to agriculture increases the amount of food available to consumers all over the world. Science, for example, in the development of the refrigerator (the first true refrigerated ship, the *Strathleven*, went into use in 1871), allowed a perishable commodity like meat to be transported from New Zealand to Great Britain halfway round the globe. By making use of the single biological discovery that, whereas most perishable foods keep better if they are cooled, bananas, on the export of which whole communities depend for their livelihood, can be shipped across the sea provided their temperature is *not* permitted to fall below 13°C (55°F), great benefits accrued. But not only has one of the most important scientific feats of this century been to increase the amount of food available, the aesthetic quality has also been raised. To make margarine (and, for that matter, butter, too) on a large scale to a uniform standard, colour must be added, emulsifiers incorporated to ensure the consistency, and vitamins A and D added to improve the nutritional value. All these are categorized as 'additives'. Great pains are taken to ensure the freedom of such additives from toxicity. Although the major diseases capable of being spread by food, for example, typhoid and botulism, have been virtually extinguished, food poisoning, mainly due to infection by salmonella, is still a common modern hazard. As more knowledge is gained in the late twentieth century about the role of diet in specific conditions, so nutritional recommendations for special diets change. There is often some controversy amongst experts regarding the best dietary approach to controlling disease – and a great deal more variety of medical opinion about the best approach to that twentieth-century obsession, slimming. It is not our aim in this book to give advice on these matters; that is what doctors are for, and throughout the world nutritional experts are at work to raise the level of people's dietary habits. What can be said with confidence, however, is that a generation which has never seen a bad egg and enjoys a wide variety of foods, many of which come from far corners of the world, has cause to be grateful for the application of science to food and agriculture.

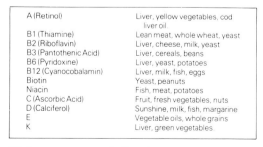

A (Retinol)	Liver, yellow vegetables, cod liver oil.
B1 (Thiamine)	Lean meat, whole wheat, yeast
B2 (Riboflavin)	Liver, cheese, milk, yeast
B3 (Pantothenic Acid)	Liver, cereals, beans
B6 (Pyridoxine)	Liver, yeast, potatoes
B12 (Cyanocobalamin)	Liver, milk, fish, eggs
Biotin	Yeast, peanuts
Niacin	Fish, meat, potatoes
C (Ascorbic Acid)	Fruit, fresh vegetables, nuts
D (Calciferol)	Sunshine, milk, fish, margarine
E	Vegetable oils, whole grains
K	Liver, green vegetables.

Dietary sources of vitamins

Carbohydrates	Approx. % of total CHO	Chief food sources	End products of digestion
Polysaccharides			
(a) Indigestible			0
1. Celluloses and hemicelluloses	3	Stalks and leaves of vegetables outer covering of seeds	
2. Pectins[1]		Fruits	0
(b) Partially digestible			
1. Inulin		Jerusalem artichokes, onions, garlic	Fructose
2. Galactogens		Snails	Galactose
3. Mannosans	2	Legumes	Mannose
4. Raffinose		Sugar beets	Glucose, fructose, and galactose
5. Pentosans		Fruits and gums	Pentoses
(c) Digestible			
1. Starch and dextrins	50	Grains, vegetables (especially tubers and legumes)	Glucose
2. Glycogen	Negligible	Meat products and seafood	Glucose
Disaccharides			
(a) Sucrose	25	Cane and beet sugars, molasses, maple syrup	Glucose and fructose
(b) Lactose	10	Milk and milk products	Glucose and galactose
(c) Maltose	Negligible	Malt products	Glucose
Monosaccharides			
(a) Hexoses			
1. Glucose	5	Fruits, honey, corn syrup	Glucose
2. Fructose	5	Fruits, honey	Fructose
3. Galactose[2]	0	0	Galactose
4. Mannose[2]	0	0	Mannose
(b) Pentoses			
1. Ribose[3]	0	0	Ribose
2. Xylose[3]	0	0	Xylose
3. Arabinase[3]	0	0	Arabinose

Source: 'Nutrition, An Integrated Approach'. R.L. Pike and M.L. Brox Brown, J. Wiley & Sons, 1967. Adapted from S. Soskin and R. Levine, 'Role of Carbohydrates in the Diet', Modern Nutrition in Health and Disease, M.G. Wohl and R.S. Goodhart, (Eds) Lea and Febiger, Philadelphia, Pa., 1965, p. 195.

[1]Chemical hydrolysis yields galactose and arabinose.
[2]These monosaccharides do not occur in free form in foods (see under lactose and mannosans).
[3]These monosaccharides do not occur in free form in foods. They are derived from pentosans of fruits and from the nucleic acids of meat products and seafood.

A summary of the role that different carbohydrates play in Western diets

Calorie count

Here are the numbers of Calories contained in 1-oz portions of a variety of foods commonly found in the British diet.

Source: Medical Research Council.

Meat and Poultry	Calories per 1 oz.		Calories per 1 oz.
		Ham, lean with fat	125
Beef, roast, lean	70	lean only	60
Steak, grilled	85	Bacon, streaky fried	150
Lamb, roast	85	gammon, fried	125
chop, grilled	140	Ox tongue	90
Pork, roast	90	Liver, fried	75
chop, grilled	155	Kidney, fried	55
Veal, roast	65	Chicken, Turkey, roast	55

	Calories per 1 oz.
Grouse	50
Partridge, Pheasant	60
Sausages, pork, fried	95
beef, fried	80
Corned beef	65

Fish

Cod, steamed	25
fried	40
Haddock, steamed	30
fried	50
Herring, fried	60
soused	50
Kipper	55
Plaice, steamed	25
fried	65
Salmon, fresh, grilled	50
Canned	40
Sardines, canned	85
Oysters	15
Prawns, shrimps	30

Dairy Produce

Milk (per fluid oz.)	20
fresh skimmed	10
dried skimmed	93
evaporated	45
Butter	225
Cream, double	130
single	60
Cheese, Cheddar	120
Stilton	135
Cottage	7
Cheese, Cream	230
Processed	105
1 egg (average, 2-oz.) boiled	
or poached	90
fried	100

Other Fats and Oils

Margarine	225
Lard, dripping, etc.	260
Olive oil and other cooking and salad oils	265
Low-fat spreads (e.g. Outline)	108

Vegetables

Celery, Marrow, Mushrooms, French Beans, Artichokes, Cabbage, Cauliflower, Chicory, Asparagus, Lettuce, Tomatoes, Onions, Watercress	*under*	5
Brussels Sprouts, Spinach		5
Mushrooms, fried		60
Broad beans, boiled		10
Baked beans		25
Beetroot, boiled		15
Carrots, boiled		5
Leeks, boiled		5

	Calories per 1 oz.
Pulses (dried haricot and butter beans, peas, split peas and lentils)	30
Onions, fried	100
Peas (fresh), boiled	15
Potatoes, boiled	25
roast	35
chips	70
crisps	160
Tomatoes, fried	20

Fruit

Apple, dessert		15
cooking		10
Apricot, fresh		10
canned		30
dried, stewed		15
Bananas		20
Blackberries		10
Cherries		15
Blackcurrants		10
Dates, sultanas, raisins		70
Figs, green		10
dried		60
Gooseberries		10
Grapes		20
Grapefruit		5
Lemon juice	*under*	5
Melon		5
Oranges		10
Peaches, fresh		10
canned		25
Pears, eating		10
canned		20
Pineapple, fresh		15
canned		20
Plums, damsons, etc.		10
Prunes (no sugar)		20
Raspberries, strawberries and similar fruits		5
Rhubarb	*under*	5

Cereals, Bread etc.

Bread, white, brown, etc.	70
Biscuits, water	125
sweet	160
Crispbread (not starch-reduced)	100
Flour, cornflour, rice and similar cereals	100
Cornflakes, rice crispies, Weetabix, etc.	105
Macaroni, spaghetti, rice (cooked)	55

Puddings and Cakes

Baked custard	35
Steamed pudding	130
Apple pie	55
Fruit cake	110
Victoria sandwich	135

	Calories per 1 oz.		*Calories per 1 oz.*
Pastry, short	160	*Nuts*	
flaky	170	Almonds	170
Scones	105	Brazil nuts	185
Shortbread	150	Chestnuts	50
Sponge cake	90	Coconut	105
		desiccated	180
Sugar, Preserves, Sweets		Peanuts	170
Sugar	110	Walnuts	155
Honey	80		
Jam, marmalade	75	*Drinks (per normal measure)*	
Golden syrup	85	Beer, $\frac{1}{2}$ pint	100
Boiled sweets	95	Wine, 1 wineglass	90
Chocolate (milk)	170	Sherry, Port, 1 small wineglass	80
Toffees	125	Spirits, 1 tot	75
		Tea, coffee, without milk, 1 cup	*under* 5
Soups and Sauces		Bournvita ($\frac{1}{3}$ pt.)	155
Clear soup	20	Marmite and Bovril, 1 cup	*under* 5
Cream soup (e.g. Cream of Lentil)	30	Lemonade	80
White sauce	40	Ribena	65
Bottled sauce	30		
Salad cream	110		

Over 95 per cent of the fish caught in the world is caught in the northern hemisphere.

You can feed twelve men with the omelette made from one ostrich egg.

At the 1909 exhibition of German sausages, there were no fewer than 1,785 individual varieties on display.

A cow grazing one acre of pasture will produce more than one ton of milk every year.

An average human being consumes about one ton of food and drink every year.

In the middle of the last century an estimated total of 1,500,000 Irish died in the 'Potato Famine'.

More wine is drunk in Italy per person than beer is drunk in Australia.

It has been estimated that the population of the USA is collectively carrying round 2,000,000 tons of excess fat.

As late as the end of the seventeenth century, half the population of England still did not eat meat.

There is nearly three times the amount of energy obtained from 100g of butter as from 100g of steak.

The substance that makes the bubbles in bubble gum is rubber.

The area of the USA under spinach cultivation increased twenty-one times during a period of twenty years following the arrival of the cartoon character Popeye.

It was only fifty years after they were first marketed that baked beans were served with tomato sauce. Up until then they had always been served with molasses.

4

Chemistry

Early on, a man took his materials as they came to him – wood, stone, bone, hide. Then he began to mould the outer shapes of these things, polishing and sharpening stone, shaping handles. But the most important tool he learned to use and control was fire. Until that moment, man could merely observe the changes that took place in the nature of substances around him. Lightning blackened trees and turned them to ash, dead leaves withered or decayed. With fire at his disposal, a man could change the nature of things for himself – he could cook food, boil water and turn it into steam, bake soft clay into hard pottery.

By about 8000 BC, people in the Middle East had found out how to grow their own crops and domesticate animals. They settled down in communities where it became possible for some of them to concentrate on specialized jobs such as the manufacture of pottery, of glazes to make the pots water-tight and of dyes to decorate them. By 4000 BC, the separation of metal from certain earths had been achieved.

Metals have two useful properties: they are malleable and ductile, that is to say, they can be beaten to a thin leaf, or stretched to form a thin wire. The first metals were found as nuggets of gold or copper, both of which are 'soft' metals. They do not hold an edge well and can easily be bent or beaten out of shape.

It was probably around the Sinai Peninsula that it was discovered that if a peculiar bluish rock was put into a wood fire, it was changed by the fire into copper. This discovery that copper could be obtained not only by looking for bits of it lying about, but by the 'smelting' of 'ore' was a major advance in technology. A further advance occurred when copper ore accidentally mixed with tin ore was smelted on a fire. The mixture of metals thus obtained was bronze, an alloy which is harder than copper. By 2000 BC, bronze was being used for weapons, jewellery and armour in Egypt, and from there it spread to Greece, where it was used in the Trojan war. Smelting is chemistry, thus 'chemical warfare' can hardly be described as new.

Iron is much more strongly bound to its ore than copper or tin and needs to be heated to a higher temperature before it can be smelted. This temperature could not be reached by a wood fire. It was some hundreds of years before charcoal fires blown with bellows and provided with good ventilation made it possible to free metallic iron from its ore. By about 1500 BC, the Hittites in Asia Minor were able to produce iron for the manufacture of tools and weapons. Pure iron, in the form of 'wrought iron', is not very hard; but if a certain amount of carbon, for example, as charcoal, is mixed with it during the smelting process, a very much stronger metal, steel, is produced.

Independently of the Egyptians and the Hittites, the Chinese of the Shang Dynasty of 1500 BC had discovered how to make bronze. The Japanese perfected the art of making flexible steel swords by AD 800.

The modern explanation of why copper and tin are soft, yet their alloys are quite hard, is that in the metals themselves all their crystals lie in parallel planes and can slide easily over each other and thus deform. In an alloy, however, a second metal with its crystals in a different plane will stop the crystals from sliding. The resulting alloy is, therefore, correspondingly harder.

But what was the explanation all that long time ago for the appearance of copper out of 'earth'? The Egyptians' name for their country was 'black earth' or 'Khem' and it was the art of the 'black land' which became 'alchemy', from which chemistry developed. The contribution of the Greeks was to try to answer fundamental questions: 'What is matter made of?' 'How can matter change from one form to another when it is burned?' Thales, a Greek philosopher living in Miletus, Iona, around 640 BC, came to the conclusion that such changes were possible because matter was made of one universal material. He concluded that this element must be water, which occurred in the atmosphere, in animals, in plants, in the earth and in rocks. Heraclitus, on the other hand, who lived about 500 BC, believed that the universal element was fire, while Anaximenes believed air to be the universal element. Another philosopher, Empedocles, believed that there were four basic elements, earth, air, fire and water, and that these four elements combined throughout the universe in different proportions under the influence of an evil and a divine power. He argued that when something burns, it is resolved back into its four basic elements – *fire* produces smoke, which vanishes into *air, water* bubbles from the ends of the burning branches, and the ash which is left is a form of *earth.*

This doctrine of the four elements was accepted by the Greek philosopher Aristotle (384–322 BC), who further argued that these elements were combinations of two pairs of opposite properties, hot and cold, and dry and moist. Hot and dry was fire, hot and moist was air, cold and dry was earth, and cold and moist was water. Aristotle opposed the 'atomic' theory of Democritus and Epicurus, which stated that matter is made up of invisible and indivisible particles, by saying that if substances were composed of such a material, then a large mass of air would be heavier than a small mass of metal. In fact, in making this statement, Aristotle overlooked the fact that Democritus had stated that these 'particles' were all of different sizes and moved at different speeds.

The remarkable properties of gold led those engaged in Alexandria in the study of matter to try to make gold from base metals. Aristotle believed that metals were formed in the earth as a result of vapours which had been given off by the sun and which had hardened. Proclus believed that various metals were produced deep in the earth under the influence of certain divinities linked to the planets. The Moon was linked with silver; the Sun with gold; Saturn with lead.

The Greeks used methods derived from the Egyptians for manufacturing artificial precious stones using mixtures of henna, mercury, indigo, resins and copper. The 'Leyden Papyrus' dated around AD 300 contains numerous recipes for colouring and imitating gold with various alloys. Yellow alloys of brass, copper, zinc and tin were prepared. Other effects were achieved by coating metals in lacquer, or by placing a layer of sulphide on an alloy. This removed the top layer, leaving the gold showing. At the same time, various mystical ideas were introduced; for example, that black ores were male, and red ores female, that metals could be conceived and born, and that a gold mine had to lie fallow for a number of years after heavy mining, so that the gold would have time to 'grow' again.

While these fanciful ideas were current, a number of useful practical techniques were being developed. In the separation of gold from its ores, 'cupellation' could be employed. This was a process in which impure gold and silver were melted together with lead. In the furnace, the molten lead oxidized, leaving a button of gold and silver alloy. The gold and silver were then separated using sulphur, antimony and sulphide. In 'amalgamation', crushed gold ores were treated with mercury. The amalgam was separated by squeezing it through leather and the residue finally removed from the gold by distillation. 'Liquation' depends on the fact that copper and lead are only slightly soluble in each other, while silver is more soluble than copper in lead. Copper ore, containing some silver and gold, is melted in three times its weight of lead. The silver and gold is taken up by the lead, leaving the copper behind.

In spite of these practical technical advances, the thoughts of many alchemists were distracted by irrational ideas, mainly to turn base metals into gold. Then about AD 700 ideas taken from the religion of Islam began to influence alchemy. Geber, a Greek convert to Mohammedanism, conceived the idea that all substances were composed of sulphur, mercury and arsenic. He asserted that all metals were composed of various proportions of these substances, gold consisting of purified mercury and sulphur. This being so, it should be possible to transform lead, copper or tin into gold by withdrawing sulphur from them, and adding mercury. He also believed that the brilliant red substance formed by the combination of sulphur and mercury showed how gold might be produced.

Yafar, another Islamic alchemist and contemporary of Geber, had a recipe for the creation of gold. Gold was mixed with three times its weight of mercury and the amalgam mixed with a distillate of ferrous sulphide. The mixture was then buried in warm horse-dung, sal ammoniac, alum, and cinnabar. Coal was then added, and the yolks of fifty eggs. When the mixture was dried it formed a red powder, a portion of which, heated over a charcoal fire on a sheet of silver, melted like wax and, when cooled in water, formed a red-gold substance.

When the Arabs invaded Spain in AD 711 they brought with them the ideas about alchemy and the notion that mercury and sulphur could be transmuted into gold. These ideas were confused still further in Europe by the addition of equally irrational Christian symbolism. Scientific study of chemistry was thus inhibited virtually up to the end of the fourteenth century.

Alchemical treatises in Latin began to appear in the eighth century. One, *Compositiones ad tingenda*, contained 'recipes' for gilding iron and dyeing and staining glass. It was more a practical handbook than a theoretical exposition. *Mappae clavicula*, written in the tenth century, contained many methods of making gold. Later, in the twelfth and thirteenth centuries, alchemy began to be couched in magical and secretive terms for the sake of obscurity itself. It was then that alchemists began to realize that alloys alone did not become transformed into gold. In place of this notion came the idea of the 'Philosopher's Stone'. It is very hard to say exactly what was meant by the Philosopher's Stone. Its main property was believed to be its power to convert base metals into gold. Every substance was examined and tested. The search was extended for the 'seed of gold', as though it were a vegetable growing in the earth. There was a general feeling that a certain pure matter existed somewhere in nature which would convert all imperfect bodies into perfect ones and hence change base metals into gold. It had many names – virgin's milk; the shadow of the sun; the water of sulphur; the spittle of Lune. By 1650, it had over 170 names. The poet Eirenaeus Philalethes wrote that 'the philosopher's stone is called a stone, not because it is like a stone, but only because, by virtue of its fixed nature, it resists the action of fire as successfully as any stone. In species, it is gold, more pure than the purest. . . . If we say that its nature is spiritual, it would be no more than the truth; if we describe it as corporeal, the expression would be equally correct.'

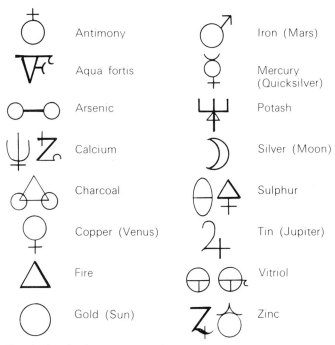

Symbols of substances used in alchemy

Alchemists, like children playing with a 'chemistry set', carried out every procedure with metals and minerals that they could think of. Mixtures were calcinated, congelated (or congealed), fixated, put into solution, 'digested' upon slow heat, distilled, sublimated (turned from solid to gas without passing through the liquid phase), condensed, separated, cerated (mixed with fats) and fermented. The longer the list of procedures became, the higher was the alchemist's reputation. It was believed that the Great Work could last up to two years, though some even stated twelve. During this time everything was couched in symbolism, all the substances used had to 'mean' something, and secret alphabets were used not only as a shorthand, but so that no one from outside the alchemists' circle would be able to understand, let alone copy their recipes. Some of the signs were from ancient runes, or from Egypt and Greece, and others were symbols from astrology. Certain chemicals were depicted by stylized drawings of animals and mythological beasts.

The obscurantism of alchemy began to decline with the introduction of printing. By 1500, over 9,000,000 books were in existence, covering a wide area of knowledge. A number of books on scientific processes began to appear, such as *De Re Metallica* by Agricola, a handbook on metallurgy.

Andreas Libau, or Libavius, compiled a book in 1595 containing all the existing chemical knowledge. Libau described the preparation of hydrochloric acid, tin tetrachloride, and ammonium sulphate, and described the manufacture of aqua regia (hydrochloric acid and nitric acid) which dissolves gold. Bernard Palissy developed an improved enamel for ceramics by careful experimentation. Unlike many of his time, he had no preconceived ideas. He wrote a book on slate, and one on alchemy, where he stated that he believed it impossible to transmute other metals into gold. In 1574 Lazarus Ercker wrote *A Treatise describing the foremost kinds of metallic Ores and Minerals*, in which he gave a detailed description of many metallurgical techniques, such as 'pickling' and 'blanching', where a base-metal alloy was oxidized, leaving a layer of silver beneath the oxide layer, which was removed by boiling in tartar and salt. The mystique of many alchemical techniques was removed finally when several books on precise assaying were printed, allowing anyone to test for themselves the claims of alchemists to have made gold. Another book, containing detailed accounts of medical preparations and drugs, was written in 1660 by Nicholas le Fevre, Royal Professor in Chemistry to Charles II. His *Traicte de la Chymie* (or *A Compleat Body of Chymistry*) was used as a standard reference book for over a century.

But the book which finally destroyed the credibility of alchemy was *The Sceptical Chymist: or Chymico-Physical Doubts and Paradoxes*, written by Robert Boyle in 1661. Boyle was the originator of the modern scientific method in chemistry. He believed that experimentation, observation and accurate measurement of results were the most important aspects of a chemist's work. Once these ideas had become assimilated by the world of scholarship, the pseudo-science of alchemy was on the road to its conversion into the exact science of chemistry. Rightly was Robert Boyle described as the Father of Chemistry.

Modern Chemistry

The first step towards modern chemistry was the study of gases. Understanding of physics was already far ahead of that of chemistry, perhaps because it is easier to measure things in the physical world than analyse and measure chemical reactions. Newton had advanced the understanding of the physical world to a state where things could be predicted, where laws worked, where order reigned. However, when it came to alchemy, even Newton believed in the transmutation of metals into gold, and no state of predictability had been reached in chemistry by the seventeenth century.

The Italian physicist, Torricelli, showed that air could exert pressure, by supporting a column of mercury thirty inches high on it. Air was thus a substance like any other matter. Then Otto von Guericke invented an air pump which could pump the air out of two metal hemispheres, which then became jammed together, as though with the most powerful glue, by the outside atmospheric pressure. Even two teams of horses could not pull them apart. But when the two hemispheres were allowed to fill with air, they fell apart.

Robert Boyle decided to do the opposite to air – to compress it. Almost immediately he found a simple inverse law governing the volume of air and the pressure exerted upon it. He exerted the pressure upon a small volume of air within a closed tube, using a column of mercury. He found that when he put twice as much mercury above the air, the volume of air was halved; and if he trebled the weight of mercury (thus trebling the pressure) the volume of air shrank to a third. This relationship only existed as long as the temperature was kept constant. Boyle's experiments with the elasticity, weight and compressibility of air, enshrined in Boyle's Law of 1660–1, were important in giving an early insight into the fundamental structure of matter.

In 1661 Boyle published *The Sceptical Chymist* in which he overthrew the Aristotelian conception of the four elements and substituted the modern idea of an element – a substance that cannot be decomposed into simpler ones. His book was certainly the foundation stone of modern chemistry, although, in some ways, he was simply supporting the notion, put forward by Thales, in the seventh century BC, that an element is a particle of substance which could not be split into other substances, whatever was done to it. Boyle believed that it should be possible to test whether a substance *was* in fact an element which could not be split into anything else.

At this time, people were interested in the nature of combustion. The

Greeks had believed that fire was one of the four main 'elements' that made up the universe, and that sulphur was the principle which caused a substance to be inflammable. In the late seventeenth century, however, the 'Phlogiston theory' was evolved to account for combustion. It was originated by Georg Stahl, a German chemist. He believed that all objects which were combustible were rich in phlogiston. When they burned, phlogiston was released into the air. What was left behind after combustion was empty of phlogiston and therefore could not be made to burn. The amount of phlogiston in a substance could be judged by measuring how much ash was left after combustion. Wood was thought to contain a lot of phlogiston, and consequently left only a very little ash, while metals had only a little phlogiston and left behind a great deal of ash or calx. The rusting of metals was considered to be the same as the burning of wood. The conversion of rock ores into metal was explained by assuming that an ore, poor in phlogiston, when heated with charcoal rich in phlogiston received some of the phlogiston from the charcoal, giving ash poor in phlogiston and metal rich in it.

Robert Boyle, the 'Father of Chemistry', whose book, *The Sceptical Chymist*, destroyed the credibility of alchemy

Air acted as a carrier of the phlogiston from one substance to another during the process of combustion. One difficulty in this theory arose from the fact that, although when fats or wood were burned they left behind ash weighing less than the original wood or fat, when metals rusted, the rust was *heavier* than the original metal. Stahl explained this by postulating that phlogiston had a *negative* weight. Even though this was an unsatisfactory explanation the phlogiston theory flourished because knowledge of gases was lacking. It is now known that when a metal rusts, it does not lose phlogiston, it gains oxygen, which explains the increase in weight.

Towards the end of the seventeenth century, John Mayow had the idea that there was something in the air which was necessary to both fire and life. He called this a 'vital, fiery and fermentative spirit'. He believed this spirit was also found in gunpowder, which was easily ignited. This 'fiery spirit' consisted of 'igneo-aerial particles'. When a metal formed rust, it increased in weight because the metal had combined with some of the 'igneo-aerial particles'. Another chemist, Stephen Hales, succeeded in collecting separate gases over water, by leading the vapours from a chemical reaction through a tube into an inverted jar of water standing in a basin of water. Then a Scottish chemist, Joseph Black, heated limestone (calcium carbonate) which gave off a gas; when this gas was left in contact with the residue of the calcium carbonate, it re-combined with it to form the calcium carbonate again. This was the first experiment which showed that a gas could enter into a chemical reaction with a solid. Black called this gas 'fixed air' as it could be 'fixed' to form a solid. He also noticed that when the residue of the heating of calcium carbonate was left standing in the air, it gradually turned into calcium carbonate again. He decided that this must mean that there was 'fixed air' in the atmosphere. (This 'fixed air' was what we now know to be carbon dioxide.) Black found that 'fixed air' did not support a flame. He also found that when he absorbed this carbon dioxide chemically there still remained some unknown gas which did not burn a flame either. His assistant separated this gas (which was nitrogen) and called it 'phlogisticated air'.

Other gases were soon discovered. Henry Cavendish observed that a gas was released when an acid reacted with a metal. He weighed equal volumes of the different gases then known, and established that the new gas, hydrogen, was the lightest of all, being one-fourteenth the weight of air.

Joseph Priestley, noticing that carbon dioxide was soluble in water (giving, in fact, soda water), was struck with the idea that he might be missing other water-soluble gases by attempting to collect them over water. Instead he tried to collect them over mercury. By this means he obtained nitrous oxide, ammonia, hydrogen chloride and sulphur dioxide from various chemical reactions.

Priestley's discovery of oxygen was a lucky accident. He was heating the red oxide of mercury in a sealed test tube, using sunlight concentrated by a lens as a source of heat. To his surprise the oxide broke down to metallic mercury while releasing a gas which caused things to burn in it with an unexpected brightness. He argued that if carbon dioxide had absorbed phlogiston until it was saturated and hence could not support a flame, then this new gas, which made things burn unnaturally brightly, must be lacking in phlogiston and absorbed it quickly. Consequently, he called this new gas 'dephlogisticated air' (it was later called 'oxygen').

Towards the end of the eighteenth century, the true explanation of combustion was reached by Antoine Lavoisier in France. Lavoisier heated metals in closed vessels containing a small amount of air and found that the metals formed a layer of calx on their surface, and weighed more than they had to begin with. Since the container had not changed in weight, the increase must come from the air inside. When he opened the vessel he found that the air had in fact been absorbed and that a partial vacuum had been formed.

This led Lavoisier to propose that the process of heating a metal ore (the oxide of the metal) was in fact the opposite to that of Stahl's phlogiston theory. This evidence showed that when an ore was heated with charcoal, the ore released a gas (oxygen) and passed it on to the charcoal (carbon). The charcoal combined with the oxygen to give another gas, carbon dioxide. Lavoisier's theory accounted for the changes in weight found. He discovered the processes involved in the combustion of many other materials and observed that, even though weight would appear sometimes to be lost or gained, when account was taken of the gases produced and all the deposits remaining, no net change in weight ever occurred. Mass was never created nor destroyed, but merely converted into another form. When Lavoisier met Priestley and heard about his newly discovered 'dephlogisticated air' he realized that it was the same gas as that which was produced by heating metal ore. He called it 'oxygen' meaning 'to give an acid' (which actually it does not do). Lavoisier then went on to study whether the chemistry of life, as exemplified in breathing, was the same as the chemistry of fire, that is, combustion. In both, oxygen is taken in and carbon dioxide given off. He measured the quantity of oxygen used in respiration and the amount of carbon dioxide produced. He found that the oxygen taken in did not match the amount of oxygen in the carbon dioxide.

It was Henry Cavendish, the discoverer of hydrogen, who explained the discrepancy. He found that when he burned hydrogen in a closed container, the gases produced condensed on the side of the vessel to become water. Water was therefore not an element, as the ancients had believed, but a compound of hydrogen and oxygen. Respiration involved the oxidation of hydrogen as well as carbon. Lavoisier deduced from this that food contained carbon and hydrogen, and that both substances took part in the life processes, hydrogen combining with the oxygen breathed in to form water, and carbon combining with the oxygen inhaled to produce carbon dioxide.

In the late eighteenth century many new elements were being discovered. Karl Scheele, a Swedish chemist, discovered molybdenum, tungsten, barium, and manganese. He also discovered chlorine, although he thought it was a compound. Scheele also isolated a number of organic acids: tartaric acid, oxalic acid, citric acid, benzoic acid, malic acid and gallic acid from plants, and lactic acid, uric acid, molybdic acid, and arsenious acid from animal sources.

Air and what it's made of

Gas	Formula	% by volume
Nitrogen	N_2	78.110
Oxygen	O_2	20.953
Argon	Ar	0.934
Neon	Ne	0.001818
Helium	He	0.000524
Methane	CH_4	0.0002
Krypton	Kr	0.000114
Hydrogen	H_2	0.00005
Nitrous Oxide	N_2O	0.00005
Xenon	Xe	0.0000087
		99.9997647%

Variable Components		
Water Vapour	H_2O	0 to 7·0
Carbon dioxide	CO_2	0.01 to 0.10, average 0.034
Ozone	O_3	0 to 0.000007

Contaminants		
Sulphur dioxide	SO_2	up to 0.0001
Nitrogen dioxide	NO_2	up to 0.000002
Ammonia	NH_3	trace
Carbon monoxide	CO	trace

In the second half of the eighteenth century, nickel, manganese and cobalt were added to the list. The use by Axel Cronstadt of the blowpipe advanced the analysis of minerals. The blowpipe enabled high temperatures to be reached. Minerals could then be identified by the colours of the flames produced when they were heated, and substances could be identified by their chemical compositions. Thus, salt could be called 'sodium chloride' because it was made of sodium and chlorine. How much of each element there was in a substance was indicated by using prefixes 'mon' for 'one', 'di' for 'two', while 'ate' means 'very oxidised' and 'ite' less so. Using this nomenclature it was clear that carbon dioxide contained twice as much oxygen as carbon monoxide.

In 1789 Lavoisier published a book explaining these ideas. Called *Elementary Treatise on Chemistry* it exerted an important influence on contemporary thought. The table overleaf, taken from this book, shows that the modern age of science had truly begun.

Gases	*Non-metals*	*Metals*		*Earths*
Light	Sulphur	Antimony	Mercury	Lime
Caloric (heat)	Phosphorus	Silver	Molybdenum	Barytes
Oxygen	Carbon	Arsenic	Nickel	Magnesia
Azote (nitrogen)	Muriatic radical	Bismuth	Gold	Argill
Hydrogen	Fluoric radical	Cobalt	Platinum	Silex
	Boracic radical	Copper	Lead	
		Tin	Tungsten	
		Iron	Zinc	
		Manganese		

Chemists everywhere adopted Lavoisier's systematic nomenclature. They also began to study chemical reactions in a quantitative manner. It was from the measurements of the amounts of substances entering reactions that the modern theory of atoms and molecules was to evolve.

One set of reactions which was studied was that involving acids and bases (or alkalis). When these two 'opposites' combined, they formed an almost neutral solution of a 'salt'. For example, hydrochloric acid (containing hydrogen and chlorine) reacted with sodium hydroxide (containing sodium and hydrogen and oxygen), to produce sodium chloride (common salt). Richter in Germany measured the exact amounts of each substance required to neutralize a given quantity of the other. He found that an exact fixed amount was always needed. Claude Berthollet in France had extended this idea that substances combined with each other in fixed and invariable proportions. Did a compound such as water or salt always contain the same proportion of the two substances? He believed that possibly the methods of preparation might alter the proportions. Also in France, Joseph Proust believed that two elements would *always* combine in the same proportions to form a particular compound, in whatever way it had been prepared. He showed this by preparing copper carbonate in various ways. The proportions of its components were always 5.3 of copper to 4 of oxygen to 1 of carbon.

These results led back to the idea of atomism that had been considered long before by the Greeks. This time, however, the theory was based on the evidence of practical experiment, rather than on intuition. The existence of 'atoms' would explain why substances always combined in definite proportions.

John Dalton followed up these ideas in a series of experiments which led him to a more 'solid', almost 'two-dimensional' picture of the structure of 'molecules'. He visualized atoms as being 'real', and found how neatly an atomist viewpoint explained the fact that eight parts of oxygen (by weight) would combine with three parts of carbon, forming carbon dioxide, and three parts of carbon and four parts of oxygen formed carbon monoxide, a gas with completely different properties. This 'law of multiple proportions' as it was called, enabled Dalton to propose that carbon monoxide contained one atom of carbon and one of oxygen, and that carbon dioxide contained one atom of carbon and two atoms of oxygen. Dalton published his ideas in 1808 in *A New System of Chemical Philosophy*. Using his ideas, it was possible to 'measure' the weights of individual atoms within any one element, by finding out in what proportions different elements combined with each other. Dalton decided to call hydrogen weight 1 (which was quite logical, as hydrogen is the lightest element known). He then devised a list of atomic weights. This was a good idea even though his calculations were often wrong. He believed that most molecules were formed by single atoms combining with other single atoms. This led him to assign the wrong weights to some elements. For example, Dalton called water HO instead of H_2O. He did not use initials to symbolize elements, but little signs within circles. For example,

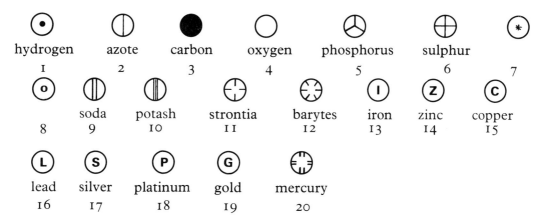

Direct proof that the one-to-one proportions in which Dalton believed the atoms to combine were incorrect came from an unexpected source, electrolysis. In 1800 Alessandro Volta had discovered the electric battery, with which he produced an electric current. He found that two different metals separated by an acid solution produced an electric current. Nicholson and Carlisle showed that the opposite could be made to occur, that is, if a current was run through such a system where the strips were separated by water, bubbles began to appear at each of the metal strips, oxygen from one and hydrogen from the other. What is more, these gases could be collected and their volumes measured. When this was done it was found that for each unit volume of oxygen there were two volumes of hydrogen. There was indeed one weight of hydrogen for each eight weights of oxygen. Nevertheless the results showed that there was one oxygen atom to *two* hydrogen atoms in this same weight proportion, so the weight of oxygen relative to hydrogen must be 16, not 8.

Joseph Gay-Lussac also found that gases always combined in fixed whole-number ratios to form compounds. Thus, two volumes of hydrogen always combined with one volume of oxygen at the same temperature and pressure to form two volumes of water vapour under the same conditions. To form ammonia, four hydrogen volumes always combined with one nitrogen

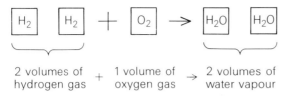

2 volumes of hydrogen gas + 1 volume of oxygen gas → 2 volumes of water vapour

Atom and Atomic Theory

volume. It seemed therefore that the number of atoms combining must be reflected in this volume ratio. Amedeo Avogadro in Italy proposed that equal numbers of gas particles take up an equal space. This hypothesis gave an important clue to the state in which gases exist; it indicated that nitrogen and oxygen and other gases must exist as molecules in their free state, not as single atoms, for when one volume of nitrogen combines with one volume of oxygen, it produces two volumes of nitrogen dioxide, not one, as would be expected if all the gas atoms existed singly.

Other ways of estimating atomic weight were being discovered. The French chemist, Pierre Dulong, found that the specific heat of an element varied inversely with its atomic weight. This implied that an element whose atomic weight was half that of another, would have twice the specific heat.

A further advance in the measurement of atomic weight was made by Jons Berzelius in Sweden. He produced a table of atomic weights which were not whole numbers as Dalton's had been. This was because more accurate techniques were being used from which it was becoming clear that the weights of elements were not whole number multiples of the weight of hydrogen. As oxygen was the element which was most often used in establishing the proportions in which particular elements combined, it was inconvenient to have its weight fixed at, say, 15.9, just to make hydrogen equal to 1. It seemed more sensible to call oxygen 16, and to recalculate every other element accordingly. This gave hydrogen an atomic weight of 1.008. Berzelius also adapted Dalton's system of symbols by using the initial of the element's name in Latin. This simplification enabled the number of atoms in a molecule to be indicated by writing the number behind the initial of the element, as in H_2O, which contains two hydrogen atoms and one oxygen atom. In this way, equations could be written which were balanced, so that the number of atoms and molecules taking part could be set down, as in, for example, $2H_2 + O_2 \rightarrow 2H_2O$.

The process of electrolysis led to the isolation of new elements. Humphry Davy, in London, devised a new system whereby solids were melted and an electric current then passed through them. By means of this technique, Davy isolated potassium from potassium carbonate; sodium from sodium carbonate; magnesium from its oxide; strontium from strontia; barium from baryta; and calcium from 'lime'. He also rediscovered chlorine and showed that hydro-chloric acid contained no oxygen, as Lavoisier had believed.

Michael Faraday (1791–1867), who studied the principles of electricity and magnetism. Among his discoveries was the condensation of gases into liquids by pressure

Michael Faraday, in Davy's laboratory, continued his work with electrolysis. He coined many of the words used today; electrode was the name used to describe the terminals dipping into the conducting solution. The solution was called the electrolyte. The electrode which carried the positive current was called the anode, and the electrode carrying the negative was called the cathode. Faraday believed the electric current to be carried in two opposite directions through the solution by two different sorts of particles, one sort called cations, moving towards the cathode, and the other, called anions, moving towards the anode. Faraday unravelled a number of laws governing the release of metals due to the electric current. He found that the amount of metal released was always proportional to the amount of electricity passed through the solution, and that the weight of metal released by a standard quantity of electricity was proportional to the equivalent weight of the metal. A further important law, discovered towards the end of the nineteenth century, stated that the mass of a metal liberated was inversely proportional to the 'binding power' of the element, that is the strength with which atoms were bonded together in compounds. This meant that the amount of electricity required to liberate the weight of an element equivalent to its atomic weight (i.e., 20.04 grams of calcium), varied from element to element. The 'equivalent weight' is the atomic weight, divided by the valence – as though one particle of electricity was required to split a 1-valent element from its bond, while 2 particles of electricity were required to transport a 2-valent element. In honour of the great strides made in electrolysis by Faraday, the unit of electricity required to liberate the 'equivalent weight' of an element was called a 'Faraday'.

By 1830, fifty-five different elements were known. There seemed to be no relationship between one element and the next. Then Johann Döbereiner, a German, realized that chlorine, iodine and bromine had similar colour and chemical properties and that the atomic weights of the three elements increased in regular steps. He also noticed that calcium, strontium and barium seemed to form a group of their own, as did sulphur, selenium and tellurium, each with increasing atomic weights. In 1864 John Newlands, an English chemist, arranged the elements in order of their atomic weights. When he ranked them in vertical columns of seven, he noticed that similar elements tended to form into horizontal rows. Fluorine was next to chlorine, and lithium, magnesium and potassium were in the same row. Newlands called this arrangement the 'law of octaves'.

At about this time, Dmitri Mendeleev, in Russia, ranked the elements in order of their atomic weights. At the same time he took account of their 'binding-power'. This was called 'valence' in 1852 by Frankland, who showed that each element always combined with a certain number of other elements or groups of elements. For example, sodium always combined with one, as did lithium, while calcium and magnesium always combined with two other atoms or radicals.

Mendeleev found that in the early part of his list, the valence rose and fell at regular intervals similar to those observed by Newlands. Mendeleev mapped out a table showing these periods in a chart known ever since as the 'Periodic Table of the Elements' published in 1869. The remarkable feature about this table was that Mendeleev left gaps where no element that he knew of had the appropriate valence, properties and atomic weight to fill the slot in the column. He prognosticated that the gap would be filled by a new element which had not then been discovered. He was even able to predict the properties and atomic weights which the new elements would have when they *were* discovered! It was not until the end of the nineteenth century that these predictions were fulfilled.

By the mid-nineteenth century, a new device for determining the composition of unknown minerals was being developed. This was the spectroscope which still remains one of the most important tools in analytical chemistry today. Gustave Kirchhoff, a German physicist, observed that when different minerals were placed in a hot flame they produced a characteristic colour, as had been shown by Cronstadt in the eighteenth century. When he viewed the flame through a slit and then a prism, he found the light was split into a pattern of coloured lines. These spectra were characteristic for each element. By studying their spectra it was possible to identify any substance under analysis or, indeed, to identify the components of the sun. Using spectroscopic methods Kirchhoff and Bunsen discovered caesium and rubidium. Other chemists using the same technique discovered the element gallium, which fitted one of the gaps in Mendeleev's table. Later, two other gaps were filled with the discovery of scandium and germanium.

During the mid-nineteenth century four 'rare-earth' elements were identified, lanthanum, erbium, terbium and didymium. Later, other rare-earth elements were discovered which brought the number of these elements up to fourteen.

Element	Symbol	Approx. at. wt.	At. no.	Element	Symbol	Approx. at. wt.	At. no.
Actinium	Ac	229	89	Mendelevium	Md	256	101
Aluminium	Al	27	13	Mercury (hydrargyrum)	Hg	200·6	80
Americium	Am	243	95	Molybdenum	Mo	96	42
Antimony (stibium)	Sb	122	51	Neodymium	Nd	144·5	60
Argon	A	40	18	Neon	Ne	20	10
Arsenic	As	75	33	Neptunium	Np	237	93
Astatine	At	210	85	Nickel	Ni	58·7	28
Barium	Ba	137·5	56	Niobium (columbium)	Nb	93	41
Berkelium	Bk	245	97	Nitrogen	N	14	7
Beryllium (glucinum)	Be	9	4	Nobelium	No	253	102
Bismuth	Bi	209	83	Osmium	Os	191	76
Boron	B	11	5	Oxygen	O	16	8
Bromine	Br	80	35	Palladium	Pd	106·5	46
Cadmium	Cd	112·5	48	Phosphorus	P	31	15
Caesium	Cs	133	55	Platinum	Pt	195	78
Calcium	Ca	40	20	Plutonium	Pu	242	94
Californium	Cf	246	98	Polonium	Po	210	84
Carbon	C	12	6	Potassium (kalium)	K	39	19
Cerium	Ce	140	58	Praseodymium	Pr	141	59
Caesium	Cs	132·9	55	Promethium (illinium)	Pm	147	61
Chlorine	Cl	35·5	17	Protoactinium	Pa	234	91
Chromium	Cr	52	24	Radium	Ra	226	88
Cobalt	Co	59	27	Radon (niton)	Rn	222	86
Copper (cuprum)	Cu	63·5	29	Rhenium	Re	187	75
Curium	Cm	243	96	Rhodium	Rh	103	45
Dysprosium	Dy	162·5	66	Rubidium	Rb	85·5	37
Einsteinium	Es	254	99	Ruthenium	Ru	101·5	44
Erbium	Er	167·5	68	Rutherfordium	Rf	—	104
Europium	Eu	152	63	Samarium	Sm	150·5	62
Fermium	Fm	253	100	Scandium	Sc	45	21
Fluorine	F	19	9	Selenium	Se	79	34
Francium	Fr	223	87	Silicon	Si	28	14
Gadolinium	Gd	157	64	Silver (argentum)	Ag	108	47
Gallium	Ga	69·5	31	Sodium (natrium)	Na	23	11
Germanium	Ge	72·5	32	Strontium	Sr	87·5	38
Gold (aurum)	Au	197	79	Sulphur	S	32	16
Hafnium	Hf	178·5	72	Tantalum	Ta	181·5	73
Hahnium	Ha	—	105	Technetium	Tc	98	43
Helium	He	4	2	Tellurium	Te	127·5	52
Holmium	Ho	163·5	67	Terbium	Tb	159	65
Hydrogen	H	1	1	Thallium	Tl	204·5	81
Indium	In	115	49	Thorium	Th	232	90
Iodine	I	127	53	Thulium	Tm	169·5	69
Iridium	Ir	193	77	Tin (stannum)	Sn	118·5	50
Iron (ferrum)	Fe	56	26	Titanium	Ti	48	22
Krypton	Kr	83	36	Tungsten (wolfium)	W	184	74
Lanthanum	La	139	57	Uranium	U	238	92
Lawrencium	Lw	257	103	Vanadium	V	51	23
Lead (plumbum)	Pb	207	82	Xenon	Xe	130	54
Lithium	Li	7	3	Ytterbium (neo-ytterbium)	Yb	173·5	70
Lutecium	Lu	175	71	Yttrium	Y	89	39
Magnesium	Mg	24·3	12	Zinc	Zn	65·5	30
Manganese	Mn	55	25	Zirconium	Zr	91	40

Table of elements, listing alternative Latin or Greek names, symbols, atomic numbers and approximate atomic weights. The Periodic Table of Elements was first devised by the Russian scientist, Mendeleev, in the 1860s

Another group of elements to be discovered was that of the 'inert' gases. The first member of this group, 'argon', was discovered by William Ramsay in 1894. He repeated an experiment first performed by Henry Cavendish in the late eighteenth century, when, after causing atmospheric nitrogen and oxygen to combine, he found a small volume of gas which would not combine when left over. Ramsay discovered that the residual gas emitted a novel spectrum. It was a new element, argon, which, not combining with any other element, was given a valence of 'o'. Four more inert gases were discovered by Ramsay and others – helium, neon, krypton and xenon. These inert gases fitted in between the vertical column containing chlorine and bromine and that containing sodium and potassium, both columns containing elements with a valence of 1. This completed the modern Periodic Table used today, apart from the new elements artificially produced after the 1940s.

The concept of 'valence' or binding power made it possible to work out the structures of organic molecules, largely composed of carbon. These tend to fall into 'groups', where a single mathematical formula will cover a family of compounds. For the alcohols, the formula $C_nH_{2n+1}OH$ covers the simplest alcohol, methanol, CH_3OH, through ethanol C_2H_5OH to increasingly bigger molecules. Other groups are the alkanes (methane, CH_4, ethane C_2H_6, propane C_3H_8, etc., where the structural formula for the group is C_nH_{2n+2}). A Scottish chemist, Archibald Cooper, proposed that the bonds between atoms should be indicated by short dashes, so that a two-dimensional 'picture' of the arrangement of the atoms within a molecule could be written down. The German chemist, Friedrich Kekulé, elaborated the system of writing down the structural formulae of organic molecules. He pointed out that carbon was unique in being able to use one or more of its four valence bonds to create long complex molecules. According to the new system of writing, methane CH_4 could be written as:

$$
\begin{array}{c}
H \\
| \\
H-C-H \\
| \\
H
\end{array}
$$

ethane as:
$$
\begin{array}{c}
H\ H \\
|\ | \\
H-C-C-H \\
|\ | \\
H\ H
\end{array}
$$
and propane:
$$
\begin{array}{c}
H\ H\ H \\
|\ |\ | \\
H-C-C-C-H \\
|\ |\ | \\
H\ H\ H
\end{array}
$$
etc.

Sometimes it was necessary to 'dispose' of an extra bond by adding it on to one already existing, producing a 'double bond', as in another series, the alkenes (covered by the formula C_nH_{2n}) where the molecule ethylene was depicted as:

$$
\begin{array}{c}
H-C=C-H \\
|\ \ \ | \\
H\ \ \ H
\end{array}
$$

One molecule which had not fitted into the diagrams of chains, was that of benzene, with the formula C_6H_6. It was Kekulé who hit upon the idea of arranging the atoms in the form of a ring, thus:

A peculiar problem arose to account for the molecular structure for 'optical isomers'. Optical isomers were identical in chemical terms. The difference between them was that one isomer would deflect a beam of polarized light shone through it to the left and the other to the right. It was Louis Pasteur, who in 1848 observed that a sample of the compound, sodium ammonium tartrate, which did not affect polarized light, was made up of a mixture of crystals, part of which had a left-handed geometrical structure and part of which was composed of the opposite, right-handed crystals. Solutions of these two types deflected polarized light, one to the left, the other to the right. Later, Jacobus Van't Hoff and Joseph Le Bel proposed that in the carbon atom, which has the capacity to form four bonds, these four bonds lie towards the corners of a tetrahedron, with the carbon atom at the centre, i.e.,

In this way, optical isomers could be visualized as being three-dimensional mirror-images of each other, where the carbon atom was attached to three different radicals or atoms, while optical activity was absent when two or more of the bonds were attached to similar groups.

Alfred Werner in Germany extended the three-dimensional view of chemical bonding to atoms other than carbon. He proposed a 'co-ordinate theory' of molecular structure, where complex inorganic molecules (molecules without carbon atoms) could form a molecular structure around a central atom without adhering strictly to the bonding laws of the valence of the atoms. Another German chemist, Johann Baeyer, put forward a theory which accounted for why there was a tendency for there to be more six- or five-carbon ringed molecules in existence in nature than any other number. He calculated that all other numbers would place the bonds at such a small angle that they would be under considerable strain. Only when there were five or six carbon atoms in a ring was the strain less.

Metal	Symbol	Atomic Number	Atomic Weight	Melting Point, °C.	Specific Gravity	Specific Heat
Lithium	Li	3	6·94	186	0·534	0·94
Beryllium	Be	4	9·02	1300	1·85	0·38
Sodium	Na	11	22·997	97·5	0·98	0·28
Magnesium	Mg	12	24·32	650	1·74	0·25
Aluminium	Al	13	26·97	658	2·7	0·218
Potassium	K	19	39·096	62·5	0·86	0·166
Calcium	Ca	20	40·07	810	1·54	0·15
Scandium	Sc	21	45·10	1200	2·5	
Titanium	Ti	22	48·10	1665	4·5	0·113
Vanadium	V	23	50·96	1720	6	0·12
Chromium	Cr	24	52·01	1550	6·9	0·12
Manganese	Mn	25	54·93	1260	7·2	0·107
Iron	Fe	26	55·84	1535	7·86	0·11
Cobalt	Co	27	58·94	1480	8	0·106
Nickel	Ni	28	58·69	1452	8·8	0·103
Copper	Cu	29	63·57	1083	8·95	0·092
Zinc	Zn	30	65·38	419·4	6·92	0·096
Gallium	Ga	31	69·72	30	5·9	0·079
Germanium	Ge	32	72·60	958	5·4	0·074
Arsenic	As	33	74·96	Sublimes	5·73	0·08
Rubidium	Rb	37	85·44	38	1·52	0·019
Strontium	Sr	38	87·63	800	2·63	0·074
Yttrium	Y	39	88·9	1490	5·5	
Zirconium	Zr	40	91·0	1530	6·4	0·07
Niobium	Nb	41	93·1	2478	12·7	0·071
Molybdenum	Mo	42	96·0	2620	10·2	0·065
Ruthenium	Ru	44	101·7	1900	12·1	0·061
Rhodium	Rh	45	102·91	1910	12·1	0·058
Palladium	Pd	46	106·7	1550	12	0·058
Silver	Ag	47	107·88	960	10·5	0·055
Cadmium	Cd	48	112·41	320·9	8·65	0·057
Indium	In	49	114·8	155	7·3	0·057
Tin (Tetragonal)	Sn	50	118·7	231·9	7·31	0·056
Antimony	Sb	51	121·77	630	6·68	0·051
Caesium	Cs	55	132·81	26	1·9	0·048
Barium	Ba	56	137·37	850	3·7	0·068
Lanthanum	La	57	138·90	810	6·16	0·045
Cerium	Ce	58	140·25	630	6·9	0·05
Praseodymium	Pr	59	140·92	940	6·48	0·045
Neodymium	Nd	60	144·27	840	6·96	
Prometheum	Pm	61	147·0			
Samarium	Sm	62	150·43	1300	7·8	
Europium	Eu	63	152·0			
Gadolinium	Gd	64	157·26			
Terbium	Tb	65	159·2			
Dysprosium	Dy	66	162·52			
Holmium	Ho	67	163·4			
Erbium	Er	68	167·7			
Thulium	Tm	69	169·4	300	11·9	0·033
Ytterbium	Yb	70	173·6			
Lutecium	Lu	71	175·0			
Hafnium	Hf	72	180·8	1700		
Tantalum	Ta	73	181·5	2996		
Technetium	Tc	43				
Tungsten	W	74	184·0	3370	18·7	0·0358
Rhenium	Re	75		3180		
Osmium	Os	76	190·8	2600	24	0·0312
Iridium	Ir	77	193·1	2290	22·4	0·032
Platinum	Pt	78	195·23	1755	21·5	0·032
Gold	Au	79	197·2	1060	19·3	0·031
Mercury	Hg	80	200·61	−38·9	13·595	0·033
Thallium	Tl	81	204·39	304	11·85	0·033
Lead	Pb	82	207·20	327	11·35	0·031
Bismuth	Bi	83	209·0	271	9·78	0·030
Radium	Ra	88	225·95	?700	?5	
Thorium	Th	90	232·15	1450	11·1	0·028
Uranium	U	92	238·17	?1850	18·7	0·028
Neptunium	Np	93	237*			
Plutonium	Pu	94	244*			
Americium	Am	95	241*			
Curium	Cm	96	247*			
Berkelium	Bk	97	249*			
Californium	Cf	98	251*			
Einsteinium	ES	99	254*			
Fermium	Fm	100	257*			
Mendelevium	Md	101	258*			
Nobelium	No	102	254*			
Lawrencium	Lr	103	257*	*Most stable isotope.		

Table of metals, showing symbols, atomic numbers and weights, melting points, specific gravities and specific heats

Thermodynamics and Physical Chemistry

When electricity entered the world of chemistry by way of electrolysis, it became obvious that physics and chemistry had overlapped. Heat was also involved in chemical reactions, whether it was being emitted or absorbed. In 1840, in Germany, Germain Hess showed that when substance A changes to substance E, whether it follows a direct reaction A→E, one more convoluted, such as A→B→E; or A→B→C→E or A→B→C→D→E, the amount of heat that has been absorbed or emitted will always be the same, whatever route the reaction follows.

In the early nineteenth century, two laws had emerged in physics. The first law of thermodynamics stated that energy could neither be created nor destroyed, but merely changed into another form, and the second law of thermodynamics stated that heat always flowed from high to low, and that it was the difference in heat levels that made 'work' from heat possible. This decay towards uniform heat levels was called 'entropy'.

In fact there was nothing new in these two laws of thermodynamics. The Roman philosopher, Epicurus, in 100 BC, stated: 'Nothing can ever be created by divine power out of nothing . . . nature resolves everything into its component atoms, and never reduces anything to nothing. We see no diminution in the sum of things. This is because the bodies that are shed by one thing, lessen it by their departure, but enlarge another by their coming; here they bring decay, there full bloom, but they do not linger there. So the sum of things is perpetually renewed. . . .'

However, it was new to apply physical concepts to chemical reactions. The French chemist, Pierre Berthelot, put forward the hypothesis that most reactions which emitted heat were easy to initiate and hard to reverse. Usually the reverse reaction required quite a large input of energy to make them begin and keep them going. There were exceptions to Berthelot's rule. Some spontaneous reactions absorb heat, while there are other reactions which are naturally reversible, the reaction proceeding with equal ease in either direction, whether heat is absorbed or emitted. Such reversible reactions, however, eventually come to a state of equilibrium with the proportions of end-products and initial products in balance while the reaction oscillates backwards and forwards.

Two Norwegian chemists, Cato Guldberg and Peter Waage, put forward the theory that the concentration of the substances reacting had a great deal to do with the direction of the reaction. In their theory, if there was more of the substances on the left of the equation, the reaction would move to the right, producing the right-hand product much faster than the left-hand. But once the reaction had reached equilibrium, the concentrations of the two substances on either side, when multiplied together, remained constant, i.e. $\dfrac{[C \times D]}{[A \times B]} = K$, where 'K' is the equilibrium constant.

An American, Josiah Gibbs, proposed the concept of 'free energy' which was easier to measure than 'entropy', but gave an indication of the increase or decrease of entropy in a reaction. When entropy increased, 'free energy' decreased. Gibbs also found that the free energy of a reaction changed in response to changes in concentration. He devised a rule from which it was possible to predict how changes in pressure, temperature and concentration would affect the 'state' of the substances taking part (whether they were solid, liquid or gas).

Then in Germany, Friedrich Östwald, continuing where Gibbs had left off, applied his ideas to catalysis. A catalyst is a substance which speeds up the rate of a reaction without itself being changed in the process. Östwald stated that the catalyst in any reaction combined with the reacting substance forming an intermediate substance which broke up to give the final product, freeing the catalyst for further action.

How much there is of this, to be sure! There was Henri Louis Le Chatelier who discovered that when any change is made in the temperature or pressure of a reaction, the system will adjust to reduce this effect; for example, if the temperature is raised, the reaction will begin to absorb heat. And there was Svante Arrhenius, who was aware that when a substance was dissolved in a liquid, the resulting solution tended to have a lower freezing point than the liquid alone. When salt (sodium chloride) is dissolved, it depresses the freezing point as though there were twice the number of particles present than there are. In a substance which has three atoms in every molecule, the freezing point is lowered as though there were three times as many particles in solution. It seemed to Arrhenius as though the molecules were actually splitting up into their separate atoms when they were dissolved. Only substances which broke down conducted electricity. Sugar, which does not break down into atoms when it is dissolved, does not conduct electric current. Arrhenius proposed that the atoms carried either a positive or a negative electric charge. All this knowledge gives modern chemists the ability to do the things they now do.

Gases, Liquids, Solids and Atoms

In the last century there were still many gaps in the understanding of the different states of matter, solid, liquid and gas. Why, for instance, did the state of a substance change from one to another when it was cooled or heated or put under pressure? James Clerk Maxwell and Ludwig Boltzmann came to the conclusion that gases were randomly-moving molecules, widely spaced. Johannes Van der Waals added that there were very slight attractive forces between these randomly-moving molecules. Liquids were assumed to have their molecules more closely packed and to be moving more slowly, while the molecules in solids were so closely packed as merely to be able to oscillate. If this was so, it should be possible to change gases to liquids or even to solids by lowering the temperature, thus slowing the molecules down, and increasing the pressure to squeeze the molecules more closely together.

Faraday had liquefied chlorine and sulphur dioxide gases under pressure in 1845. Later, he was able to liquefy carbon dioxide. However, gases such as nitrogen, hydrogen and oxygen refused to liquefy, whatever the pressures they were put under. In the 1860s Thomas Andrews noticed that it was possible to keep carbon dioxide in liquid form by raising the pressure as the temperature crept up, until a critical temperature was reached. At this point, no pressure could compensate for the temperature and the liquid became gas. It was, however, possible to achieve very low temperatures by allowing a gas to expand. This caused it to cool rapidly. It was then compressed without being allowed to regain any heat. This process was repeated many times, each repetition lowering the temperature of the gas until its own particular threshold temperature was reached. Then when pressure was applied, the molecules could be pushed closely enough together to liquefy the gas.

How cold could one go to? In 1848, William Thomson developed the ideas arising from Charles's discovery that gases lost 1/273rd of their volume for every degree centigrade drop in temperature. He proposed that the energy of the individual gas molecules was the factor that was being reduced when the temperature was lowered. This meant that at $-273°C$ all the molecules in the gas would reach an energy level of zero. This temperature would be the lowest temperature possible for all matter. ($-273°C$ was called 'absolute zero' because there could be no temperature that was lower.)

In 1898, James Dewar managed to liquefy hydrogen at only 20°C above absolute zero, and, in 1908, Heike Onnes liquefied helium at a temperature of only 4°C above absolute zero.

However advanced are the practical applications of such ideas, the concept of moving particles in matter is not new. Epicurus, writing in the first century BC, was remarkably accurate in many of his thermodynamic concepts:

'. . . It clearly follows that no rest is given to the atoms in their course through the depths of space. Driven along in an incessant, but variable movement, some of them bounce far apart after a collision, while others recoil only a short distance from the impact. From those that do not recoil far, being driven into a closer union, and half there by the entanglement of their own interlocking shapes, are composed firmly rooted rocks, the stubborn strength of steel and the like. Those others that move freely through larger tracts of space, springing far apart, and carried far by the rebound – these provide for us thin air . . .'

Epicurus even understood the significance of 'Brownian motion' – the random movement of small particles suspended in water. It was Albert Einstein, in 1909, who proposed that this movement was caused by the bombardment of the water molecules in the vessel. Epicurus had said,

> Observe what happens when sunbeams are admitted into a building and shed light in shadowy places. You will see a multitude of tiny particles mingling in a multitude of ways in empty space within the light of the beam, as though contending in everlasting conflict, rushing into battle rank upon rank with never a moment's pause in a rapid sequence of union and disunions. From this you may picture what it is for the atoms to be perpetually tossed about in the illimitable void. To some extent a small thing may afford an illustration and an imperfect image of great things. Besides, there is a further reason why you should give your mind to these particles that are seen dancing in a sunbeam: their dancing is an actual indication of underlying movements of matter that are hidden from our sight. There you will see many particles under the impact of invisible blows, changing their course and driven back upon their tracks, this way and that in all directions . . .

It took Einstein, all those centuries later, to pin down what Epicurus had realized so long ago!

Organic Chemistry and Vitalism

Tyndall, a British physicist of the 1870s, wrote in a book called *Fragments of Science for Unscientific People*, 'Does life belong to what we call matter, or is it an independent principle inserted into matter at some suitable epoch, when the physical conditions became such as to permit the development of life?' Was the chemistry of 'matter' derived from living sources different from that of non-living matter?

By the nineteenth century, although living matter could readily be converted into its non-living components, by boiling, heating in strong acids, or by incineration, no one had been able to create the substances which were created by life from non-living materials. Stahl suggested that some special influence, or 'vital force', was necessary to convert non-living matter into the matter making up a living creature. Yet it had been realized that all living substances contained hydrogen and carbon. Such carbon compounds were termed 'organic' to distinguish them from the 'inorganic', non-carbon compounds of the inanimate world.

When Friedrich Wöhler succeeded in synthesizing the organic substance, urea, by heating ammonium cyanate, it began to appear that substances produced by life processes, just like inorganic materials, fell within the ambit of chemistry. It was not long before Adolph Kolbe synthesized acetic acid from hydrogen, oxygen and carbon. Pierre Berthelot also synthesized methyl alcohol, ethyl alcohol, benzene, acetylene and methane.

The assertion made by Lavoisier towards the end of the eighteenth century that 'life is a chemical process' could be seen to be true by the end of the nineteenth century. It was then clear that protein, the main component of flesh, was composed of a network of 'amino acids', several of which (cystine, tryosine, leucine) had been isolated in pure form and their chemical structure established. As early as 1901, Emil Fischer had linked a number of amino acids together in the way they are linked in nature. New techniques – ultracentrifugation, electrophoresis, dialysis, chromatography and – in our own time – paper chromatography – gradually enabled more and more exact analysis of protein to be carried out.

The technique of X-ray crystallography was used to determine the spacing and structure of proteins and to determine how the different amino acids are arranged. By this means it could be observed that when a fully stretched fibrous polypeptide was examined, it seemed that the amino acid units formed a straight line. When the fibres were relaxed, they fell back into a complicated spiral pattern. The precise turn and shape of the helix was determined by Linus Pauling and Robert Corey in America. It appeared that the helix was held together by a weak chemical bond between a hydrogen atom and a nitrogen or an oxygen atom.

By 1953, Sanger and Tuppy had worked out the detailed chemical structure of the protein, insulin. A few years later they succeeded in making in the laboratory another protein, oxytocin.

The knowledge of the order of the amino acids in a protein chain was not the entire story of the understanding of a protein molecule. In view of the fact that keratin (the main protein of finger nails) and fibroin existed naturally in spiral form, what form did other protein molecules take up? Using X-ray diffraction pictures, as had been done with keratin, Max Perutz and John Kendrew discovered the precise 'three-dimensional' form of haemoglobin and myoglobin, two very large and complex molecules. The three-dimensional structure of insulin was worked out by Dorothy Hodgkin in 1969.

Protein is the substance from which the living tissues are made. But what is it that controls how the tisues grow? The great achievement of chemistry in the twentieth century has been to discover that a chemical molecule controls our development. This is a molecule of nucleic acid (actually deoxyribonucleic acid).

Nucleic acids were first noticed towards the end of the nineteenth century by a Swiss chemist, Friedrich Miescher, who found these substances in the nucleus of cells. He also discovered the presence of nucleic acids in sperm. Another sort of nucleic acid was also discovered in yeast. In 1910 Kossel, in Germany, split up the nucleic acid molecule and found it to contain the compounds adenine, guanine, cytosine and thymine. The first two compounds belong to the chemical category called 'purines', while the other two are 'pyrimidines'. Then a year later, an American biochemist, Phoebus Levene, showed that nucleic acids were linked to a five-carbon sugar molecule of ribose and, what is more, found that in the yeast nucleic acid the sugar was ribose, while in the animal nucleic acid the ribose was lacking an oxygen atom. While the former, therefore, was 'ribonucleic acid', the latter was 'deoxyribonucleic acid', abbreviated to RNA and DNA respectively. Levene also noticed that the RNA molecule had a different pyrimidine molecule, uracil, in place of the thymine.

Nucleic acids were found in all the nuclei of both animal and plant cells, and were particularly conspicuous in chromosomes, the substances on which heredity depends. The importance of chromosomes had been realized in 1904. Caspersson, a Swede, using ultra-violet light to pick out the DNA or RNA in the cell, found that the DNA seemed to lie in varying 'bands' along the chromosome threads. It was concluded that DNA could be the chemical molecule of heredity. Was it possible to discover its precise structure and then perhaps deduce the mechanism by which it worked? However, even by the 1940s there was still no *direct* evidence to show that DNA *was* the hereditary material. It could still be protein which operated within the chromosome.

Then in 1944 three American biochemists, Avery, MacLeod, and McCarthy, found that DNA alone could transform one strain of bacteria into another. DNA seemed to be acting like the genes which geneticists had believed existed. Could DNA actually *be* the substance which made up the genes? If so, how did it work? How could a chemical molecule, however complex, contain enough information to tell a newly-generated cell what sort of creature to turn into? It was obvious that the DNA chains must somehow have a complex structure or pattern where instructions could be stored.

William Astbury, working with F. Bell in London, took the first X-ray diffraction picture of DNA and found it to be a repeating structure in which flat planes of purine and pyrimidine bases occurred repeatedly at right angles to the long axis of the molecule. Next, Maurice Wilkins and Rosalind Franklin, in London, developed a technique by which DNA could be drawn out into long fibres, and deduced that the DNA molecule must possess some sort of helical structure. Various teams of workers postulated various types of structure but none of these exactly fitted the chemical evidence. Then in 1953 Wilkins joined two other scientists, James Watson, an American, and Francis Crick, an Englishman, in their attempt to build molecular models of DNA. They knew from Wilkins's earlier work that the width of the DNA molecule was 20 ångströms (an ångström is a millionth of a centimetre), and they knew that 10 nucleotides (phosphate, base and sugar) fitted into every complete turn of 34 ångströms from their X-ray diffraction pictures. From this, they were able to calculate the density of the DNA molecule. The result indicated that the DNA molecule must consist of two chains.

When they began to build models of two nucleotide chains to see how they might fit together, they used the information, discovered by Chargaff, that there were always equal numbers of adenine and thymine bases and equal numbers of guanine and cytosine. Watson and Crick concluded that this implied that these bases might be paired with each other. When they designed a model with the base-pairs facing inwards, like rungs in a helical ladder, with the bases joined together by hydrogen bonds, the structure of DNA fell into place. It appeared that the workings of heredity were now being revealed at the level of molecular chemistry.

Synthetic Organic Chemistry

Dyes By the mid-nineteenth century, chemists were beginning to conceive the possibilities of creating completely new substances, synthesizing substances which previously could only be obtained from natural sources. The first such substances were the dyes. Hardly more than a hundred years ago the dyes most commonly in use dated back to Roman and Anglo-Saxon times. There was dark blue 'woad', indigo, Tyrian purple from a snail found in Tyre and alizarin from the madder plant.

Then William Perkin, trying to synthesize quinine, stumbled on something new. He was working with coal-tar compounds. At one stage in his study he noticed that a purplish substance had been produced. When he added alcohol, the purple appeared throughout the solution. Perkin had the wit to patent his process. The product became the first of a series of synthetic dyes. He called it 'mauveine'. In 1858, August Hofmann, Perkin's teacher, manufactured the dye, magenta. Before long, such dyes as alizarin and indigo were quickly produced synthetically and indigo farmers of India were put out of business.

Drugs By the late nineteenth century knowledge had become available to allow chemists to modify organic structures virtually at will. By 1944 quinine had been synthesized in the laboratory. In 1954 strychnine was also synthesized. Cocaine had been synthesized in 1923. In the 1940s, the molecular structure of cocaine was modified and an artificial drug, more stable chemically than cocaine, was produced. This was procaine (also called novocaine). Morphine yielded to chemical study, and a compound of morphine – diacetyl-morphine – produced heroin.

Barbituric acid had been identified as a sleep-inducing drug in 1864, but it was in 1902 that barbiturates were manufactured on a commercial scale. In 1935 it was found that a red dye, 'prontosil rubra', protected mice against streptococcal infections and that the active antibacterial agent was a breakdown product of the red dye, called 'sulphanilamide'. Following this discovery, hundreds of similar drugs were produced by chemical synthesis.

Explosives The explosive industry began in 1845 when a German chemist, Christian Schönbein, accidentally spilled a mixture of nitric and sulphuric acid on a cotton apron, which he then hung up to dry. But as soon as the apron was dry, it exploded. Schönbein had produced nitrocellulose (guncotton). The explosive properties of nitrocellulose were due to the fact that the 'nitro' group provided a source of oxygen within the molecule itself, whereas in gunpowder the saltpetre providing oxygen needed to be mechanically mixed with the sulphur and charcoal.

Another high explosive was discovered by accident – nitroglycerine. It was prepared by an Italian chemist, Ascanio Sobrero, by adding glycerine to a mixture of nitric and sulphuric acids. Nitroglycerine was so sensitive that it was almost too dangerous to use. It was forty years before the Swedish chemist, Alfred Nobel, found that its power could be controlled by absorbing it on an appropriate earth to produce dynamite. In the 1950s trinitrotoluene (TNT) was developed.

Major twentieth-century explosions

Date	Location	Deaths	Date	Location	Deaths
1910 Oct 1	Los Angeles Times Bldg	21	1962 Jan 16	Gas pipeline, Alberta, Canada	19
1913 Mar 7	Dynamite, Baltimore Harbor	55	1962 Mar 3	Gasoline truck, Syria	31
1915 Sept 27	Gasoline tank car, Ardmore, Okla.	47	1962 Oct 3	Telephone Co. office, N.Y. City	23
1917 Apr 10	Munitions plant, Eddystone, Pa.	133	1963 Jan 2	Packing plant, Terre Haute, Ind.	16
1917 Dec 6	Halifax Harbor, Canada	1,654	1963 Mar 9	Dynamite plant, S. Africa	45
1918 May 18	Chemical Plant, Oakdale, Pa.	193	1963 Mar 9	Steel plant, Belecke, W. Germany	19
1918 July 2	Explosives, Split Rock, N.Y.	50	1963 Aug 13	Explosive dump, Gauhiti, India	32
1918 Oct 4	Shell plant, Morgan Station, N.J.	64	1963 Oct 31	State Fair Coliseum, Indianapolis	73
1919 May 22	Food plant. Cedar Rapids, Ia.	44	1964 July 23	Bone, Algeria, harbor munitions	100
1920 Sept 16	Wall Street, New York, bomb	30	1965 Mar 4	Gas pipeline, Natchitoches, La.	17
1924 Jan 3	Food plant, Pekin, Ill.	42	1965 Aug 9	Missile silo, Searcy, Ark.	53
1928 April 13	Dance hall, West Plains, Mo.	40	1965 Oct 21	Bridge, Tila Bund, Pakistan	80
1937 Mar 18	New London, Tex., school	294	1965 Oct 30	Cartagena, Colombia	48
1940 Sept 11	Hercules Powder, Kenvil, N.J.	51	1965 Nov 24	Armory, Keokuk, Ia.	20
1942 June 5	Ordnance plant, Elwood, Ill.	49	1966 Oct 13	Chemical plant, La Salle, Que.	11
1944 Apr 14	Bombay, India, harbor	700	1967 Feb 17	Chemical plant, Hawthorne, N.J.	11
1944 July 17	Port Chicago, Cal., pier	322	1967 Dec 25	Apartment bldg., Moscow	20
1944 Oct 21	Liquid gas tank, Cleveland	135	1968 Apr 6	Sports store, Richmond, Ind.	43
1947 Apr 16	Texas City, Tex., pier	561	1970 Apr 8	Subway construction, Osaka, Japan	73
1948 July 28	Farben works, Ludwigshafen, Ger.	184	1971 June 24	Tunnel, Sylmar, Cal.	17
1950 May 19	Munitions barges, S. Amboy, N.J.	30	1971 June 28	School, fireworks, Pueblo, Mex.	13
1956 Aug 7	Dynamite trucks, Cali, Colombia	1,100	1971 Oct 21	Shopping center, Glasgow, Scot.	20
1958 Apr 18	Sunken munitions ship, Okinawa	40	1973 Feb 10	Liquified gas tank, Staten Is., N.Y.	40
1958 May 22	Nike missiles, Leonardo, N.J.	10	1975 Dec 27	Chasnala, India, mine	431
1959 Apr 10	World War II bomb, Philippines	38	1976 Apr 13	Lapua, Finland, munitions works	45
1959 June 28	Rail tank cars, Maldrin, Ga.	25	1977 Nov 11	Freight train, Iri, S. Korea	57
1959 Aug 7	Dynamite truck, Roseburg, Ore	13	1977 Dec 22	Grain elevator, Westwego, La.	35
1959 Nov 2	Jamuri Bazar, India, explosives	46	1978 Feb 24	Derailed tank car, Waverly, Tenn.	12
1959 Dec 13	Dortmund, Ger., 2 apt. bldgs.	26	1978 July 11	Propylene tank truck, Spanish	
1960 Mar 4	Belgian munitions ship, Havana	100		coastal campsite	150
1960 Oct 25	Gas, Windsor, Ont., store	11			

Polymers If in the manufacture of nitrocellulose, the treatment of cellulose with nitric acid is adjusted so that only part of the molecule is nitrated, the material formed, after being dissolved in alcohol, can be produced in the form of collodion, a strong skin-like film. It was later found that if this material was combined with camphor, a useful 'plastic' was produced. This was 'celluloid'. By replacing the nitrate groups by acetate groups, 'cellulose acetate' was obtained, which was used on a large scale for photographic films.

In 1900, Leo Baekland, an American of Belgian origin, studied the gummy residues which were formed by reacting phenol with formaldehyde. In due course he produced the plastic, 'bakelite', which was hard, durable, capable of being moulded and a good insulator.

Another plastic of wide utility was polyethylene (often called by its trade name, polythene). It was produced by subjecting the gas, ethylene, to appropriate conditions of pressure and temperature. Propylene, containing 3 carbon atoms in its molecule where ethylene contained 2, could be similarly treated to yield the plastic polypropylene. When chlorinated ethylene was used, polyvinyl chloride (PVC) was produced. Later, after World War II, fluorine was introduced into the molecule and tetrafluorethylene obtained. This has the useful property of not being able to be made wet. It is marketed as Teflon, used in things like non-stick saucepans.

The chemistry of rubber has been extensively studied, leading to the production of artificial rubber by polymerising butadiene and styrene. Later, a chlorine atom was introduced into the molecule to produce Neoprene which possessed greater resistance to oil and many solvents.

The natural polymers – wool, cotton, silk, as well as the muscle fibres of which flesh is largely composed – are, in chemical terms, long complex chains of carbon atoms combined with nitrogen and sulphur. Similarly, the artificial polymers – the plastics – with which we are familiar – are also based on carbon chains. The silicones are a curious group of substances, originally discovered by E.S.Kipping, based on chains not of carbon, but of silicon. One of the useful properties of the silicones is that they are water-repellent.

Fibres The first of the man-made fibres, rayon, was made by Louis Chardonnet in 1884. It was prepared by treating cellulose with caustic soda, drying it and then treating it with carbon disulphide. The product when dissolved in caustic soda and squeezed through the fine holes of a spinneret produced threads of 'artificial silk'.

The most useful of the purely artificial fibres which came later was nylon. This was produced after many years of research in the laboratory of the American company, Du Pont. It is a polymer based on the two monomers, hexamethylene-diamine and adipic acid. It represents a milestone in the history of chemistry because Wallace Carothers, who came from Harvard to lead the team by which it was produced, set out to make a purely synthetic fibre with the properties, which was finally achieved.

In its 'relaxed' state, the molecules of nylon are folded, the folds being held together by hydrogen bonding between the -NH- and the -CO- groups. When it is straightened, it unfolds and the molecules straighten parallel to each other.

This links adjacent molecules to each other, and increases the total strength.

Nylon has many useful properties – it is strong, will drip dry, possesses elasticity and tensile strength. It is used for parachute cords, climbing rope, and, because it does not rot, for fishing nets. It is also used for delicate stockings and beautiful fabrics.

Terylene, another purely artificial fibre, used widely today, is a polymer of terephthalic acid and polyesters.

Insecticides   Chemistry has scored outstanding success in the production of synthetic insecticides. Although mosquitoes, for example, may begin to develop immunity to what has been the most successful of all the insecticides, namely DDT, this does not detract from the fact that millions of people have been saved from illness and death from malaria. Other chemical compounds – BHC, aldrin, dieldrin, carbonates and many more have increased food supplies in a hungry world.

Great things are also being achieved by chemistry in the production of herbicides – phenoxy compounds, carbamates, urea compounds, amides, triazines, dinitroaniline herbicides.

Detergents   The first synthetic detergents, made by the Germans after the First World War, were good wetting agents (and they reduced the surface tension of the water, allowing it to wet the fibres that were being washed). These first detergents were alkyl naphthalene sulphonates. After World War II, alkyl benzene was used. The use of alkyl benzene sulphate compounds revolutionized the economics of soap manufacture.

Scientists have come far since those distant days when fire was first used to separate copper from its ore. Today, the understanding of the 92 diverse elements which naturally occur on earth has provided the chemist with a store of ingredients from which the chromium-plated bumpers of his car, the special alloys for his aircraft and the means by which his television tube produces the subtlety of a coloured picture are all derived. Perhaps more noteworthy still has been the accumulation of knowledge by which the precise structure of the complex network of interlocking carbon atoms can be made plain. Not only can the chemist understand the exact three-dimensional structure of a molecule of quinine or morphia, of insulin or vitamin B_{12}, but he can also construct such molecules for himself. These are the achievements of modern chemical synthesis.

Only a few of the modern achievements of chemistry have been described in the last sections of this chapter. There have been many more. Indeed, the time is virtually in sight when there are few materials – whether they are artificial like nylon or natural like cotton – which *cannot* be made by a chemist in a laboratory. It does not follow, of course, that because something *can* be done, it *will* be done. Rubber, for example, can be got from a tree or from a laboratory and, in practice, tyres are made of rubber derived from both sources. Perhaps it is simplest to think of a substance, not as a 'chemical' or a 'natural product' but, regardless of its source, as a legitimate target for chemical investigation. After all, chemistry is the science of the composition of matter – not just of 'chemicals', but of every substance there is.

There are at least as many molecules in one teaspoonful of water as there are teaspoonfuls of water in the Atlantic Ocean.

Two gases, helium and hydrogen, together represent 95 per cent of the sun's matter.

Bright yellow is the colour signifying danger in scientific laboratories.

Ether was used as an anaesthetic after an American chemistry student had observed its effects on young people who sniffed it at parties.

70 per cent of the world's bromine comes from the Atlantic Ocean.

There are about 7,000,000 tons of Epsom salts in every cubic mile of sea water.

In every cubic mile of sea water there are about 170,000,000 tons of chemical compounds (not counting the water) of which 4,000,000 tons are magnesium.

The earth is five-and-a-half times denser than water.

If the nucleus of an atom was scaled up to the size of a marble measuring half an inch in diameter, it would have a mass of 100,000,000 tons. If a chain of a rubber molecule containing 15,000 carbon atoms were scaled up to the same size, the molecule would stretch from London to Mecca. And if DNA was straightened out on the same scale it would reach from London to Calcutta.

5

Energy

The Need For Energy

It is only since 1785, when steam engines designed and built by James Watt began to come into use, that sources of energy, in the sense with which the term is used today, became a topic of any practical interest. Coal had been mentioned in English chronicles as early as AD 852, but so far as the energy for producing work was concerned, this was supplied throughout Europe by the muscles of labourers, horses and oxen, supplemented by the sails of ships and of windmills and, in certain favoured places, by the flow of water to turn mill-wheels. Wood from the forests was used, as well as coal, for heat and for the smelting of iron ore. Indeed, the great weald of England had been almost devastated to provide the iron the nation needed.

James Watt was not the first man to construct a workable steam engine but his engine, based on his better understanding of the scientific principles involved, represented a major advance. In 1698 Thomas Savery had devised an engine using the principle that the vacuum formed when steam, contained within a cylinder, was condensed, could be used to pull up a piston. In 1712, Thomas Newcomen invented a machine using a similar principle in which, after the cylinder had been filled with steam, which pushed on a piston, a cold water jet was squirted into the cylinder to condense the steam and thus create a vacuum to pull the piston and with it a great beam which could be coupled to a pump. Newcomen engines were installed in a number of mines to work the pumps to prevent flooding. The Newcomen system was, however, very inefficient, principally because so much of the heat energy from the coal with which the engines were fuelled was wasted by the repeated injection of cold water. It often happened that the amount of coal burnt to keep the pump going represented a significant proportion of the coal recovered from the mine in which the pump was installed.

James Watt understood the importance of a then current discovery by Joseph Black of the 'latent heat of steam'. This was the amount of heat that needed to be put into water at its boiling point in order to convert it into steam at the very same temperature. This led him to provide two vessels in his steam engine. The first was the boiler in which the steam was generated. This vessel was maintained continuously at a high temperature. The second, quite separate vessel was the condenser, in which the temperature was lower and the steam was condensed to produce the vacuum. The engine allowed the steam alternately to push on one side of the piston at the same time that the vacuum pulled on the other. At the end of the stroke, the two forces were reversed.

Soon Watt's steam engines were being used to operate factories, work hammers and other power machinery, operate air blowers in iron smelters and in due course, after modification by a series of gifted engineers, initiate the age of steam locomotives and the period of 'railway fever' characteristic of the middle of the nineteenth century. And the uncertainty of journeys by sea under

1 Wears
2 Brake and break wheel
3 Spindle beam
4 Wallower (gear-wheel)
5 Stone nut
6 Runner stone
7 Bed stone
8 Governor
9 Crown tree
10 Horse
11 Post
12 Sack hoist
13 Quarter bars
14 Vanes with
   wind-controlled
   setting
15 Whip
16 Cross-trees
17 Fantail or fly
18 Fan carriage
19 Striking chain
20 Windshaft

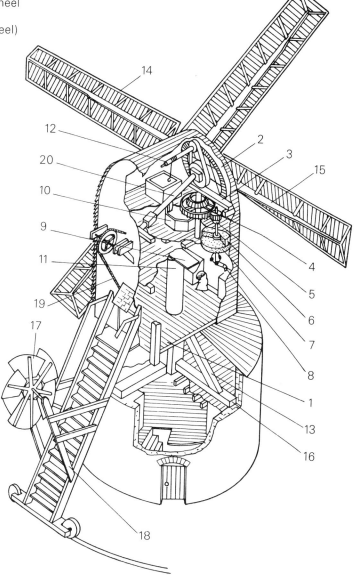

Until the fourteenth century windmills
were of the post mill type. The sails
were attached to a wooden or
cast-iron windshaft, which carried a
large, wood-toothed gear-wheel,
which in turn drove the horizontal
millstones through a small piston or
hoist. At one time there may have been
as many as 10,000 windmills working
in England

Boulton and Watt's rotative beam engine, 1788 (front view)

sail gave way, as a result of Charles Parsons' application of the steam turbine in the 1880s, to the steamer. Suddenly after millennia of horse-, ox- and man-power, the industrial age in which we now live had begun, with its dependence, first on coal and later on petroleum – the so-called 'energy sources'.

It was estimated that in 1870 the total amount of coal used throughout the world was 277,000,000 tons a year; by 1900 it had risen to 912,000,000 tons. Thereafter the figure gradually rose to about 2,000,000,000 tons by the 1940s. Yet even in these same 1940s, the estimated reserves of coal yet undug were about 5,000,000,000,000 tons, that is some 2,500 years' supply. Although it can be argued that one day this source of energy will be exhausted, it can hardly be taken as a matter of immediate world concern (although UK reserves of coal are not much more than 300 years' supply). Furthermore, although the bulk of the world's coal deposits appear to be in Europe, Asia and North America, coal is also to be found in the other continents. Coal has, in the main, been used for heating, for the production of steam to obtain power from steam engines, some of which have been used to operate electric generators and thus convert the chemical energy of the coal into electricity (the chemistry by which energy is released from coal is the combination of the carbon in the coal with the oxygen in the atmosphere with the resultant formation of carbon dioxide gas).

World Coal Resources

United States	$1,486 \times 10^9$ metric tons
North America outside US	601×10^9 metric tons
Western Europe	377×10^9 metric tons
USSR (including European part)	$4,310 \times 10^9$ metric tons
Asia (excluding USSR)	681×10^9 metric tons
South and Central America	14×10^9 metric tons
Oceania (including Australia)	59×10^9 metric tons
Africa	109×10^9 metric tons
Total world resources	$7,637 \times 10^9$ metric tons

In the early nineteenth century, the Scottish inventor, William Murdoch, discovered that when coal was heated in the absence of oxygen, it produced readily combustible coal gas. For the first fifty years or so after its discovery, coal gas, piped into people's houses, was used to produce light. We then find the chemical energy of coal having been converted into heat, thence into mechanical work, then – or a little later – into electricity, and now into light. An alternative process for obtaining light from coal was the invention, by a Boston pharmaceutical firm in 1852, of a method of distilling 'coal oil' from coal tar. This oil, marketed as 'kerosene', was widely used in lamps.

Petroleum, like coal, was known to the ancients, although it was not widely available. The Babylonians used it in lamps as did the inhabitants of Agrigentum in Sicily, where there was a petroleum spring. The Assyrians had access to petroleum in the form of naphtha, which they used to set fire to enemy ships. Veritably, the history of petrol bombs is a long one. But the use of petroleum as a fuel from which to obtain mechanical energy only dates from 1857, when the first commercial oil well was drilled, quickly followed by the opening of wells in the United States in 1859. By 1900, the world usage was 150,000,000 barrels. Another half century saw the annual world usage at more than 4,000,000,000 barrels and since then demand has steadily increased.

World oil reserves – the ten largest national deposits

		Proven Reserves (in billions of barrels)
1	Saudi Arabia	165.7
2	Union of Soviet Socialist Republics	71.0
3	Kuwait	66.2
4	Iran	59.0
5	Iraq	32.1
6	Abu Dhabi (of the United Arab Emirates)	30.0
7	United States	28.5
8	Libya	24.3
9	People's Republic of China	20.0
10	Nigeria	18.2

Source: *Oil and Gas Journal*, December 25, 1978. © Petroleum Publishing Co.

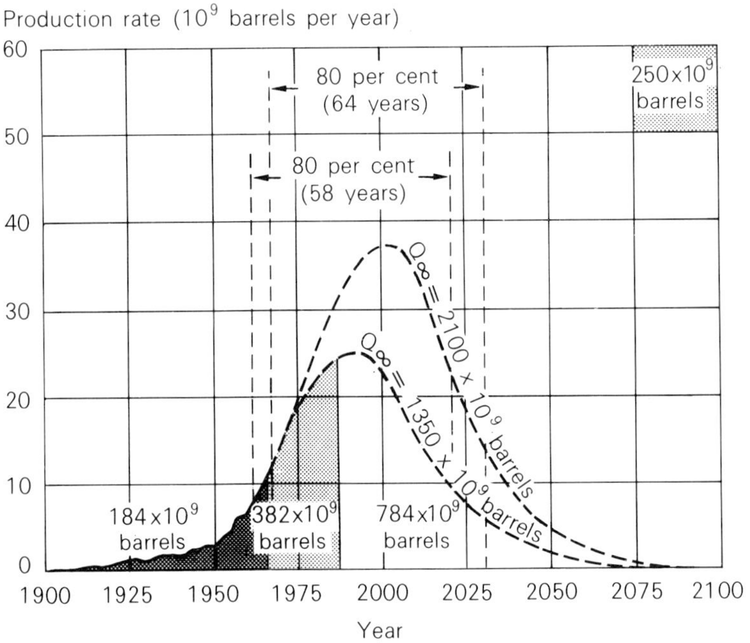

Production rate (10^9 barrels per year)

```
60
         |         | 80 per cent |  |        |      |250x10⁹|
         |         | (64 years)  |  |        |      |barrels|
50
         |      | | 80 per cent  |  |        |
40       |      | | (58 years)   |  |        |
         |      | |              |  |        |
30       |      | |      ___     |  |        |
         |      | |   __/   \__  | Q∞ = 2100 × 10⁹ barrels
20       |      | |  /       \   | Q∞ = 1350 × 10⁹ barrels
         |      | | /         \  |
10   184x10⁹   |382x10⁹|  784x10⁹ |
     barrels   |barrels|  barrels |
 0
   1900  1925  1950  1975  2000  2025  2050  2075  2100
                        Year
```

Such is the level of world oil consumption that 80 per cent of the oil reserves may well have been consumed by the year 2020. The rate of oil consumption has doubled every twelve years during the twentieth century. This diagram shows the upper and lower limits of estimated world reserves

Oil production by the world's top twenty producers (1979)

Nation	Daily production	% of total world production
1. USSR	4,186,550	18.6%
2. Saudi Arabia	3,374,425	14.7
3. United States	3,111,625	13.7
4. Iraq	1,253,775	5.5
5. Iran	1,107,775	5.0
6. Venezuela	859,575	3.8
7. Nigeria	841,325	3.7
8. Kuwait	808,475	3.5
9. People's Republic of China	773,800	3.4
10. Libya	753,725	3.3
11. United Arab Emirates	669,775	2.9
12. Indonesia	580,350	2.5
13. United Kingdom	573,050	2.5
14. Canada	545,675	2.4
15. Mexico	532,900	2.3
16. Algeria	414,275	1.8
17. Neutral Zone	206,225	0.9
18. Egypt	186,150	0.8
19. Qatar	184,325	0.8
20. Brunei-Malaysia	182,500	0.8
Total World	22,765,050	100.0

The moral arising from the recent unfolding of history is that science has been unable to make any reliable estimate of the total stock of this particular fuel existing in the world as a whole. The scale of usage appears to be high and it has been fashionable to forecast the exhaustion of supplies within a century. Yet no sooner is a forecast published than another oil deposit – in the Middle East, the Gulf of Mexico, Alaska and the North Sea – comes to light. Furthermore, arising from the discovery made in 1912 in Germany by Friedrich Bergius of a method of treating coal and heavy oil with hydrogen, it is possible to convert some of the immense stocks of coal into petrol.

The huge demand for petrol which, starting in the 1850s and growing rapidly to the end of the nineteenth century, expanded to become the major economic preoccupation it is today, was caused by the invention of the internal combustion engine. In spite of the improvement in the efficiency of the steam engine brought about by Watt, it remained a cumbersome machine in which, of the total energy of the coal combusted, only about ten per cent might be recovered in the work developed to pull a train or run a factory. In 1860, a French engineer, Jean Lenoir, produced an engine freed from the necessity of heating water to produce steam as a means of doing work. Lenoir's device called for the combustion of a mixture of air and an inflammable gas actually within the cylinder in which the piston was situated. This internal combustion engine was used to power the first motor vehicle. A later German model designed by Nicholas Otto employed a 4-stroke cycle in which (1) the injection of the gas-air

Semi-submersible drilling rig in the North Sea, capable of working in depths down to about 900 feet

mixture was followed by (2) a compression stage (3) an ignition stage and (4) the ejection of the spent explosion products. In 1885, Gottlieb Daimler patented a single-cylinder high-speed engine and, gradually, as one modification followed another, the modern petrol engine was developed.

An important feat of scientific insight from which great developments have already come and which may lead to more in the future arose from the work of Rudolf Diesel. As a young man, listening to a lecture on the progress of the steam engine, he was struck, not only by its merits but by its continuing inefficiency as a means for converting the potential energy of coal into work. He considered the problem over a period of several years and in 1893 he published a long paper entitled 'The Theory and Construction of a Rational Heat Engine'. This was a description of what has since become known as the 'Diesel engine', which so far has achieved its most notable achievement, among many, in pulling railway trains. One of the basic principles of Diesel's design was to use the heat of very high compression in the cylinders to combust the fuel. In the early models the fuel was still coal, as used in the steam engines they were to supersede, which was blown into the cylinders through a valve as finely divided coal dust. As far as we know, no one has considered whether this principle could be re-adapted to meet modern circumstances in which coal is more readily available than fuel oil. At present, though, private motor cars are usually powered by four-stroke petrol engines, while diesel engines are mostly used for heavy transport – lorries and locomotives, for instance.

World energy consumption – the top twenty

		Energy Units per Capita/per Year*
1	U.S. Virgin Islands	54,283
2	Qatar	25,236
3	Wake Island	24,025
4	Netherlands Antilles	22,836
5	Christmas Island	20,537
6	Luxembourg	15,788
7	Brunei	14,209
8	Panama Canal Zone	13,685
9	United Arab Emirates	13,322
10	Bahrain	11,998
11	United States	11,554
12	Canada	9,950
13	Kuwait	9,198
14	Guam	9,081
15	New Caledonia	7,687
16	Czechoslovakia	7,397
17	Bahamas	7,286
18	East Germany	6,789
19	Australia	6,657
20	Nauru	6,430

* 1 energy unit equals 10 kilowatt-hours

World energy consumption – the bottom twenty

		Energy Units per Capita/per Year
1	Nepal	11
2	Burundi	12
3	East Timor	16
3	Kampuchea	16
5	Rwanda	17
6	Upper Volta	18
7	Chad	23
8	Ethiopia	27
8	Mali	27
10	Haiti	28
11	Bangladesh	33
12	Niger	35
13	Afghanistan	41
13	Central African Empire	41
13	Yemen	41
16	Somalia	47
17	Uganda	48
18	Benin	49
18	Burma	49
20	Malawi	56

Source: *World Energy Supplies*, Statistical Papers, Series J, No. 21. New York: United Nations, 1978.

The efficiency of twenty energy converters

A variety of means of converting energy from one form to another is essential if the limited range of primary fuels is to meet the needs of modern society. Yet many common systems are surprisingly inefficient in energy conversion.

Watt engine	1%	Aircraft gas turbine	36%
Incandescent lamp	5%	Nuclear reactor	39%
Steam locomotive	8%	Steam turbine	46%
Solar cell	10%	Liquid fuel rocket	47%
Rotary engine (Wankel)	18%	Fuel cell (hydrogen-oxygen)	60%
Fluorescent lamp	20%	Electric storage battery	72%
Internal combustion engine	25%	Home gas boiler	85%
Solid state laser	30%	Dry cell battery	90%
Steam power plant with generator	32.5%	Electric motor	93%
Industrial gas turbine	34%	Electric generator	98%

Ideas About Energy

The notion of energy as uniform stuff which was measureable and could be thought of as being always the same, even when manifest in different forms, is a comparatively modern one. Ideas were different in the eighteenth century. Then, light was thought of as consisting of material particles of some sort of luminous stuff; things were hot, it was thought, because they contained the element 'caloric'; magnetized bodies contained the 'magnetic effluvia', and living animals were full of vital spirit. There was no more reason to believe that these bore any more direct relationship to each other than did, say, charcoal to sulphur. Gradually, however, as the nineteenth century progressed, it became clear that the energy of motion, heat, light, electricity, chemical action and magnetism could all be converted into one another and could be thought of as manifestations of the same thing, namely, energy. Since life was established as chemistry, its energy was also the same stuff. Then, in the middle of the nineteenth century, J.P.Joule worked out how much heat could be obtained from a given amount of work. By means of a piece of apparatus worked by weights like a grandfather clock he found that a paddle-wheel immersed in water made the water warmer by stirring it. He showed that 772 foot-pounds of work were needed to provide enough heat to raise the temperature of a pound of water by $1°F$. He also showed, while on a journey in Switzerland, that a sensitive thermometer could demonstrate that water at the bottom of a waterfall was warmer than at the top.

Static electricity had been observed as long ago as in Greek times. It was also known that if two electrically charged objects were brought close together they sometimes attracted and sometimes repelled each other; furthermore, the Italian scientists, Luigi Galvani and Alessandro Volta, had, in the 1770s, made some early experiments into the relationship of electricity to animal muscular movement, and André Ampère anticipated the advent of electromagnetism when he noticed that a spiral of wire containing a current might act like an ordinary bar magnet. In 1820 Hans Oersted showed that an electric current flowing in a wire could deflect a magnetic needle.

But it was Michael Faraday who showed that mechanical motion could actually be converted into electricity. By moving a metal conductor so as to cut the lines of force of a magnetic field, electric current was produced. The same thing happened if the magnet producing the lines of force was moved and the conductor was kept still. This observation not only showed the interchangeability of mechanical work and electricity but also made possible the modern electrical industry that was to follow. Electrical generators produce electrical energy when power is used to spin conducting wires across magnetic fields. Alternatively, when electrical energy is fed into a similar system, the conductors cutting the lines of force will be made to move and an electric motor result converting electrical into mechanical energy.

In 1847 ideas about energy were assuming their modern form. It was in this year that Hermann Helmholtz in Germany conceived what has now become the 'First Law of Thermodynamics'. This states that energy cannot be created or destroyed but can only be converted from one form to another. Thus work and heat are equivalent energy forms. This is also known as the 'conservation of energy'. Joule elaborated and confirmed this hypothesis and showed that in locating the final destination of, for example, a certain amount of mechanical energy, it might be necessary to take account not only of work done and heat given off, but also of the sound produced as well, since energy is needed to vibrate the air that transmits the sound.

Ideas about energy moved forward a further step by the middle of the nineteenth century. It was then that James Clerk Maxwell pointed out that at any particular temperature the molecules of a gas would be moving at a particular speed. If more energy was contributed to the system and the gas heated, its molecules would move faster. William Thomson Kelvin took the matter a stage further. It had been shown by 'Charles' Law' that the volume of a gas is reduced by 1/273rd for every drop in temperature of 1°C. Kelvin considered this phenomenon and concluded that the *energy* within a gas, represented by the *movement* of its molecules, would be reduced to zero if the gas were cooled to −273°C. This temperature, at which all the energy is gone and the molecules have stopped moving, is now called 'Absolute Zero', and temperature measured from Absolute Zero upwards is called the Kelvin Scale. On this scale, the freezing point of water is 273°K. In 1850 Rudolf Clausius defined and named the property, entropy, that is, the thermodynamic state of a body, and enunciated the second Law of Thermodynamics, which states that the passage of heat from a colder to a hotter body cannot take place without compensation.

Fahrenheit and centigrade compared

1	Absolute Zero	= −273.16°C.	= −459.69°F.
2	Point of Equality	= −40.0°C.	= −40.0°F.
3	Zero Fahrenheit	= −17.8°C.	= 0.0°F.
4	Freezing Point	= 0.0°C.	= 32°F.
5	Normal Human Blood Temperature	= 36.9°C.	= 98.4°F.
6	100 Degrees F.	= 37.8°C.	= 100°F.
7	Boiling Point	= 100.0°C.	= 212°F.

Where the electricity goes in the home

	Average Wattage	Kilowatt-hours Consumed Annually		Average Wattage	Kilowatt-hours Consumed Annually
Comfort			*Food*		
air-conditioner (room)	1,566	1,389	blender	386	15
electric blanket	177	147	carving knife	92	8
dehumidifier	257	377	coffee maker	894	106
fan (rollaway)	171	138	deep fryer	1,448	83
heater (portable)	1,322	176	dishwasher	1,201	363
humidifier	177	163	freezer		
lighting	—	1,800	(frostless, 15 cu ft)	440	1,761
			frying pan	1,196	186
Health			mixer	127	13
hair dryer	381	14	oven, microwave	1,500	300
shaver	14	1.8	oven, self-cleaning	4,800	1,146
sun lamp	279		range	8,200	1,175
toothbrush	7	0.5	refrigerator		
			(frostless, 12 cu ft)	321	1,217
Entertainment			toaster	1,146	39
radio	71	86	waste disposer	445	30
radio-record player	109	109			
colour television	332	502	*Laundry*		
			clothes dryer	4,856	993
Housewares			iron (hand)	1,008	144
clock	2	17	washing machine	512	103
floor polisher	305	15	water heater (standard)	2,475	4,219
sewing machine	75	11			
vacuum cleaner	630	46			

Light As Energy

We know that light is a form of energy. It is light, shining on the green pigment in leaves, that salvages the spent fuel from the atmosphere, the carbon dioxide gas which we, our steam engines and our motor cars breathe out, with the spent hydrogen from water, and builds them back into sugar and thence into the complex structures of plants. Light, therefore, is the energy of the food we eat. It was also the source from which coal and oil, the crushed residues of great plants which flourished over the millennia long ago, were derived. Light's

An engraving of Sir Isaac Newton 'investigating light', with his telescope on the desk

energy also provides the oxygen we and our engines require to keep going because it is in prising the carbon off the carbon dioxide and the hydrogen off the H_2O that light and green plants release for us free oxygen. Moreover, in the electric light bulb, pioneered in the nineteenth century, and now widely used in varying, sophisticated versions, man created for himself a form of light that was 'artificial', shaped to his own needs.

Light has been studied for a very long time. The way it behaves when it is reflected was worked out by the Greeks; Snell in Holland established the laws of refraction in 1621. This is the bending of light rays passing from air to water, or water to glass. Newton in 1666 split white light into the coloured components of which it is composed. He collated the evidence supporting the conclusion that light was composed of particles of energy. Other evidence, however, notably that derived from experiments carried out by Thomas Young in 1803, seemed to imply that light was a series of waves which, if sent through a narrow slit, could be diffracted round corners. Other experiments, by David Brewster and Augustin Fresnel, of passing light through crystals of Iceland spar, were interpreted as supporting the wave hypothesis. In 1905 Einstein postulated that light is composed of units of energy or 'quanta'. In the same year, in his special theory of relativity, he argued that if, for all frames of reference, the speed of light is constant, and if all natural laws are the same, then both time and motion are found to be relative to the observer. In a mathematical application of the theory Einstein went on to show that mass and energy are related and he put forward the famous formula:

$$E \text{ (energy)} = m \text{ (the mass of matter involved)} \times c^2$$
$$\text{(c being the velocity of light)}$$

The energy of light is responsible for the energy stored in food crops and the consequent energy derived from horses, oxen and men. There are current schemes for making use of light energy to run motor cars by growing – possibly in wet tropical countries – quick-maturing starchy crops such as cassava from which alcohol could be produced as a motor fuel. In general, however, light energy occurs in a dispersed form. But in the 1960s, Theodore Maiman constructed a device in which light was fed into a ruby cylinder. The colour of the light was selected to fit exactly the colour best absorbed by the ruby. Under appropriate conditions this caused a rapid series of flashes to be produced resulting in there being emitted from the end of the cylinder a narrow beam of so-called 'coherent' light possessing the property of travelling for long distances without spreading. Light energy thus concentrated was powerful indeed. It could be used to cut through metal or, in the hands of a surgeon, dissect tissues with high precision. The process by which the energy of light is thus concentrated is called 'Light Amplification by the Stimulated Emission of Radiation', or LASER for short.

Light can be defined as electromagnetic radiation, the pulses of which it is composed striking our eyes with the frequencies which we perceive as light. As the wavelengths become shorter, so the energy and 'penetrating power' of the rays increase. X-rays, discovered by Wilhelm Röntgen in 1895, are capable of passing through solid matter, while gamma rays, discovered by Antoine Becquerel in 1896, possess the most energy of all. The table below shows how narrow is the band of light which we can see, around which is electromagnetic energy which we are not capable of seeing.

As might be expected, light is not the only wavelength of electromagnetic radiation which has been utilized by modern technology. Microwaves, to take a single example, are already used in radar (radio detecting and ranging), a method of detecting otherwise invisible objects by bouncing radio pulses off them, and are today being adapted to project energy into the cooking of food, where the microwave is converted into heat by which the food is cooked.

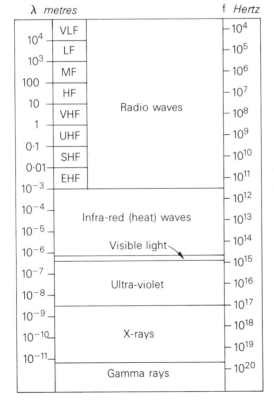

The spectrum of electromagnetic waves. The lower the frequency, the longer the wavelength; the higher the frequency the shorter the wavelength. Hertz measurements are used for low frequency waves, and wavelength measurements for higher frequency waves. VLF=Very Low Frequency; EHF waves are sometimes called 'millimetre' waves; SHF are often called 'microwaves'. Infra-red waves are heat waves. The diagram shows clearly how only a very narrow band of wavelengths is visible as light to the human eye

Nuclear Energy

From the dawn of history until 1934, every form of energy then known was derived either from the chemistry of combustion, which it was increasingly within the bounds of human intellect to influence, or from the sun, which it was not. Light, originally derived from the process of direct burning, that is, the chemical combination of carbon and hydrogen from oil, wax or gas with oxygen from the air, as in a candle or lamp, led to the release of heat sufficient to render particles of burning fuel incandescent. Later, after the primary fuels had been used to produce mechanical power, light was derived from the heat produced by electrical energy, derived from a steam-driven generator, forcing its way against the resistance of a metal filament. In scientific terms, all this energy came from chemical reactions involving only the electron shells within which resided the nucleus of an oxygen atom or a carbon atom. Then in 1934, Enrico Fermi exposed uranium to bombardment by neutrons. Neutrons can be specially produced in the laboratory from the nucleus of, say, beryllium, by an appropriate exposure to radioactivity. The result of his experiment was to split the atom of uranium into two radioactive atoms of barium with the release of an amount of energy greater by several orders of magnitude than anything attainable by chemical reaction.

The Hiroshima atomic bomb, 1945 – at that date, the greatest release of man-made energy in history.

In 1942, Fermi and Leo Szilard produced a chain reaction. By bombarding uranium 235, one neutron in splitting the atom caused the release of two neutrons which then caused other nearby uranium atoms to be split without the need for any further outside source of neutrons. In Fermi and Szilard's 'pile' the uranium blocks were separated by graphite which put a brake on the neutron bombardment. It was also possible to insert into the pile cadmium rods capable of absorbing neutrons and, if necessary, bringing the reactor to a stop. Energy released as heat was drawn away from the pile eventually to produce steam and, from it, mechanical power. Here, then, for the first time on earth, was a new source of energy. Today, forty years later, several important communities, the French, the Indians, the citizens of the United States, Great Britain and many other countries, have already generated a significant proportion of their energy needs by this means. Further possibilities are attainable. In 1951 Walter Zinn succeeded in designing a nuclear reactor which, once started up on uranium 235, was capable of producing from an otherwise unusable isotope of uranium, more uranium 235 than it had started with. This is a so-called 'breeder' reactor. It is estimated that a large nuclear reactor will produce heat equivalent to the output of 4,000,000 single-bar electric fires. But it ought to be said that controversy still reigns over the safety aspects of large reactors; in 1979 an 'impossible' accident at Three Mile Island in America nearly caused nuclear disaster.

Over the horizon lies nuclear fusion. So far nuclear energy has been produced on an industrial scale by fission. That is to say the uranium nucleus is split into two. Under extreme conditions, however, it is known that even more energy can be obtained by the fusion of the nuclei of light atoms, for example, that of hydrogen. So far, however, this reaction has only been achieved when an atomic bomb, depending on fission, is used as a means of reaching the very high temperature required to bring about the fusion process. This was the so-called 'hydrogen bomb'. This reaction has not so far been achieved in a power station.

If the use of nuclear reactors is the most advanced scientific approach to the provision of energy, it is fitting that attention should also be given to the sun as an energy source. We are not proposing that a study of the nuclear reactors, which follow the same principles as the sun in the production of heat and light, would necessarily be fruitful. Rather it could be productive to consider the wind by which the earth's atmosphere is stirred under the rays of the sun. The application of modern aerodynamics to the use of wind-power to drive ships at sea and work machinery on land is already under way. Some progress has already been made in harnessing the restless motion of the waves, stirred by the winds, to the generation of power. By all these means, as well as by the search for coal and oil, the management of biological fermentation to supplement whatever renewable fuels there may be, and by the use, where this is feasible, of geological heat deep within the earth's crust, can man's need for energy be met.

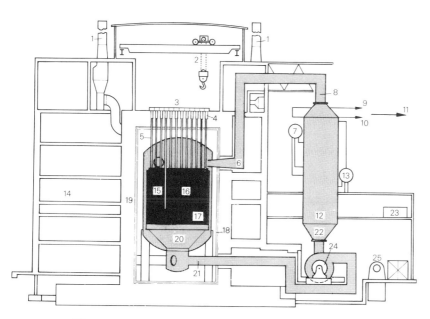

1 Chimneys for cooling air
2 Overhead crane
3 Control charge face
4 Charging tubes
5 Control rods
6 Hot gas duct
7 High pressure steam drum
8 Hot gas
9 High pressure steam
10 Low pressure steam
11 Steam to conventional steam
   turbine generating plant
12 Heat exchanger
13 Low pressure steam drum
14 Control and switchgear block
15 Control rod
16 Uranium rods
17 Graphite moderator
18 Thermal shield
19 Biological shield
20 Pressure vessel
21 Cool gas duct
22 Cool gas
23 Overhead crane
24 Electrically driven coolant
   circulating blower
25 Motor generator

The resources of nuclear power derivable from the fission process are many times larger than the energy available from existing, economic fossil fuel reserves. The first commercial application of nuclear power was the UK Calder Hall power station, 1956, here seen in cross-section showing the pressure vessel and one of the heat exchangers (UK Atomic Energy Authority)

World nuclear power – capacity and distribution

Country	Operational reactors	Capacity[1]	Generation[2] 1979
Argentina	1	360	2.7
Belgium	3	1,740	11.4
Canada	8	5,590	38.4
Finland	2	1,150	6.7
France	15	7,800	39·9
Germany, W.	10	7,050	40.4
Great Britain	33	9,040	38·6
India	3	620	2·9
Italy	4	1,490	2.6
Japan	20	12,840	62·0
Netherlands	2	520	3.5
Pakistan	1	140	0
South Korea	1	590	3·2
Spain	3	1,120	6·7
Sweden	6	3,850	21.0
Switzerland	3	1,060	11·8
Taiwan	2	1,270	6·3
U.S.	71	54,180	270.7
Total[3]	189	110,410[4]	568.8

(1) Thousand kilowatts. (2) Billion kilowatt hours. (3) Non-Communist countries.
(4) Total may not equal sum of components due to independent rounding.

Source: Energy Information Agency, U.S. Energy Department

Energy from food

Calories or Joules are a measure of the energy and heat that your body can obtain from the food and drink that you consume. A rough guide to the number of calories you can get from various types of food is:

Carbohydrates and protein: 4 Calories or approximately 17 kilojoules per Gram.

Fat: 9 Calories or approximately 38 kilojoules per Gram.

The number of Calories required by each individual depends on their age, sex and occupation. A person doing heavy manual work, or a sportsman taking a lot of exercise, will require more Calories (3000–4000 a day) than someone leading a sedentary life (1500–2000 Calories a day). Ideally, your Calorie intake should equal your Calorie output. (One Calorie is the equivalent of 4.19 kilojoules, or one kilocalorie, or 1000 calories.)

Calories/Joules

Each of the following contains 10 Grams Carbohydrate and 30 Calories (126 Joules)

	Grams weight
Grapes, whole	60
Milk, sweetened condensed	20
Nectarines	90
Plantains	37
Sweet potato	37

Each of the following contains 10 Grams Carbohydrate and 40 Calories (168 Joules)

Apples, baked (with skin)	120
Apples, stewed	150
Apples, raw (with skin and core)	120
Apricots, dried, stewed	75
Apricots, fresh, stewed (with stones)	180
Bananas, ripe (without skin)	60
Bananas, green	60
Carrots, boiled	240
Cherries, raw (with stones)	120
Cherries, stewed (with stones)	120
Currants, dried	15
Damsons, stewed (with stones)	150
Dates (with stones)	20
Dates (without stones)	15
Figs, dried, raw	20
Figs, dried, stewed	45
Gooseberries, dessert, raw	120
Greengages, raw (with stones)	90
Greengages, stewed (with stones)	120
Jelly, in packet	15
Melon (without skin)	210
Oranges (without peel)	120
Peaches, fresh (with stones)	120
Peaches, dried, raw	20
Peaches, raw (with skin and core)	120
Pears, stewed	150
Pineapple, fresh (edible part)	90
Plums, desert, raw (with stones)	120
Potato crisps	20
Prunes, dry, raw (with stones)	30
Raisins, dried	15

	Grams weight
Raspberries, raw	180
Raspberries, stewed	180
Rice, boiled	30
Strawberries, fresh, ripe	180
Sultanas, dried	15
Sweet corn (edible part)	45
Syrup	15
Tangerines (with peel)	180
Treacle	15

Each of the following contains 10 Grams Carbohydrate and 50 Calories (210 Joules)

Allbran	20
Apricots, dried, raw	30
Apricots, fresh (with stones)	180
Beans, baked, tinned	60
Beans, butter, boiled	60
Beans, haricot, boiled	60
Beetroot, boiled	120
Bournvita	15
Bread, brown or white	20
Chestnuts	30
Corn on the cob (edible part)	90
Cornflakes or other unsweetened breakfast cereal	15
Cornflour, before cooking	15
Custard powder, before cooking	15
Figs, green, raw	120
Flour	15
Horlicks	15
Lentils, boiled	60
Macaroni, raw	15
Noodles, raw	15
Ovaltine	15
Parsnips, boiled	90
Peas, tinned	60
Plums, stewed (with stones)	240
Porridge, cooked with water	120
Potatoes, boiled	60
Potatoes, roast	45
Rice, before cooking	15

	Grams weight
Ryvita	15
Sago, before cooking	15
Semolina, before cooking	15
Spaghetti, raw	15
Tapioca, before cooking	15

Each of the following contains 10 Grams
Carbohydrate and 60 Calories (251 Joules)

	Grams weight
Beans, broad, boiled	150
Biscuits, plain or semi-sweet	15
Lemon curd	22
Vitawheat	15

Each of the following contains 10 Grams
Carbohydrate and 70 Calories (293 Joules)

	Millilitres
Milk, evaporated, unsweetened	75
Milk, powdered. skimmed (reconstituted according to directions)	175

	Grams weight
Potatoes, chipped	30
Potatoes, mashed	60

Each of the following contains 10 Grams
Carbohydrate and the stated amount
of Calories/Joules

	Grams weight	Calories	Joules
Almonds, shelled	240	1360	4441
Barcelona nuts, shelled	210	1323	4286
Brazil nuts, shelled	240	1464	4458
Chipolatas, cooked	90	246	1031
Cocoa powder	30	128	536
Ice cream, plain	60	112	469
Onions, fried	120	404	1693
Peanuts, shelled	120	684	2447
Sausages, cooked	90	279	1169
Walnuts, shelled	210	1092	4843
Yoghurt, plain	210	100	419

	Milli-litres	Calories	Joules
Milk, fresh	175	133	557

	Pints	Milli-litres	Calories	Joules
Ale, strong	½	250	147	616
Beer, bottled	1	500	160	670
Beer, draught bitter	¾	375	135	566
Cider, bottled, dry	¾	375	150	628
Cider, bottled, sweet	½	250	120	503
Stout, bottled	½	250	100	419

PROTEINS	Per 30 grams weight	
Cheese	Calories	Joules
Camembert	88	369
Cheddar	120	503
Cheshire	110	461
Cream	232	972
Danish blue	103	427
Edam	88	369
Gorgonzola	112	469
Gouda	96	402
Gruyère	132	553
Parmesan	118	494
Processed	106	444
Spread	82	344
St. Ivel	108	452
Stilton	135	566
Wensleydale	115	482
Eggs		
Boiled	46	193
Fried	68	285
Poached	45	189
Fish		
Cod, steamed	23	96
Cod, fried	40	168
Crab, boiled, shelled	36	151
Dover sole, steamed	24	100
Dover sole, fried	68	285
Haddock, steamed	28	117
Haddock, fried	50	210
Haddock, smoked, steamed	28	117
Hake, steamed	24	100
Halibut, steamed	37	155
Herrings, baked, in vinegar	50	210
Kippers, baked	31	139
Lemon sole, steamed	18	75
Lemon sole, fried	62	260
Lobster, boiled, shelled	34	142
Oysters, raw	14	57
Pilchards, canned fish only	54	226
Plaice, steamed	26	109
Plaice, fried	66	277
Prawns, shelled	30	126
Salmon, canned	84	352
Shrimps, shelled	32	134
Turbot, steamed	28	117
Whitebait, fried	152	637
Meat		
Bacon, fried	142	595
Beef, corned	66	277
Beef, silverside, boiled	86	360
Beef, roast	83	348
Beef, steak, grilled	86	360
Chicken, boiled (meat only)	58	243
Chicken, roast (meat only)	54	226
Ham, boiled (lean only)	62	260
Liver, fried	74	310
Luncheon meat, tinned	95	398

	Per 30 grams weight	
	Calories	*Joules*
Mutton, roast	83	348
Mutton chop, grilled (with bone)	108	452
Pork, roast	90	377
Pork chop, grilled (with bone)	128	536
Veal, roast	66	277
FATS		
Butter	226	947
Cream, single	62	260
Cream, double	131	549
Lard	262	1098
Margarine	226	947
Oils	264	1106
Suet	262	1098

Source: British Diabetic Association.

The highest temperature in the Universe is probably 120,000 times the temperature of the Sun's interior (14,000,000°C).

It takes the energy from one ton of coal to make one ton of paper.

In ancient Greece marble used to be split with wedges of cork. The cork was forced into cracks in the rock and then water was poured over to saturate it. As the cork expanded the rock cracked.

The most efficient form of light production that has been discovered so far is the glow worm.

Drops of water that land on a red-hot surface never actually touch the surface. They rest on a cushion of vapour while they boil away and in the end they evaporate.

Between 1783 and 1857 over 111,000 inhabitants of the kingdom of Naples were killed in earthquakes. The mortality rate in those seventy-five years was nearly 1,500 deaths per annum.

The Great Fire of London in 1666 claimed only six lives.

A nineteenth-century Scots inventor, David Hutton, invented a tiny mill for twisting twine that ran on mouse power. Originally he employed the services of only one mouse. However, plans for harnessing the collective power of 10,000 mice were regrettably forestalled by Hutton's death.

To work off 1lb of fat you would need to walk 34 miles.

6

Time

For primitive man, the day was (and still is) the simplest and most obvious unit of time. The peoples of the Malay Archipelago, the Comanche Indians, the North Luzon tribes, all reckoned time in 'suns'. In contrast, the Greenlanders, the Polynesians, the Indians of Pennsylvania (and the early Germans and English) reckoned in 'nights'.

Many different peoples used to divide the day into portions, depending upon the sun's position in the sky. The Cross River natives of Nigeria, East African tribes, and Australian aborigines used to point to the position the sun would be in in the sky to indicate a particular time. A Swahili tribe used to plant a special flower in every garden, whose petals began to open at sunrise, were wide open by noon, and closed again between noon and sunset.

If the day was divided into smaller sections, the divisions chosen often reflected activities in daily life, or changes in people's surroundings. The Baganda divided day and night into NIGHT, COCK-CROW (early dawn), LITTLE-SUN (morning), BROAD-DAYLIGHT and SUN-UP-ABOVE (noon). The Thonga of South Africa divided the day in terms of temperature: COOL-DAWN, SUN-PIERC-ING, SUN-BURNING, SUN-MIDDLE-OF-THE-SKY, SUN-GOES-COOLER, REACHED-HOR-IZON. The Achenise of Sumatra divided the day into times when they tended their rice, and the Moslem divided it into prayer-times. The Antananarivo of Madagascar broke the day into quite small sections, based upon a remarkable mixture of observations and activities. Their 'time segments' began at midnight – HALVING-OF-THE-NIGHT, FROG-CROWING, COCK-CROWING, MORN-ING-AND-NIGHT-TOGETHER, CROW-CROWING, BRIGHT-HORIZON, GLIMMER-OF-DAY, COLOURS-OF-CATTLE-CAN-BE-SEEN, SUNRISE, BROAD-DAY, DEW-FALLS, CATTLE-GO-OUT, LEAVES-DRY, HOAR-FROST-DISAPPEARS, SUN-OVER-RIDGE-OF-ROOF, SUN-ENTERS-THRESHOLD-OF-ROOM, SUN-AT-RICE-POUNDING-PLACE, SUN-AT-HOUSE-POST, SUN-AT-SHEEP-PEN, CATTLE-COME-HOME, SUNSET-FLUSH, SUN-DEAD, FOWLS-COME-IN, PEOPLE-COOK-RICE, PEOPLE-EAT-RICE, PEOPLE-FINISH-EATING, GO-TO-SLEEP. Many of these descriptions are of the position the sun had reached in relation to the peoples' possessions or dwellings. A rational system of time could only arise once people had broken away from this sort of simple and repetitive existence.

The first realization of periods of time related to the seasons was linked to perception of changes in the weather from hot to cold, and from dry to wet. The plants and animals around them gave people additional clues about the passage of time. In the tropics, indeed, the principal change from one season to the next is often when it starts to rain or becomes dry. For instance, the Indians of Orinoco knew the rainy season was about to begin when they heard the scream of monkeys at midnight and when certain trees began to blossom. The tribe of Bigambul in Australia have four seasons, denoted by the blossoming of certain trees.

In other parts of the world there were even more remarkable ways of measuring the passing of the seasons. The Hidatsa Indians reckoned in terms of the gestation period of a buffalo calf. The Dayak tribe of Borneo had eight different seasons according to the different work to be done in the rice fields, and the Balinese derived their seasons from the different monsoon winds blowing across the country. The Chinese had a particularly elegant system for measuring the passing of the seasons. Their twenty-four divisions of the year were partly based on what they were doing and partly determined by astronomical observations. The seasons averaged 15 days in length. There was a season of rainwater (15 days); season of moving snakes (15); Spring equinox (15); season of pure brightness (15); season of sowing rain and season of dawn of summer (31); season of little fruitfulness and season of corn in the beard (31); Summer solstice (16); season of beginning of heat (16); season of great heat and season of signs of Autumn (31); season of end of heat and season of white dew (31); season of cold dew (15); Autumn equinox (15); season of hoar frost (15); season of signs of Winter (15); season of beginning of snow and season of Great Snow (29); Winter solstice (15); season of little cold (15); season of great cold (15); season of dawn of Spring (15).

The idea of a 'year' as a unit of time was derived from the repetitive nature of many natural phenomena. This sometimes led to a 'year' lasting for six months, as in Bali, where there are two identical periods of dry and wet seasons, each lasting for six months. This same 'six-month year' also occurred in the Samoan islands, East Africa, New Guinea, and the Bismarck Archipelago. In certain agricultural communities such as the Dayaks of Borneo, the year ran parallel with the growth of rice, until the time of its harvest, after which there was a 'gap'.

Sometimes there may be one particular event which has been observed to occur at a predictable time and acts as a 'marker' as each year comes round. In Brazil, the cashew tree blossoms once a year, and this was used as an annual sign. Often the choice reflects what is considered to be the most important annual event in the life of the community. Thus, the Paez of Colombia reckoned years by 'fishing-summers', the medieval Swiss reckoned by 'leaf-fall', while the old Norse, the Eskimos, and the North American Indians reckoned the passing of the years by the winters.

At last people began to judge their year by the annually recurring phase of the stars, and they recognized and named many constellations. Perhaps the most important for measuring time was the Pleiades, which was easy to recognize, and which also coincided with a number of important phases in the growth of plenty. The Chuckchee Indians called the Pole Star the *stuck star*, Orion, *the archer who shot a copper arrow*, and Capella, *a reindeer buck tied behind the sledge of a man driving two reindeer*.

The idea of a year as a unit of time is quite an advanced concept, and does not serve much purpose within a small isolated community. The peoples of the Torres Straits never counted years and none of them knew how old he or she was in numerical terms. A complex method of reckoning by generations had evolved in the Masai, where alternate groups of children were circumcised in four-year intervals, and each alternate group was given distinguishing names.

Another means of identifying years, with which we are more familiar today, is to assign a particular event to a particular year, or a number of years and not a number, as Westerners do now. We are accustomed to learning dates in history covering the reigns of kings, the duration of wars or the signing of treaties. Much the same system was used by the Dayaks who recalled two eclipses of the sun as a fixed date in relation to which other events could be timed. The Batak of Sumatra believed that smallpox epidemics returned at nine-year intervals, and used this (untrue) idea in reckoning time.

In Babylonia in the days of the Sumerian Kingdom of Ur, in the second half of the third millenium BC, the first complete year of a reign of a particular king was called, 'The Year of King X'. National events marked the other years. Sometimes a year was named after some violent catastrophe. But if no important event had occurred, the year was named 'the year following such-and-such a year'.

In the earlier period of Egyptian history, each year of the king's reign was described by an official name borrowed from festivals, buildings or wars. Gradually the simple counting of the years of the reign appeared alongside the names and, from the end of the Old Empire, supplanted the names.

In practically every language in the world, and among every group of peoples, whether primitive or sophisticated, the word MONTH is similar to that of MOON.

Even when the lunar month was used as a unit of time, many of those who did so did not count the number of days in each month, but just waited until the moon disappeared. The correlation between nine of these months and the time it took for a human child to be born was observed very early.

Even though they did not count the days, nearly all those who used the moon to measure time noticed its phases. Sometimes they merely observed new moon and full moon. More often, however, the month was divided up into smaller units, sometimes only of three or four days, each group of days named after a particular phase of the moon.

In present time-reckoning, the month has become a conventional sub-division of the year, and is now independent of the moon. By contrast, early peoples tried to adjust the 'year' by the moon, by adopting years of 12 or 13 months. Some descriptions of the month were not named directly after the moon itself, but still clung to the natural phenomena occurring at the time. This linking of a natural event or seasonal occupation to a month, so that each month could be distinguished, connected the seasons to the moon. For instance, the Voguls had 13 months: Little Autumn hunting month, Great Autumn hunting month, Winter Month, Month of light, Ski month, Month of the thawing snow crust, Month of thaw, Sap-in-furs month, Sap-in-birches month, Middle of summer month, Little summer month, Month of young razor bills, Elk running month.

In some parts of the world, months were named after stars. The Maoris of New Zealand named four months out of their 13 after stars: Month of the Great White Star, Month of another star, Spring begins, Tree flowering month, Cuckoo arrives, Rewarewa flowers, nga flowers, Great summer star, dry and scarce month, Harvest, Cuckoo leaves, Winter star, Grumbling month.

Early peoples had little need to measure very short periods of time. When a unit was employed it was often a standard cooking time. However, every pot and every fire were different, so that such a unit could not claim to be standard. The Malays and Javanese used a blink of the eyes as a second, the time it took to chew a quid of betel nut as an approximate five-minute unit, the time to cook a 'kay' of rice as about half-an-hour, and the time needed to cook a 'gantong' of rice as about one-and-a-half hours.

The great ancient civilizations of the Mayas, Babylonians and Egyptians progressed far beyond these primitive methods of measuring time. They mastered the fundamental laws of mathematics, and were able to keep records and make accurate observations of the movements of the stars and planets. However, their concepts of time were complex and different from our own. The Mayas pictured the divisions of time as burdens carried by a regiment of divine bearers, some of whom were days, others months, others years, and yet others decades. Events were believed to move in a circle, each circle being a recurring spell of duty for each god in the succession of bearers. The idea of a sequence of cycles for each division of time led the Mayas to devote more attention to the past than to the future. History was expected to repeat itself in cycles of 260 years.

The Babylonians originated the idea that celestial occurrences can influence events on earth. It is possible to trace back to them, by way of the Hebrews, the origin of our seven-day week, associated with the sun, moon, and the five planets they had discovered.

In India in 500 BC, it was believed that matter was discontinuous and so was time. This implied that everything existed for a moment, and was replaced the next moment by a facsimile of itself. Time was a series of momentary existences, which replaced each other so fast that people were not aware of the break.

It was the Ionian Greeks, with their command of mathematical astronomy, who placed the planets in a certain order and at certain distances from the earth, and enabled the late Hellenistic astrologers to construct a Pagan week. By the end of the third century AD, the Christians, who had previously used the Jewish seven-day week, in which the days simply had numbers, began to be influenced by astrological beliefs that the stars were demons, capable of affecting the fate of man. Of more importance than this, however, was one of the central doctrines of Christianity, that the crucifixion was a unique event, never to be repeated. This led the Christians to stress the linear nature of time, which moved on like a flowing river, in place of the idea of time as a circular progress endlessly repeating itself, a notion held by other civilizations.

Measurement of Time

Fo-hi, the first Emperor of China, devised in about 3000 BC a simple clock by which the day could be divided into approximately equal parts. A horizontal metal rod was covered with tar and sawdust. One end of it was set alight in the morning and the flame moved steadily along as time went by. When it had reached a certain distance along the rod, it burnt through a thread on which a ball was hung allowing the ball to fall onto a gong. The flame of burning tar and sawdust continued to move along the rod until it reached a second ball suitably spaced, and so on.

Later, the Chinese measured the length of the seasons, days and months by observing the movements of the moon, the sun and the stars. They divided the path of the moon into 28 'mansions'. The sun was thought of as the hand of a huge clock, whose path was divided into twelve discs, each symbolized by an animal. The night discs (or yin discs) were black and the day discs (or yang discs) were white, with grey discs showing the sunrise or sunset. Midnight was the 'dark hour' or 'rat', noon was a horse, before noon was 'before horse' symbolized by a dragon or snake. The afternoon, or 'after horse' was symbolized by a sheep and monkey. The evening was called 'dog', after which there began the new mansion of the moon.

Babylonian priests kept accurate records for 4000 years, and it was Nabu-rimanni, a Babylonian living around 500 BC, who calculated the time taken for the earth to rotate on its axis (a day) and the time taken for the earth to revolve around the sun (a year). From this he was able to calculate the length of the year in terms of days and parts of days. He concluded that one year was equal to 365 days, 6 hours, 15 minutes and four seconds. The remarkable accuracy of Nabu-rimanni's calculations is apparent by comparison with modern estimates of 365 days, 6 hours, 41 minutes and 59 seconds.

Originally the Romans had based their year upon the lunar month, and their earliest calendars had ten months in a year. Then Numa Pompilius devised a calendar of twelve months, with the year beginning in the spring. Six of these months were named, the others numbered. Having twelve months meant that six of the months would have an even number of days in them, which was considered unlucky, so they alternated with twenty-nine and thirty-one days, giving a year of 360 days, which was $5\frac{1}{4}$ days shorter than the solar year. They then modified the year from 360 to 355 days, which was much nearer the lunar year, by reducing the days in February from 31 to 28, and only having 29 days in December instead of 31. The beginning of the year was changed from March 1st to January 1st.

Julius Caesar abandoned the lunar month, and took the solar year to be $365\frac{1}{4}$ days. Each fourth year an extra day was added to account for the quarter day (as in our leap year).

Comparative time chart (1 billion=one thousand million)

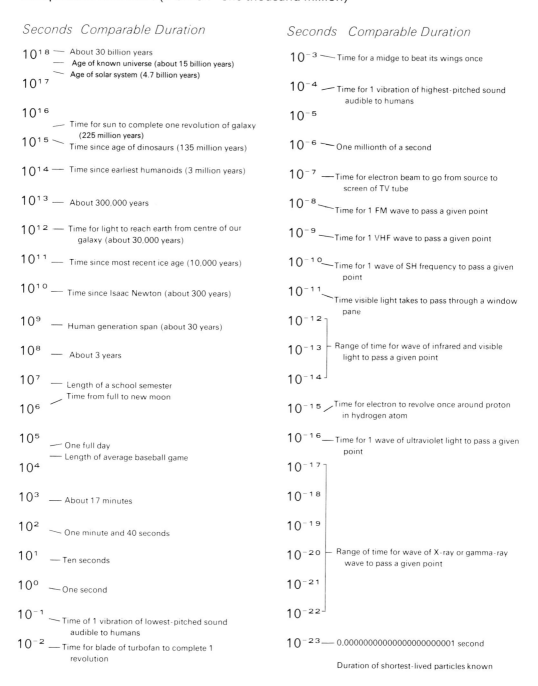

Seconds Comparable Duration

10^{18} — About 30 billion years
— Age of known universe (about 15 billion years)
— Age of solar system (4.7 billion years)
10^{17}

10^{16}
— Time for sun to complete one revolution of galaxy (225 million years)
10^{15}
— Time since age of dinosaurs (135 million years)

10^{14} — Time since earliest humanoids (3 million years)

10^{13} — About 300,000 years

10^{12} — Time for light to reach earth from centre of our galaxy (about 30,000 years)

10^{11} — Time since most recent ice age (10,000 years)

10^{10} — Time since Isaac Newton (about 300 years)

10^{9} — Human generation span (about 30 years)

10^{8} — About 3 years

10^{7} — Length of a school semester
— Time from full to new moon
10^{6}

10^{5} — One full day
— Length of average baseball game
10^{4}

10^{3} — About 17 minutes

10^{2} — One minute and 40 seconds

10^{1} — Ten seconds

10^{0} — One second

10^{-1} — Time of 1 vibration of lowest-pitched sound audible to humans
10^{-2} — Time for blade of turbofan to complete 1 revolution

Seconds Comparable Duration

10^{-3} — Time for a midge to beat its wings once

10^{-4} — Time for 1 vibration of highest-pitched sound audible to humans

10^{-5}

10^{-6} — One millionth of a second

10^{-7} — Time for electron beam to go from source to screen of TV tube

10^{-8} — Time for 1 FM wave to pass a given point

10^{-9} — Time for 1 VHF wave to pass a given point

10^{-10} — Time for 1 wave of SH frequency to pass a given point

10^{-11} — Time visible light takes to pass through a window pane

10^{-12}
10^{-13} — Range of time for wave of infrared and visible light to pass a given point
10^{-14}

10^{-15} — Time for electron to revolve once around proton in hydrogen atom

10^{-16} — Time for 1 wave of ultraviolet light to pass a given point

10^{-17}
10^{-18}

10^{-19}

10^{-20} — Range of time for wave of X-ray or gamma-ray wave to pass a given point

10^{-21}

10^{-22}

10^{-23} — 0.00000000000000000000001 second

Duration of shortest-lived particles known

This is a logarithmic scale, in which the time interval increases by a factor of 10 with each division of the scale.

From AD 8 the Julian calendar, with every fourth year a leap year, was used without alteration until 1582, by which time the cumulative difference between the calendar year of 365.25 days and the solar year of 365.2422 days had resulted in the vernal equinox being on 11 March, while Easter, which was intended to coincide with the Jewish Passover, but whose date was determined from tables drawn up in AD 325 by the Council of Nicaea, had moved forward towards the summer. To rectify this situation Pope Gregory XIII ruled that the vernal equinox should be restored to 21 March, its date at the time of the Council of Nicaea, by making the day following 4 October 1582, 15 October; that the length of the average calendar year should be altered to 365.2425 days by making the centurial years leap years only if they are divisible by 400; that the rules for determining the date of Easter should be modified.

The Gregorian calendar was adopted immediately in Roman Catholic countries, but reluctantly and at various dates in Protestant and Orthodox countries. In Great Britain and the American Colonies it was not adopted till 1752 when 2 September was followed immediately by 14 September. In Russia the change was not made till 1918, the day after Julian date 31 January becoming Gregorian date 14 February. In other Orthodox countries the change was made in October 1923, and a slightly modified rule was adopted for leap years, viz., centurial years are to be leap years only when the century number divided by 9 leaves a remainder of 2 or 6. The first difference from the usual rule does not occur until 2800. In none of these calendar changes has the sequence of the days of the week been interrupted.

Sundials probably existed as early as 2000 BC in Babylonia. As the sun progressed round the sky, the shadow of an upright stick traced out a path on a curve marked out on the ground. In early sun dials, this path was divided into equal parts, thus giving 'hours' which, to our modern way of thinking, were of unequal length. Later, when clepsydrae (water-clocks) came into use, they were sometimes made to record such unequal hours.

Sundials were very common in Saxon and Norman England, and were usually placed on the south walls of country churches. The Saxons divided up their sundials into eight tides, though only four could be recorded in daylight. The 'tides' in the Saxon day were:

4.30 am – 7.30 am	Morgan	4.30 pm – 7.30 pm	Mid-aften
7.30 am –10.30 am	Dael-mael	7.30 pm –10.30 pm	Ondverthnott
10.30 am – 1.30 pm	Mid-daeg	10.30 pm – 1.30 am	Mid-niht
1.30 pm – 4.30 pm	Ofanverthrdagr	1.30 am – 4.30 am	Ofanverthnott

The Greeks employed different time measurements and dates in each City State, with the year beginning on different dates, with different lengths to each month. The Greek Olympiad, held every four years, was a useful means of correlating happenings in different City States with a national set of dates. However from 747 BC a continuous record of solar and lunar eclipses was kept, and continued right through to the time of Ptolemy of Alexandria in AD 150. The Greeks also designed the astrolabe, a sophisticated sundial, which consisted of a circular disc suspended from a point on its circumference. A pointer with sights was fixed at the centre of the circle like an hour hand, and turned towards the sun. The pointer could be adjusted to show the time of day on the rim of the disc. The astrolabe came to Europe around AD 1300 and was used by navigators at sea to give longitude and the time of day until well into the 1700s, when it was replaced by the quadrant. Sand clocks were used around that time in Europe to determine a ship's speed.

Astrolabe of the time of Christopher Columbus, used by navigators to determine the time in a given longitude

Another early method of measuring time was the wick clock and lamp clock. Knots were tied at equal distances in a length of wick, which was lit at one end, and allowed to smoulder. It is said that King Alfred used to tell the time by wax candles marked off in inches, which he protected from draughts by a thin horn window. Wick and lamp clocks were used as late as the eighteenth century.

Egyptian water clocks, also called clepsydrae, could be used in the day or in the night. They were rather inaccurate. In one version, a cylinder floated on a bowl of water in which was a small hole, to allow the water to escape. As the water drained away, the cylinder sank and a pointer attached to it recorded the time on a numbered board. In another version, a pot with a small hole at the bottom was filled with water. As it emptied, the lines of a graduated scale would gradually be revealed, thus giving the time. When shorter periods of time were to be measured, the Egyptians devised a small pot with a hole in the bottom. This was floated in a bowl of water and the time taken for it to fill and sink was a measure of the interval required.

Types of clepsydra were in use in China around 6000 years ago. Many of them were quite complex. To obtain a uniform flow of water, the clocks were designed so as to keep the pressure head constant. In order to indicate 'temporal' hours, either the rate of flow, or the scale of hours had to be varied according to the time of year. This included a good deal of gadgetry. In 1092 Su Sung developed a water clock which used an escapement action, which was only to come to Europe in the fourteenth century. Water was allowed to run at a steady rate into a spoked wheel carrying cups. This caused the weight of water in a cup to press down once every 24 seconds, with a trip against a counter-weighted horizontal beam. This allowed the wheel to revolve by one spoke, thus placing the next empty cup under the spout, to repeat the process. In Alexandria in Egypt, Ctesibus made a clepsydra which was designed to be accurate and self-adjusting. Water was allowed to run into a small funnel and from thence into a reservoir. In the funnel, there was a float which held a thin pillar on top of which was the figure of a man holding a pointer against a graduated column. The divisions on the column were drawn at a slant, so that hours of different lengths could be measured. When water overflowed from the funnel down a looped tube, it entered a drum which revolved as each of its compartments became filled. This drum was connected to the hour column by means of wheels and a tall spindle which caused the column to revolve and the pointer to move up and down.

The idea of using weights to turn the wheels of a clock could not be utilized until some means had been invented to control the rate at which the wheels were turned. The first escapement device to do this was the foliot. This consisted of two weights, one attached at each end of a bar. The whole thing oscillated first one way then the other. At each oscillation, two flat plates, called pallets, allowed a toothed wheel to turn, one tooth at a time, and thus control the clock.

Mechanical Clocks

Mechanical clocks spread across Europe during the beginning of the fourteenth century. Many of these clocks lost or gained as much as an hour a day, but despite such inaccuracy, clocks that struck the hours were installed in the church steeples of many European towns. One of the most elaborate was the Strasbourg clock built in 1352. Other early clocks were at Salisbury and Wells. The clock at Wells showed the phase of the moon, and when the hour struck, moving figures were set in motion.

Until the invention of the mechanical clock, the day and night were kept separate, with twelve hours each. This implied that as midsummer approached, the hours in the day became longer while the night hours became shorter, and in winter the night hours became longer and the day hours shorter. With the introduction of the mechanical clock, day and night were combined into one continuous block of twenty-four equal hours.

Fourteenth-century clock in Wells Cathedral, Somerset, showing the phases of the moon. When the hour struck, the moving figures appeared

Towards the end of the fourteenth century, clocks began to be accurate to within fifteen minutes a day. During this time, it was common for only one hand to be fitted, as being sufficient to show the hours and the quarters. Time-keeping did not become accurate enough to record the passing of minutes until the mid-seventeenth century.

Dials were first fitted to clock faces in the mid-sixteenth century, one of the oldest being on a clock in Amsterdam. At this time a few 'chamber clocks' were made, but they were used only by royalty and other affluent people, and were first made of wrought iron. Later they were made of brass, which allowed finer and more delicate workmanship. These domestic clocks were heavy and were usually placed in the hall where everyone could hear them. But by the end of the seventeenth century elaborate clocks were being made, some of which, besides striking the hours, played music. These clocks had a balance-wheel regulator. This balance wheel was fitted to the verge, taking the place of the foliot.

As time went on, clocks became more accurate and smaller. Early in the sixteenth century, a locksmith from Nuremburg, Peter Henlein, produced a clock which was driven by a spring. Early spring-driven clocks were drum-shaped, usually about six inches across. The dial was viewed through a metal plate pierced with holes. These first spring-driven time-pieces tended to run faster when the spring was fully wound and slower as the spring became more loosely coiled. The 'fusee' was one solution to this problem. The power of the spring was transmitted to the clock through a wire or chain wound round a spiral drum, narrower at one end than the other. When the spring was fully wound, it uncoiled the wire from the part of the drum with the smallest diameter. As the spring unwound and became weaker, the pull of the wire was applied to the drum where the diameter was largest. By this means, the spring was able to drive the clock mechanism at a uniform rate throughout.

The measurement of time became more accurate following the discovery that the swing of a pendulum is uniform and that its oscillation is closely proportional to its length. It is said that Galileo first noticed this phenomenon by watching the swinging lamps in Pisa Cathedral and timing them by counting his pulse.

After Galileo's death, Christaan Huygens (1629–95) used the principle of the pendulum to regulate weight-driven clocks. He realized that the highest accuracy could only be obtained if the pendulum described a cycloidal, not a circular arc. He therefore devised a system whereby the weights of the clock only transmitted just enough energy to the pendulum to keep it from coming to rest. At that time, however, there were two factors detracting from the accuracy of the clock. The first was temperature. A rise in temperature causing the pendulum to expand and become longer would make the clock run slow. The second was that the verge escapement impeded the natural motion of the pendulum's swing. In 1676, Robert Hooke devised the 'anchor escapement'. The escape wheel was set in the vertical plane, and a double claw like an anchor

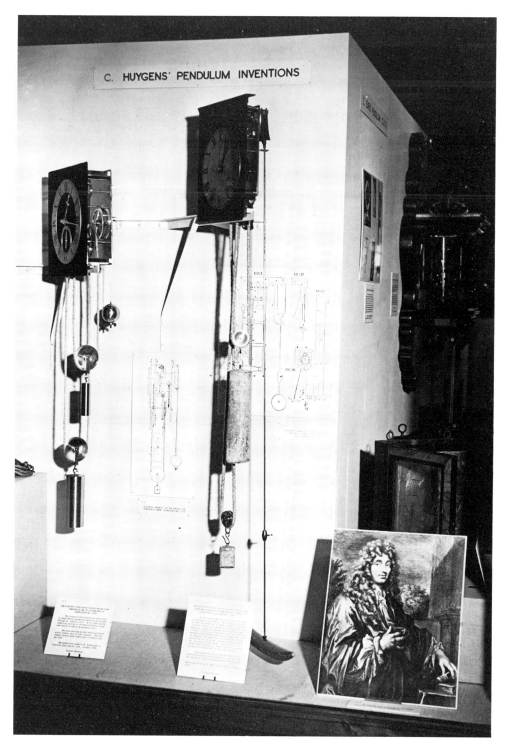

In 1655 Christaan Huygens applied the pendulum to time measurement, immediately rendering the clock accurate to within a minute or two a day

Greenwich Observatory, established in 1675

oscillated by the pendulum allowed the escape wheel to turn a half-tooth space at every tick. The improved accuracy thus obtained allowed clocks to be made to run for a month at a time. A pendulum which oscillates every second must be 39.11 inches long in Edinburgh, 39.10 inches long in London and just 39.00 inches long at the equator. The differences are related to the different pulls of gravity at these different locations.

In the eighteenth century, clocks were gradually made to achieve greater accuracy. George Graham developed both the 'dead-beat' escapement and the 'mercurial compensation' pendulum. The dead-beat escapement produced less wear and friction than the anchor escapement. And the 'mercurial compensation' pendulum was one device among several which counteracted the effect of changes of temperature on the effective length of the pendulum.

Greenwich Observatory had been established in 1675. In 1714 the British Longitude Board offered a prize of £10,000 to the person who could design a ship's chronometer, so that an accurate record of Greenwich time could be kept while at sea, to allow ships' masters to determine longitude. Another prize of £20,000 was offered if the chronometer could be made accurate to allow navigation to within thirty miles over the distance to the West Indies and back. One degree of longitude is equal to four minutes, so this was quite a tall order, requiring that the chronometer did not have an error of more than half a degree.

John Harrison, the British horologist (1693–1776), not only devised an improved escapement but also a way to compensate automatically for changes in temperature. He mounted pins at one end of a system of bi-metallic strips, leaving the other end free to move. When the temperature rose, the strip became convex on the brass side, and concave on the steel side, and the pins were moved along the balance spring. When the length of the pin was adjusted, the amount of movement in the watch's working would shorten the spring exactly enough to compensate for the slowing effect produced by any rise in temperature. Harrison sailed from Portsmouth to Jamaica, and after 156 days, his chronometer had gained only 54 seconds – under half a second a day! Harrison had a long struggle with the British Government before he could claim his full reward. From 1850 onwards, ship's chronometers were being designed which were accurate even after having been exposed to a temperature of 100° F. Such means of time-keeping were the only way a ship could work out its longitude until the development of the radio time signal in the twentieth century.

Electric Clocks, Atomic Clocks and Modern Developments

In 1940, Alexander Bain, a Scottish clock-maker, devised a method whereby a number of clocks could be controlled by one master clock. He did this by transmitting an electric pulse to each every second. Today there are four main types of electric clock: self-contained clocks worked by their own batteries; master clocks controlling a number of slaves; electrically wound clocks; and synchronous clocks which keep in time with the dynamo from which their electric supply is derived. In the first type, a solenoid pendulum weight swings over an electro-magnet operated by the clock's battery. When the pendulum comes to the limit of its swing, a pin completes the electric circuit and the electro-magnet gives the pendulum a push.

All the clocks in a master clock circuit show the same time. In order that this is as closely correct as possible, the master clock is commonly controlled by a Shortt Free Pendulum. This is a device developed in 1921 which has a daily variation of only a few thousandths of a second a day. The free pendulum does not actually have to turn the count wheel; another clock does this. This clock releases an arm every thirty seconds, carrying a 'jewel' which falls upon a wheel attached to the free pendulum. When it rolls off the wheel, it gives the pendulum a small push and transmits a synchronizing signal to the support clock.

Although clocks which are wound automatically by an electric motor are kept going by electricity, they are, for all practical purposes, no different from other mechanical time-pieces. Synchronous clocks are entirely regulated by a master clock in a power station. The master clock is set by the radio pips or Greenwich time. The main drawback to this system is that it is susceptible to any breakdown or stoppage at the power station.

The quartz crystal clock was the first major improvement in the accuracy with which time can be measured since Harrison's chronometer of the eighteenth century (perhaps with the exception of the Shortt Free Pendulum). The first quartz clock was made in America in 1929. The quartz clock depends for its accuracy on the 'piezoelectric effect' of quartz crystals which emit fixed and unchanging radio frequencies at low pressures. These regular natural frequencies can be used to control an oscillator which itself controls the clock. The accuracy of the best mechanical pendulum clock is about three seconds a year. That of a quartz clock is from three seconds per century up to three seconds per 1000 years. Within the last few years, a clock based on the atomic vibrations of the element caesium has been constructed, which can achieve an accuracy within one second in 150,000 years.

It is estimated from fossil remains that 600,000,000 years ago the length of the day was less than 21 hours. Our present 24 hours a day is due to the gradual slowing of the earth's rotation. In 1967, the second was re-defined as 9,192,631,770 periods of caesium vibration. In 1971 Greenwich Mean Time was moved back by one-tenth of a second. It appeared that small, unpredictable variations in the earth's rotation had caused Greenwich Time to lose 9.9 seconds when compared with Atomic Time International with which it had been synchronized on 1 January 1958. It will probably be necessary to insert a 'leap second' when the gap becomes larger in the future.

Noon, when the sun is at the zenith, varies from place to place, being earlier as one travels to the East, and later as one travels to the West. Time changes according to the longitude, with one hour corresponding to a 15° change in longitude. Britain has a relatively short axis from East to West compared with many other countries. Even so, there is a ten-minute difference in time between Bristol and Greenwich, though, for practical convenience, the whole of Britain works on standard national time.

Time around the world

Area	Standard time only (difference from GMT in hours)
Afghanistan	$+4\frac{1}{2}$
Albania	+1
Algeria	GMT
Andorra	+1
Angola	+1
Antigua	−4
Argentina	−3
Australia	
a New South Wales, Tasmania, Victoria	+10
b Queensland	+10
c Northern Territory	$+9\frac{1}{2}$
d South Australia	$+9\frac{1}{2}$
e Western Australia	+8
Austria	+1
Bahamas	−5
Bahrain	+3
Bangladesh	+6
Barbados	−4
Belgium	+1
Belize	−6
Benin	+1
Bermuda	−4
Bhutan	$+5\frac{1}{2}$
Bolivia	−4
Botswana	+2
Brazil	
a East	−3
b West	−4
c Territory of Acre	−5
Brunei	+8
Bulgaria	+2
Burma	$+6\frac{1}{2}$
Burundi	+2
Cameroon	+1
Canada	
a Newfoundland	$-3\frac{1}{2}$
b Atlantic Zone	−4

Area	Standard time only (difference from GMT in hours)
c Jekastern Zone	−5
d Central Zone	−6
e Mountain Zone	−7
f Pacific Zone	−8
g Yukon Territory: Whitehorse and Watson Lake	−8
Dawson City and Mayo	−9
Cape Verde Islands	−1
Cayman Islands	−5
Central African Republic	+1
Chad	+1
Chile	−4
China	
a Zone 1 (Urumchi)	+6
b Zone II–IV (Chunking, Lanchow, Peking, Shanghai, Harbin)	+8
Christmas Island	+7
Cocos Islands	$+6\frac{1}{2}$
Colombia	−5
Comoro Islands	+3
Congo	+1
Costa Rica	−6
Cuba	−5
Cyprus	+2
Czechoslovakia	+1
Denmark	+1
Djibouti	+3
Dominica	−4
Dominican Republic	−4
Ecuador	−5
Egypt	+2
El Salvador	−6
Equatorial Guinea	+1
Ethiopia	+3
Falkland Islands	−4

Area	Standard time only (difference from GMT in hours)	Area	Standard time only (difference from GMT in hours)
Faröe Islands	GMT	Martinique	−4
Fiji	+12	Mauretania	GMT
Finland	+2	Mauritius	+4
France	+1	Mexico	−6
French Guyana	−3	*a* Mexico City	−6
French Polynesia	−10	*b* Baja California Sur, States of	
Gabon	+1	Sonora, Sinaloa, Nayarit	−7
Gambia	GMT	Mongolia	+8
Germany, East	+1	Morocco	GMT
Germany, West	+1	Mozambique	+2
Ghana	GMT	Namibia	+2
Gibraltar	+1	Nauru	+11½
Greece	+2	Nepal	+5.40 minutes
Greenland		Netherlands	+1
East	−2	Netherlands Antilles	−4
West	−3	New Caledonia	+11
Thule	−4	New Zealand	+12
Grenada	−4	Nicaragua	−6
Guadeloupe	−4	Niger	+1
Guatemala	−6	Nigeria	+1
Guinea	GMT	Niue	+11
Guinea Bissau	−1	Norway	+1
Guyana	−3	Oman	+4
Haiti	−5	Pakistan	+5
Honduras	−6	Panama	−5
Hong Kong	+8	Papua New Guinea	+10
Hungary	+1	Paraguay	−4
Iceland	GMT	Peru	−5
India	+5½	Philippines	+8
Indonesia		Pitcairn Island	−9
a Western Zone	+7	Poland	+1
b Central Zone	+8	Portugal	GMT
c Eastern Zone	+9	Qatar	+3
Iran	+3½	Reunion	+4
Iraq	+3	Rumania	+2
Ireland	GMT	Rwanda	+2
Israel	+2	Saint Helena	GMT
Italy	+1	St. Kitts-Nevis, Anguilla	−4
Ivory Coast	GMT	Samoa, American	−11
Jamaica	−5	Samoa, Western	−11
Japan	+9	São-Tomé and Principe	GMT
Johnston Island	−11	Saudi Arabia	+3
Jordan	+2	Senegal	GMT
Kampuchea	+7	Seychelles	+4
Kenya	+3	Sierra Leone	GMT
Korea, North	+9	Singapore	+7½
Korea, South	+9	Somalia	+3
Kuwait	+3	South Africa	+2
Laos	+7	Spain	+1
Lebanon	+2	Sri Lanka	+5½
Lesotho	+2	Sudan	+2
Liberia	GMT	Surinam	−3½
Libya	+2	Swaziland	+2
Liechtenstein	+1	Sweden	+1
Luxembourg	+1	Switzerland	+1
Macao	+8	Syria	+2
Madagascar	+3	Taiwan	+8
Malawi	+2	Tanzania	+3
Malaysia		Thailand	+7
a Peninsular mainland	+7½	Togo	GMT
b Sabah, Sarawak	+8	Tonga	+13
Maldives	+5	Trinidad and Tobago	−4
Mali	GMT	Tunisia	+1
Malta	+1	Turkey	+2

Area	Standard time only (difference from GMT in hours)	Area	Standard time only (difference from GMT in hours)
Turks and Caicos Islands	−5	d Alma-Ata, Karaganda, Omsk	+6
Tuvalu	+12	e Novosibirsk, Krasnoyarsk	+7
Uganda	+3	f Irkutsk	+8
United Arab Emirates	+4	g Yakutsk	+9
United States		h Khabarovsk, Vladivostok	+10
a Eastern Zone	−5	i Magadan, Yuzhno-	
b Central Zone	−6	Sakhalinsk	+11
c Mountain Zone	−7	j Petropavlovsk-	
d Pacific Zone	−8	Kamchatskiy	+12
e Alaska (Ketchikan to		Vanuatu	+11
Skagway)	−8	Venezuela	−4
f Skagway to 141°W	−9	Vietnam	+7
g 141°W to 162°W	−10	Virgin Islands – British	−4
h 162°W to Westernmost Point	−11	Virgin Islands – US	−4
i Hawaii	−10	Yemen, North	+3
Upper Volta	GMT	Yemen, South	+3
Uruguay	−3	Yugoslavia	+1
USSR		Zaire	
a Kiev, Leningrad, Moscow,		a Kinshasa, Mbandaka	+1
Odessa	+3	b Shaba, Kasai, Kivu	+2
b Archangel, Volograd, Tbilisi	+4	Zambia	+2
c Ashkhabad, Sverdlovsk	+5	Zimbabwe	+2

In 1895 it was decided that the base-line for all time calculations, that is the prime meridian, should run through the Royal Greenwich Observatory, and be marked 0° longitude. However, it was not practical for the larger countries to use Greenwich as the sole reference point. Such countries were divided into official 'time zones', and their clocks were based upon Greenwich Mean Time. The 180° Meridian, exactly halfway round the world from Greenwich, is where each new calendar day begins. The International Date Line in the main follows the 180° Meridian, zig-zagging a little when it would otherwise imply that two calendar dates would exist in the same country. In order to determine the local time anywhere in the world, it is necessary to know the longitude, latitude, and Greenwich time. If the longitudinal degrees, minutes and seconds are divided by 15 (because one hour equals 15° longitude) the hours, minutes and seconds of the place ahead of or behind Greenwich Mean Time will be found.

Photo-finish timers are now used in sporting events, revealing a distance between two athletes (or, say, horses) covered in 0.01 of a second. It is not only now possible with modern chronographs to measure the speed of a missile or of a bullet fired from a gun, but also to take photographs of events taking place within a ten million-millionth of a second.

A technique for measuring time past and hence for dating archaeological findings is 'carbon-14 dating'. Radioactive carbon-14 is being continually created naturally in the atmosphere by neutron bombardment of nitrogen. This radioactive carbon has a 'half-life' of 5760 years. This means that in 5760 years only half the carbon-14 now present will remain. In the course of time, an equilibrium has been set up between the creation and decay of carbon-14 in the carbon dioxide in the atmosphere. While there is still likely to be a margin of error, any material which contains carbon originating from the atmosphere can be dated by its present carbon-14 content. Living matter, which has recently absorbed atmospheric carbon dioxide, contains a proportion of carbon-14 together with stable isotopes, such that one gramme of such carbon has a standard activity of over 15 disintegrations per minute. It can be calculated from the known half-life of carbon that the activity decreases by 1% in 80 years, and therefore by measuring the activity per gramme of carbon from a specimen, any age between 600–40,000 years can be estimated. Charcoal specimens found in the prehistoric caves of Lascaux, in France, were dated as being from fires lit about 15,000 years ago, and the Dead Sea scrolls were dated – according to one interpretation – as being from AD 33 when the linen in which they had been wrapped was examined by carbon-dating.

Modern Ideas and Concepts of Time

Newton believed both space and time to be absolute, infinite and eternal. He believed that time flowed for ever, evenly and independently of sensible motions, whether it was perceived or not.

By the eighteenth century, the concept of time had changed. Leibniz believed that space and time were mere ideas, abstracted from confused sense perceptions of the relations of real things. Immanuel Kant in the late eighteenth century believed that though time itself does not exist, our *consciousness* of time does exist.

In 1905, Einstein proposed his special theory of relativity. His theory explained the unexpected results of an experiment done by Michelson and Morley in 1887, which appeared to show that light travelled at the same speed whether one was going towards it or going away from it. Einstein explained these results by assuming that the velocity of light was always the same, with *time* as the varying factor – an idea undreamt of before.

Einstein's theory stated that all the laws of physics remained the same for all observers, wherever they were, and however fast they were moving. He assumed that there are no instantaneous connections between external events and an observer – for such information has to travel – and that the fastest means by which it can travel is by light. Einstein proposed that the speed of light was the same for all observers, whether they were at rest or moving.

If this was so, observers who were in motion would be led to assign different times to the same event, and a moving clock would therefore appear to be running slow if observed by a stationary observer.

Einstein also calculated that the mass of a body increased indefinitely the nearer its velocity aproached that of light. This meant that a given force acting

Albert Einstein (1879–1955) was responsible for the twentieth-century revolution in
the understanding of the nature of time

on the body would produce smaller and smaller changes in its velocity the faster it moved and, as a result, no particle of matter could ever reach the speed of light.

Evidence for the phenomenon of 'time dilation' or time slowing down at speeds approaching that of light is found in subatomic particles called muons. When they are speeded up in a particle accelerator, they increase their lifetime by more than twenty times to about twenty-millionths of a second, thus becoming the longest-lived sub-atomic particles (except for neutrons). As they move in the accelerator, the muons reach a speed very close to that of light and their time-dilation factor therefore reaches over twenty.

Thus, it might be argued that people living on the equator are ageing a tiny bit more slowly than those living near the North Pole. Because their velocity is greater, time will be slowed a little bit for them. By the same argument, it could be said that the centre of a well-used record is a little older than the outside.

Looked at another way, time is stuff that is made by clocks. If your clock is the incomplete circle traced by the shadow of a stick as the sun moves round the sky, and you divide the part-circle into equal sections, the hours of the day will be of unequal length. If your clock is a mechanical one controlled by a pendulum, you will probably opt for hours of equal length. If your clock is an atom of caesium, then matter will be the stuff that makes time. And before the Universe began, about 15,000,000,000 years ago, and there was no matter, we have to conclude that there was no time either.

In the Ordovician period, about 450,000,000 years ago, the South Pole was situated in what is now the Sahara desert.

The light reaching us from the Crab Nebula left there during the flowering of the Ancient Egyptian civilization.

When James Cook returned from his three-year voyage in 1772 his chronometer was found to be only 7 minutes 45 seconds slow.

The only time when there is an equal number of hours of light and darkness everywhere on earth is at the two equinoxes in March and September.

Protons are stable for 10^{28} years, while neutrons last for only 15 minutes. If the lifespan of a neutron was compared to the time taken to drink a pint of beer, you would have to drink for 20,000,000,000,000 times the lifespan of the universe to last as long as the proton.

In the Arctic there are as many hours of light when print can be read out of doors as there are in the tropics.

If Western Europe continues to subside at its present rate of one inch every ten years, in 200,000 years' time even the top of the Eiffel Tower, assuming that it was not dismantled beforehand, would have disappeared beneath the Atlantic Ocean.

Twenty successful predictions by Hugo Gernsback (1884–1967) – father of modern science fiction

1 Television	12 Automatically controlled doors
2 Photographs transmitted by radio	13 Radio transmission
3 Synthetic foods	14 Mass entertainment transmissions
4 Spaceflight	15 Artificial fibres
5 Use of geothermal power	16 First moon landing by 1975
6 Tape-recordings	17 Videotaping by 1990
7 Sound films	18 Spy satellites
8 Solar cells	19 Identification by voiceprint
9 Transatlantic flights	20 Sports stadiums automatically air-conditioned
10 Televised telephone calls	
11 Satellite television transmissions by 1970	

7

Calculation

The Early Mathematicians

Although the first method of counting was probably by using the ten fingers and thumbs on two hands, by as long ago as 3000 BC symbols to represent numbers had been invented in Egypt, Babylon, China and India, and by 2900 BC the Egyptians had begun to use numbers in a practical way and had devised a standardized system of weights and measures. This early system emphasized the importance of the human body in the establishment of units. The smallest unit of length was the 'finger'; a 'foot' equalled 20 fingers; a 'cubit' – the length from the elbow to the tip of the fingers – equalled 30 fingers; a 'pole' was 12 cubits; a surveyor's 'cord', 120 cubits; and a 'league', 180 cords. The units of weight were based on the most common medium of exchange, namely barley. Thus the smallest unit of weight was a 'grain' leading on to a 'shekel' and thence to a 'talent'.

Ancient units and their modern equivalents

Biblical		*Greek*		*Roman*	
Cubit	=21.8 inches	Cubit	=18.3 inches	Cubit	=17.5 inches
Omer	=0.45 peck	Stadion	=607.2 or 622 feet	Stadium	=202 yards
	3.964 litres	Obolos	=715.38 milligrams	As, libra,	=325.971 grams,
Ephah	=10 omers	Drachmas	=4.2923 grams	pondus	·71864 pounds
Shekel	=0.497 ounce	Mina	=0.9463 pounds		
	14.1 grams	Talent	=60 mina		

As the units of calculation became more exact, the methods and techniques of their use progressed also. The Egyptians used stretched ropes to divide land into quadrilaterals of equal area. They developed methods for working out areas and volumes of various simple geometrical shapes, although they never developed general formulae applicable to different variables, but worked out every problem afresh. One of their systems, which we use to this day, was to divide a circle into 360 portions or 'degrees'.

Geometry was the first of the branches of mathematics to be developed. The Greeks, indeed, carried geometry to the position in which it stayed until the mid-nineteenth century. But they also made advances in algebra and logic. The first mathematician whose work was recorded was Thales of Miletus. But even at that early date some of his propositions were based on still earlier Egyptian geometry. Thales' main contribution was to convert what had been a purely practical exercise into an abstract study. He developed the system of 'deductive mathematics' which was to be used subsequently by Euclid. This system set out to prove a mathematical statement by a regular series of logical arguments, proceeding step by step to the final 'proof'. It was the reasoning behind the solving of problems which mattered to the Greeks, not the actual answer itself, which could often have been found by direct measurement. In this way, the Greeks were able to draw generalized conclusions and formulae from specific examples, and apply these formulae to examples which it would have been impossible to measure directly. In fact, it was the Greeks who were the first to see that mathematics could sometimes solve problems which were impossible to solve by direct measurement alone. As mathematics progressed, it became a tool which enabled those using it to measure phenomena too fast or too small even to see. Thales discovered the axioms that 'the diameter of a circle divides the circle into two equal parts' and that 'the base angles of an isosceles triangle are equal'.

Plato, who lived in Athens around 360 BC, believed that mathematics was pure, abstract and good for the soul. Unlike Archimedes, he did not believe in the application of mathematics to practical affairs. To his mind the heavenly bodies exhibited perfect geometric form and the only five possible regular solids, the tetrahedron, the hexahedron, the octahedron, the dodecahedron and the icosahedron represented the four elements of which the world was made and the universe as a whole. The perfect curve, according to his thinking, was the circle. It followed therefore that the planets must all move in circular orbits. In these ideas, Plato was greatly influenced by Pythagoras of Samos, who, a little earlier, discovered the mathematical relationships between the length of strings struck and the pitch of notes in music. It was found that the lengths of a vibrating string which produced a particular note, its fifth, and octave, were always in the ratio 6:4:3. From this observation, Pythagoras jumped to the conclusion that these ratios must apply to the universe at large and that the distance of the planets from the earth must conform to the musical progression – to 'ring forth the music of the spheres'. The Greeks even decided that there must be ten planets, ten being the 'perfect' number. This idea, that the heavens must reflect mathematical 'perfection', persisted in astronomy until the time of Kepler.

But the 'father of geometry' was Euclid, who in about 300 BC wrote the first book on geometry, *Elements*, in which he went through numerous proofs, theorems and axioms. He made optics into a part of geometry by treating light rays as straight lines. His axioms of geometry still hold true.

Algebra, in which different categories of numbers are represented by letters, was developed in Egypt and in India in the sixth and seventh centuries AD. But the 'founder of modern algebra' could be said to be Diophantus of Greece, whose algebraic equations were translated into Arabic and finally translated into Latin in the sixteenth century.

The Greeks and the Romans were severely handicapped by the symbols which they used to represent numerals. The use of Is, Vs, Xs, Cs, Ds and Ms makes calculation particularly difficult. It was only when the Arabic numerals reached Europe in AD 1200 that mathematics of any complexity could be developed.

By 598–660, Greek learning had reached India. Hindu mathematicians were

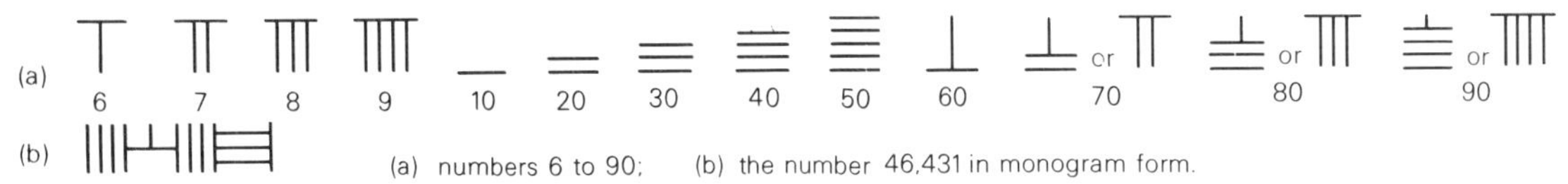

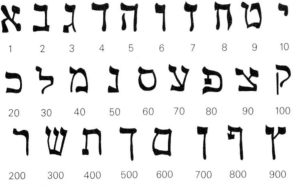

(a)
6 7 8 9 10 20 30 40 50 60 or 70 or 80 or 90
(b)
(a) numbers 6 to 90; (b) the number 46,431 in monogram form.

Fig. 1. Chinese rod numerals. The units 1–5 consist of one to five vertical strokes; 6–9 of one to four vertical strokes with superscribed bar; and the tens of horizontal strokes or of a combination of horizontal and vertical strokes (fig. 1a). The hundreds were written like the units, and so on. These numerals were frequently written in the monogram form – fig. 1b is the number 46,431.

א ב ג ד ה ו ז ח ט י
1 2 3 4 5 6 7 8 9 10
כ ל מ נ ס ע פ צ ק
20 30 40 50 60 70 80 90 100
ר ש ת ך ם ן ף ץ
200 300 400 500 600 700 800 900

Fig. 2. The later Hebrew numerical system.

Fig. 3.
Development of the Arabic numerals. 1, Devanagari letters of the 2nd century AD; 2, Arabic numerals of the 10th century; 3, the earliest examples of Arabic numerals in Latin manuscripts, Escorial Library Spain, 976; 4, other forms of the Arabic numerals, Western type; 5–8, Arabic numerals, Eastern type (8, modern Arabic numerals, as employed in Arabic script); 9–13, the so-called apices of Boethius of the 11th and 12th centuries; 14, the numerals of John Basingestokes (d. 1252); 15–17 Arabic-Byzantine numerals of the 12th to the 15th centuries; 18, numerals in a manuscript from France (now in Berlin), of the second half of the 12th century; 19, numerals in an Italian manuscript from Florence of the first half of the 14th century; 20, numerals in an Italian manuscript of the 15th century. *(Source: D. Diringer).*

1
2
3
4
5
6
7
8
9
10
11
12
13
14
15
16
17
18
19
20

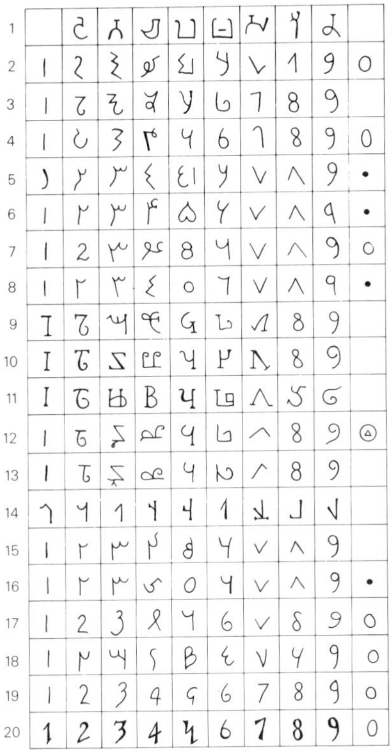

Roman numerals and their use

A bar placed over a numeral multiplies the value by 1,000, *e.g.*
$\overline{IV}$=4,000, $\overline{XL}$=40,000, etc.

1	I	500	D	or	IϽ
2	II	600	DC	or	IϽC
3	III	700	DCC	or	IϽCC
4	IV or IIII	800	DCCC	or	IϽCCC
5	V	900	CM	or	IϽCD
6	VI	1,000	M	or	CIϽ
7	VII	1,100	MC	or	CIϽC
8	VIII	1,200	MCC	or	CIϽCC
9	IX	1,300	MCCC	or	CIϽCCC
10	X	1,400	MCD	or	CIϽCD
11	XI	1,500	MD	or	CIϽD
12	XII	1,600	MDC	or	CIϽDC
13	XIII	1,700	MDCC	or	CIϽDCC
14	XIV	1,800	MDCCC	or	CIϽDCCC
15	XV	1,900	MCM	or	CIϽIϽCD
16	XVI	2,000	MM	or	CIϽCI
17	XVII	3,000	MMM		
18	XVIII	4,000	$\overline{IV}$		
19	XIX	5,000	$\overline{V}$	or	IϽϽ
20	XX	6,000	$\overline{VI}$		
30	XXX	7,000	$\overline{VII}$		
40	XL	8,000	$\overline{VIII}$		
50	L	9,000	$\overline{IX}$		
60	LX	10,000	$\overline{X}$	or	CCϽϽ
70	LXX	50,000	$\overline{L}$	or	IϽϽϽ
80	LXXX	100,000	$\overline{C}$	or	CCCIϽϽϽ
90	XC	500,000	$\overline{D}$	or	IϽϽϽϽ
100	C	1,000,000	$\overline{M}$	or	CCCCIϽϽϽϽ
200	CC				
300	CCC				
400	CD or CCCC				

using the numerals that we now use today, although it was only during the period 660–800 that they introduced a symbol for 'zero'. Only when this had been done did it become possible to use 'positional notation' and thus allow any number, no matter how large or how small, to be written with only nine numerals. In addition to the information the numerals themselves give, their *position* gives more. The Hindu numerals spread to Arabia by around 800 and to the French scholar, Gerbert, by about 1000. But it was probably the book, *Liber Abaci*, published by Leonardo Fibonacci in Italy in 1202, which convinced European mathematicians of the superiority of Arabic numerals. By 1453, the Austrian mathematician, Georg von Puerbach, used Arabic numerals to prepare a table of sines far more accurate than any which had been made at that time, thus advancing trigonometry beyond the stage reached by the Greeks.

Prime number, a whole number which cannot be divided by any other whole number (except 1) without leaving a remainder. Primes less than 100 are:—

2	13	31	53	73
3	17	37	59	79
5	19	41	61	83
7	23	43	67	89
11	29	47	71	97

Numbers above 1,000,000

U.S.	Number of zeros	French British, German	U.S.	Number of zeros	French British, German
million	6	million	sextillion	21	1,000 trillion
billion	9	milliard	septillion	24	quadrillion
trillion	12	billion	octillion	27	1,000 quadrillion
quadrillion	15	1,000 billion	nonillion	30	quintillion
quintillion	18	trillion	decillion	33	1,000 quintillion

From Descartes Onwards

In 1637 René Descartes in France combined the techniques of algebra and geometry. He saw that any point in space could be plotted in numerical terms by the use of his 'Cartesian co-ordinates'. Any point of a plane, for example, could be represented by two numbers, one being the distance along the horizontal co-ordinate, the other the distance along the vertical. Thus, in an algebraic equation, it was possible to show that one variable, designated 'y' along the vertical co-ordinate, could depend in a particular relationship upon the fluctuations of another variable, 'x' along the horizontal, as in, for example $y = 3x + 2$. Then when $x = -3$, $y = -7$; $x = -2$, $y = -4$; $x = -1$, $y = -1$; $x = 0$, $y = 2$; $x = 1$, $y = 5$; $x = 2$, $y = 8$; $x = 3$, $y = 11$, and so on. If this is plotted on a system of Cartesian co-ordinates, a straight line is obtained which cuts the vertical at a particular point. Other equations will produce curves of diverse shapes all of which can be plotted. This fusion of geometry and algebra was called 'analytical geometry'.

In the 1640s another French mathematician, Pierre de Fermat, extended the notion of Cartesian co-ordinates to account not only for a flat two-dimensional plane, but for solid three-dimensional objects. This called for the introduction of another 'axis', implying that any point in space could be represented by three numbers along three axes, x, y and z. At about the same time, Blaise Pascal published a book on the geometry of conic sections (slices taken at various angles through a conc) and brought the study of such forms far beyond the stage reached by Apollonius of Greece, who had found that all conics could be considered as sections of one cone, and introduced the names parabola, ellipse, and hyperbola.

Another discovery about curves was made by the German mathematician, Karl Friedrich Gauss, in 1795. He discovered the 'method of least squares' by which the algebraic equation for a curve best fitting a group of observations could be worked out.

In 1822 a French mathematician, Jean Poncelet, illustrated the power of mathematics in another direction by inventing 'projective geometry', a branch of geometry that ignores lengths and angles and concentrates on the shadows thrown by various geometrical forms – the properties that remain unaltered by projection.

Common fractions expressed as decimals

8ths	16ths	32nds	64ths		8ths	16ths	32nds	64ths	
			1	.015625				33	.515625
		1	2	.03125			17	34	.53125
			3	.046875				35	.046875
	1	2	4	.0625		9	18	36	.5625
			5	.078125				37	.578125
		3	6	.09375			19	38	.59375
			7	.109375				39	.609375
1	2	4	8	.125	5	10	20	40	.625
			9	.140625				41	.640625
		5	10	.15625			21	42	.65625
			11	.171875				43	.671875
	3	6	12	.1875		11	22	44	.6875
			13	.203125				45	.703125
		7	14	.21875			23	46	.71875
			15	.234375				47	.734375
2	4	8	16	.25	6	12	24	48	.75
			17	.265625				49	.765625
		9	18	·28125			25	50	.78125
			19	.296875				51	.796875
	5	10	20	.3125		13	26	52	.8125
			21	.328125				53	.828125
		11	22	.34375			27	54	.84375
			23	.359375				55	.859375
3	6	12	24	.375	7	14	28	56	.875
			25	.390625				57	.890625
		13	26	.40625			29	58	.90625
			27	.421875				59	.921875
	7	14	28	.4375		15	30	60	.9375
			29	.453125				61	.953125
		15	30	.46875			31	62	.96875
			31	.484375				63	.984375
4	8	16	32	.5	8	16	32	64	1

Geometry Beyond Euclid

Euclid dominated geometry for more than 2000 years. It almost seemed as if the truths he showed were the only truths there were. In 1844, however, the German mathematician, August Möbius, showed that there could be a different kind of geometry. For example, what would Euclid say of a figure shown on a paper strip in the form of a garter with a twist in it? Different geometrical rules would apply. Möbius developed a branch of geometry known as 'topology', which dealt with shapes and surfaces.

Euclid had postulated a number of axioms, one of which was that 'through a given point, not on a given line, one line, and one line only, can be drawn which is parallel to the given line'. In 1829 a Russian mathematician, Nikolai Lobachevski, published a treatise in which he was able to prove that, provided his conditions were accepted, the axiom could be rewritten: 'through a given point, not on a given line, *at least two lines* parallel to the given line, can be drawn'. From this axiom Lobachevski worked backwards through others of

Euclid's and devised a new but consistent geometry. In it he showed that the sum of three angles of a triangle had to be *less* than 180 degrees. (In Euclidean, as in all 'normal' geometry, the sum of all three angles *has to equal* 180 degrees.) At first it was believed that Lobachevski's geometry did not actually represent anything real. Then it was discovered that if all the manipulations were carried out upon the surface of a geometric figure known as a 'pseudosphere', they did in truth make sense.

A second type of non-Euclidean geometry was devised by a German mathematician, Georg Riemann, in 1851. Riemann's fifth axiom was that 'through a given point not on a given line, *no* line parallel to the first given line could be drawn'. In his geometry *any number* of straight lines could be drawn through two given points, and there was no such thing as a straight line of infinite length. In Riemann's geometry, the three angles of a triangle add up to *more* than 180 degrees. Again, this seemingly useless, but consistent geometry, was found to work upon the surface of a sphere. Since, in fact, most of our activities take place on the surface of a sphere, it should not have been too much of a surprise when in due course Lorentz and Fitzgerald and Einstein showed that the universe *in total* is indeed non-Euclidean. Non-Euclidean geometry was brought to England in the 1840s by Charles Babbage, Lucasian Professor of mathematics at Cambridge.

Progress in Algebra

Progress in algebra began to accelerate from the time of François Viète in the sixteenth century. Viète, using letters to represent unknown numbers in algebraic equations, employed vowels for 'unknowns' and consonants for 'constants'. The book he published in 1591, *Isogoge in artem analyticum*, was the first writing on algebra to bear any resemblance to the modern subject. Then in 1637, Descartes applied algebraic equations to the curves and straight lincs plotted on his Cartesian co-ordinates and made it possible to visualize equations as geometrical shapes. Later, in 1799 the German mathematician, Gauss, proved the fundamental theorem of algebra, that every algebraic equation has a root of the form $a + bi$ (where a and b are real numbers, and i is $\sqrt{-1}$).

In 1687 the scene was therefore ready for Isaac Newton to devise the 'binomial theorem', which enabled the sum of two functions (or equations) to be raised to a power, and then expanded into a series of terms. Without this system, the working out of a sum of two equations had been a difficult and time-consuming process. Now the matter could be readily dealt with and the solution plotted as a curve on Cartesian co-ordinates.

Both the French mathematicians, Pierre de Fermat and René Descartes, had prepared the ground for the development of 'calculus' by Isaac Newton and

Gottfried Leibniz. This was an elegant mathematical system by which a variety of computations could for the first time be achieved. In 1666, Newton developed 'integral calculus', which was virtually the opposite of the 'differential calculus'.

Powers of ten

When either very large or very small numbers have to be written it is convenient to use powers of ten in the compact form illustrated by the following table:

$$
\begin{aligned}
10^{10} &= 10,000,000,000 \\
10^{9} &= 1,000,000,000 \\
10^{8} &= 100,000,000 \\
10^{7} &= 10,000,000 \\
10^{6} &= 1,000,000 \\
10^{5} &= 100,000 \\
10^{4} &= 10,000 \\
10^{3} &= 1,000 \\
10^{2} &= 100 \\
10^{1} &= 10 \\
10^{0} &= 1 \\
10^{-1} &= 0.1 \\
10^{-2} &= 0{\cdot}01 \\
10^{-3} &= 0.001 \\
10^{-4} &= 0.0001 \\
10^{-5} &= 0.00001 \\
10^{-6} &= 0.000001 \\
10^{-7} &= 0.0000001 \\
10^{-8} &= 0.00000001 \\
10^{-9} &= 0.000000001 \\
10^{-10} &= 0.0000000001
\end{aligned}
$$

If, in algebra, letters could be used to represent numbers and manipulated to demonstrate general principles, why should not letters similarly be used to represent something other than numerals? In 1815, pursuing this line of thought, George Boole, an English mathematician, showed that it was possible to apply a set of symbols to logical propositions. In 1847, he published his first book, *An Investigation of the Laws of Thought*, which initiated the subject now known as 'symbolic logic'. Logical processes behind thought were expressed in mathematical terms. Similarly, instead of using mathematics to study the logic of thought and language, language and logic could be used to study the processes of mathematics. A number of other workers, for example, Gottlob Frege in Germany and Guiseppe Peano in Italy, took up Boole's ideas. In 1880, Peano published *A Logical Exposition of the Principles of Geometry*. Then during the period 1910–13, Alfred Whitehead and Bertrand Russell published their three-volume work, *Principia Mathematica*, in which mathematics was developed on the basis of symbolic logic.

Finally, at the end of the road, just as in physics there was an 'uncertainty principle' which prevented a physicist from knowing which particle would ultimately trigger off a nuclear reaction, so did Kurt Gödel, an Austrian mathematician, prove that in mathematics there would always be statements which could neither be proved nor disproved by mathematical logic.

Probability and Chance

Pierre de Fermat founded the theory of probability in 1650, following on from earlier discoveries made by an Italian, Cardano, in 1552. It is a branch of mathematics which provides methods of analysing problems involving randomness or unpredictability. In 1642, Blaise Pascal worked out the basic laws of probability using dice. By the use of these laws, scientists became able to calculate whether their results showed that a real effect was being observed or whether what they had found was purely a matter of chance. By the end of the eighteenth century, mathematical devices such as the Gaussian curve showed how events might be distributed by chance. It was thus possible to identify those events which did in fact deviate and then to discover what had caused their deviation.

Calculation of Probabilities

The example of throwing a die is one of the simplest situations for probability theory. There are 6 possible outcomes of the action of throwing a die. Each of them is equally likely. The problem that any one outcome will occur is therefore defined to be 1/6. Suppose two dice are thrown: what can be said of the likelihood that they will both show the same number? There are 36 possible outcomes, each equally likely; in 6 of them the two dice show the same number. The probability of showing the same number is then defined to be $6 \div 36 = 1/6$. This method of defining probabilities can be generalized. If an action can lead to a definite number of equally likely outcomes then the probability of a particular type of outcome (called a 'favourable outcome') occurring is defined to be

$$\frac{\text{number of favourable outcomes}}{\text{number of possible outcomes}}$$

This is often called the 'classical definition' of probability. There is a great deal of experimental evidence to support the following statement: if an action is repeated a large number of times then the actual frequency of occurrence of 'favourable outcomes' divided by the total number of trials will approach the probability computed from the classical definition. It is important to recognize, however, that actual frequencies come reasonably close to computed probabilities only over several thousand repetitions of an action such as throwing a die. Probability theory (and statistics, which is derived from it) describes the real world in the long-term.

Probability of card holdings in a 13-card bridge hand

Type of hand	Number of those hands[1]	Probability (%)	Approximate odds against drawing
Four aces	1,677,106,640	0.26	378 to 1
No aces	192,928,249,296	30.4	7 to 3
No card higher than a nine (Yarborough)	347,373,600	0.055	1,827 to 1
Seven-card suit or longer	25,604,567,408	4.03	24 to 1
Any 4–3–3–3 distribution	6.691×10^{10}	10.54	17 to 2
Any 5–4–2–2 distribution	6.718×10^{10}	10.58	17 to 2
Any 5–3–3–2 distribution	9.853×10^{10}	15.52	11 to 2

[1] Out of a total of 635,013,559,600 possible hands.

Methods of Calculating

(1) *The abacus*   One of the first devices to increase the ease and speed of calculation was the Chinese abacus which was invented around 550 BC. It can still be found, expertly operated, in Chinese stores in Hong Kong. The abacus is an arrangement of wooden counters strung on wires, which can be manipulated and arranged in columns.

Some mathematical formulae

To find the Circumference of a:

Circle – Multiply the diameter by 3.14159265 (usually 3.1416).

To find the Area of a:

Circle – Multiply the square of the diameter by .785398 (usually .7854).
 Rectangle – Multiply the length of the base by the height.
Sphere (surface) – Multiply the square of the radius by 3.1416 and multiply by 4.
Square – Square the length of one side.
Trapezoid – Add the two parallel sides, multiply by the height and divide by 2.
Triangle – Multiply the base by the height and divide by 2.

To find the Volume of a:

Cone – Multiply the square of the radius of the base by 3.1416, multiply by the height, and divide by 3.
Cube – Cube the length of one edge.
Cylinder – Multiply the square of the radius of the base by 3.1416 and multiply by the height.
Pyramid – Multiply the area of the base by the height and divide by 3.
Rectangular Prism – Multiply the length by the width by the height.
Sphere – Multiply the cube of the radius by 3.1416, multiply by 4 and divide by 3.

(2) *The slide rule*   In 1594 the Scottish mathematician, John Napier, had the insight to see that any number could be expressed in exponential form. For example, 8 could be written as 2^3, or 32 as 2^5. Once numbers had been expressed in this form, multiplication could be carried out by adding the exponents and division by subtracting them. This greatly increased the speed of such computations. Napier compiled a table of his 'logarithms' in 1614. In 1624 Henry Briggs devised the system of 'common logarithms' and worked out the first logarithm tables covering the numbers from 1 to 100,000. Finally, in 1622, William Oughtred arranged Napier's logarithmic scale along two rules. By sliding these rules against each other, calculations could be performed mechanically. It was this device which became known as the 'slide-rule'.

(3) *The calculating machine*   In 1642 Blaise Pascal invented a calculating machine that could add and subtract by means of cogged wheels. Gottfried Leibniz in 1671 improved Pascal's design and produced a machine which could not only add and subtract, but multiply and divide as well.

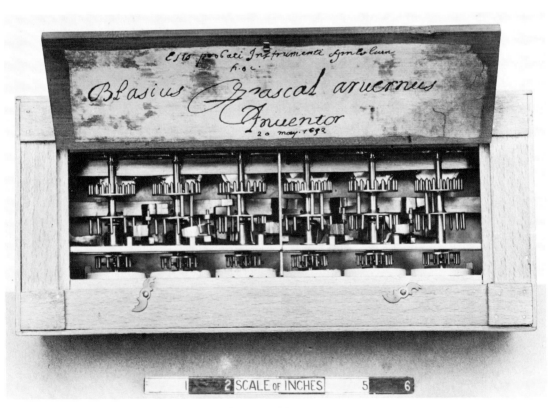

Replica of Blaise Pascal's adding machine

Pascal's triangle

Blaise Pascal devised this triangle in which each number, except for the 1's on the outside, is the sum of the two numbers immediately above it. The triangle is used to calculate probabilities.

```
                1    1
              1    2    1
            1    3    3    1
          1    4    6    4    1
        1    5   10   10    5    1
      1    6   15   20   15    6    1
    1    7   21   35   35   21    7    1
  1    8   28   56   70   56   28    8    1
1    9   36   84  126  126   84   36    9    1
1   10   45  120  210  252  210  120   45   10    1
```

(4) *The computer*   By 1833 Charles Babbage had worked out a design for a machine which could calculate, could store the results of its calculations and could then, by making use of a punched card similar to that used on Jacquard looms to weave patterned designs, be 'instructed' to perform a given series of computations. Babbage's design involved the use of cogged wheels and proved impracticable, but the principles of its design were incorporated in the

The world's first commercially available digital computer, capable then of performing 800 instructions per second

computers which came later and which operated electronically. In 1946 the first electronic computer, ENIAC, was built in America. Gradually improved designs were introduced and by 1964 a computer completed in eight seconds the calculations of the orbit of Mars which had taken Kepler four years. Today, a vast number of operations, which previously had had to be done manually, are performed by computers.

The development of the transistor and, subsequently, of the printed circuit and the 'silicon chip' on which thousands of circuits can be imprinted, allowed for the radical 'miniaturization' of computers. In 1949, Florey and Hodgkin used an electronic computer to analyse large amounts of data in their work to establish the atomic structure of penicillin.

Calculation and Science

The subject of mathematics is not strictly science. Mathematical propositions can be based, like chess, on any chosen premises. Science, on the other hand, must be grounded on observations and measurements of the natural universe. On the other hand, progress in science is only possible when mathematics and calculations are available. Calculation first showed the basic laws of motion and gravity. Archimedes observed the phenomena around him, measured what he observed and fitted a mathematical relationship to his observations. Galileo, an ardent admirer of Archimedes, also applied mathematics to his studies of the acceleration of a falling body, the rate of swing of a pendulum and the strength of a structure in relation to its proportions. But it was Johannes Kepler in Germany after 1600 who demonstrated the power of mathematics as an adjunct to science. Kepler had for some time been trying to make the numerous observations of the motion of the planets fit in with Plato's concept of a 'perfect circular orbit'. Eventually it came to him that the mathematical interpretation of his observations implied that the orbits of all the planets could be drawn as ellipses. This conclusion became known as 'Kepler's First Law'. His second law was that the closer a planet was to the sun, the faster it would move in its elliptical orbit and that this increase in speed could be expressed in mathematical terms. Kepler used Napier's newly-invented logarithms to complete a table of planetary motions which was published in 1627.

In 1687 Isaac Newton published his book *Philosophiae Naturalis Principia Mathematica* in which he had re-organized Galileo's findings into three 'laws of motion'. From these three laws Newton worked out how the gravitational force between the earth and the moon could be calculated. He found that the gravitational force was directly proportional to the product of the masses of the two bodies and was inversely proportional to the square of the distance between their centres. He expressed this in the equation:

$$F = \frac{Gm_1m_2}{d^2}$$

This law of universal gravitation explained Kepler's findings of the elliptical motions of the heavenly bodies. Newton's mathematical treatment of simple phenomena had produced an entire new way of regarding the universe. In 1795 Gauss, the German mathematician, carried the matter further by applying the 'method of least squares' to astronomy; the discovery of Ceres in 1801 led Gauss to develop his new method, which eventually contributed to the discovery of Neptune.

Mathematics in all its forms, now reinforced by the speed, flexibility and versatility of modern electronic computers, has thus been applied not only to astronomy and the laws of motion but to every branch of science. Chemistry, grounded on the law of the conservation of matter, has for long been a quantitative study. The so-called 'gas laws' can best be comprehended in mathematical terms while the modern technique of X-ray crystallography, by which the molecular configuration of complex substances can be elucidated, can only progress on the basis of modern computational facilities. And the same considerations hold for biology where genetics and the whole process of evolution and growth depend upon an underpinning of mathematics. Finally, in the field of nuclear physics, progress can only be achieved with its proper use. Indeed, the basis of this branch of science is most clearly expressed in mathematical terms as the formula $E = mc^2$.

Weights and measures – how to convert them

Multiply:	By:	To Obtain:	Multiply:	By:	To Obtain:
acres	43,560	sq. ft.	cu. feet	1728	cu. ins.
	0.4047	hectares		62.43	lbs. of water
	0.0015625	sq. mi.		7.481	gals. (liq.)
ampere-hours	3600	coulombs		0.0283	cu. m.
atmospheres	76.0	cm. of mercury	cu. ft./min.	62.43	lbs. water/min.
	33.90	ft. of water	cu. ft./sec.	448.831	gals./min.
	14.70	lbs./sq. in.	cu. inches	16.387	cu. cm.
British thermal units	1054	joules		0.0005787	cu. ft.
	777.5	ft.-lbs.	cu. metres	264.2	gals. (liq.)
	252.0	gram calories		35.3147	cu. ft.
	0.0003927	horsepower-hrs.		1.3079	cu. yds.
	0.0002928	kilowatt-hrs.	cu. yards	27	cu. ft.
B.T.U./hr	0.2928	watts		0.765	cu. m.
B.T.U./min.	12.96	ft.-lbs./sec.	days	86,400	seconds
	0.02356	horsepower	degrees/sec.	0.1667	revolutions/min.
bushels	3523.8	hectolitres	°F−32	0.5556	°C
	2150.42	cu. ins.	faradays/sec.	96,500	amperes
	35.238	litres	feet	30.48	cm.
°C+17.78	1.8	°F		0.3048	metres
centimetres	0.3937	inches		0.0001894	mi. (stat.)
cm-grams	980.1	cm.-dynes		0.0001645	mi. (Brit. naut.)
chains	66	ft.	ft. of water	62.43	lbs./sq. ft.
circumference	6.2832	radians		0.4335	lbs./sq. in.
cubic centimetres	0.0610	cu. ins.	ft./min.	0.5080	cm./sec.

Multiply:	By:	To Obtain:	Multiply:	By:	To Obtain:
ft./sec.	0.6818	mi./hr.	miles		
	0.5921	knots	statute	5280	ft.
fluid ounces	29.573	millilitres		1.609	km.
furlongs	660	feet		0.8624	mi. (Brit. naut.)
	0.125	mi.	nautical (Brit.)	6080	ft.
gallons	231	cu. ins.		1.151	mi. (stat.)
	8.345	lbs. of water	mi./hr.	1.467	ft./sec.
	8	pts.	milligrams/litre	1	parts/million
	4	qts.	millilitres	0.0338	fluid oz.
	3.785	litres	millimetres	0.03937	inches
	0·003785	cu. m.	ounces		
gals./min.	8.0208	cu. ft./hr.	avoirdupois	28.349	grams
grains	0.0648	grams		0.9115	oz. (troy)
grams	980.1	dynes		0.0625	lbs. (avdp.)
	15.43	grains	troy	31.103	grams
	0.0353	oz. (avdp.)		1.0971	oz. (avdp.)
	0.0022	lbs. (avdp.)	pecks	8.8096	litres
hectares	107,600	sq. ft.	pints		
	2.47	acres	liquid	473.2	cu. cm.
hectolitres	2.838	bushels		28.875	cu. ins.
horsepower	33,000	ft.-lbs./min.		0.473	litres
	2545	B.T.U./hr.	dry	0.550	litres
	745.7	watts	pounds		
	42·44	B.T.U./min.	avoirdupois	444,600	dynes
	0.7457	kilowatts		453.6	grams
inches	25.40	mm.		32.17	poundals
	2.540	cm.		14.58	oz. (troy)
	0.00001578	mi.		1.21	lbs. (troy)
ins. of water	0.03613	lbs./sq. in.		0.4536	kg.
kilograms	980,100	dynes	troy	0.373	kg.
	2.2046	lbs. (avdp.)	lbs. (avdp.)/sq. in.	70.22	g./sq. cm.
kg. calories	3086	ft.-lbs.		2,307	ft. of water
	3.968	B.T.U.	quarts		
kg. cal./min.	51.43	ft.-lbs./sec.	liquid	57.75	cu. ins.
	0.06972	kilowatts		32	fluid oz.
kilometres	3280.8	ft.		2	pts.
	0.621	mi.		0.946	litres
km./hr.	0.621	mi./hr.	dry	67.20	cu. ins.
	0.5396	knots		1.101	litres
kilowatts	737.6	ft.-lbs./sec.	quires	25	sheets
	56.92	B.T.U./min.	radians	3437.7	minutes
	1.341	horsepower		57.296	degrees
kilowatt-hrs.	2,655,000	ft.-lbs.	reams	500	sheets
	3415	B.T.U.	revolutions/min.	6	degrees/sec.
	1.341	horsepower-hrs.	rods	16.5	ft.
knots	6080	ft./hr.		5.5	yds.
	1.151	stat. mi./hr.		5.029	metres
	1	(Brit.) naut. mi./hr.	slugs	32.17	lbs. (mass)
litres	61.02	cu. ins.	square centimetres	0.155	sq. ins.
	2.113	pts. (liq.)	sq. feet	0.093	sq. m.
	1.057	qts. (liq.)	sq. inches	6.451	sq. cm.
	0.264	gals. (liq.)	sq. kilometres	247.1	acres
	1.816	pts. (dry)		0.3861	sq. mi.
	0·908	qts. (dry)	sq. metres	10.76	sq. ft.
	0.1135	pecks		1.1960	sq. yds.
	0.0284	bushels	sq. miles	27,878,400	sq. ft.
metres	39.37	inches		640	acres
	3.2808	ft.		2.5889	sq. km.
	1.0936	yds.	sq. yards	0.8361	sq. m.
	0.0006215	mi. (stat.)			
	0.0005396	mi. (Brit. naut.)			

Multiply	By:	To Obtain:
tons		
long	2240	lbs. (avdp.)
	1.12	short tons
	1.0160	metric tons
metric	2204.6	lbs. (avdp.)
	1000	kg.
	1.1023	short tons
	0.9842	long tons
short	2000	lbs. (avdp.)
	0.9072	metric tons
	0.8929	long tons
watts	3.415	B.T.U./hr.
	0.001341	horsepower
yards	36	inches
	3	ft.
	0.9144	metres
	0.0005682	mi. (stat.)
	0.0004934	mi. (Brit. naut.)

Number Fun

$1 \times 8 + 1 = 9$	$111 \quad 1+1+1 = 3$	$111 \div 3 = 37$
$12 \times 8 + 2 = 98$	$222 \quad 2+2+2 = 6$	$222 \div 6 = 37$
$123 \times 8 + 3 = 987$	$333 \quad 3+3+3 = 9$	$333 \div 9 = 37$
$1234 \times 8 + 4 = 9876$	$444 \quad 4+4+4 = 12$	$444 \div 12 = 37$
$12345 \times 9 + 5 = 98765$	$555 \quad 5+5+5 = 15$	$555 \div 15 = 37$
$123456 \times 8 + 6 = 987654$	$666 \quad 6+6+6 = 18$	$666 \div 18 = 37$
$1234567 \times 8 + 7 = 9876543$	$777 \quad 7+7+7 = 21$	$777 \div 21 = 37$
$12345678 \times 8 + 8 = 98765432$	$888 \quad 8+8+8 = 24$	$888 \div 24 = 37$
$123456789 \times 8 + 9 = 987654321$	$999 \quad 9+9+9 = 27$	$999 \div 27 = 37$

```
                                    1 2 3 4 5 6 7 8 9      9 8 7 6 5 4 3 2 1
         1 × 9 − 1 = 8              1 2 3 4 5 6 7 8          8 7 6 5 4 3 2 1
        21 × 9 − 1 = 188           1 2 3 4 5 6 7              7 6 5 4 3 2 1
       321 × 9 − 1 = 2888          1 2 3 4 5 6                  6 5 4 3 2 1
      4321 × 9 − 1 = 38888         1 2 3 4 5                      5 4 3 2 1
     54321 × 9 − 1 = 488888        1 2 3 4                          4 3 2 1
    654321 × 9 − 1 = 5888888       1 2 3                              3 2 1
   7654321 × 9 − 1 = 68888888      1 2                                  2 1
  87654321 × 9 − 1 = 788888888   + 1                                      1
 987654321 × 9 − 1 = 8888888888  ─────────────────      ─────────────────
                                  1 0 8 3 6 7 6 2 6 9    1 0 8 3 6 7 6 2 6 9
```

$1 \times 9 + 2 = 11$

$12 \times 9 + 3 = 111$

$123 \times 9 + 4 = 1111$

$1234 \times 9 + 5 = 11111$

$12345 \times 9 + 6 = 111111$

$123456 \times 9 + 7 = 1111111$

$1234567 \times 9 + 8 = 11111111$

$12345678 \times 9 + 9 = 111111111$

$9 \times 9 + 7 = 88$

$98 \times 9 + 6 = 888$

$987 \times 9 + 5 = 8888$

$9876 \times 9 + 4 = 88888$

$98765 \times 9 + 3 = 888888$

$987654 \times 9 + 2 = 8888888$

$9876543 \times 9 + 1 = 88888888$

$98765432 \times 9 + 0 = 888888888$

$11^2 = 121$

$111^2 = 12321$

$1111^2 = 1234321$

$11111^2 = 123454321$

$111111^2 = 12345654321$

$1111111^2 = 1234567654321$

$11111111^2 = 123456787654321$

$111111111^2 = 12345678987654321$

$33 \times 3367 = 111111$

$66 \times 3367 = 222222$

$99 \times 3367 = 333333$

$132 \times 3367 = 444444$

$165 \times 3367 = 555555$

$198 \times 3367 = 666666$

$231 \times 3367 = 777777$

$264 \times 3367 = 888888$

$297 \times 3367 = 999999$

$$
\begin{array}{r}
12345679 \\
\times\,99999999 \\
\hline
111111111 \\
111111111 \\
111111111 \\
111111111 \\
111111111 \\
111111111 \\
111111111 \\
111111111 \\
111111111 \\
\hline
1234567887654321
\end{array}
$$

In ancient Babylon zero was written with two dots, like our modern colon(:).

On the assumption that a person can count to 200 in a minute, that he or she counts for twelve hours a day, and that he or she is blessed with immortality, it would still take 19,024 years, 68 days, 10 hours and 40 minutes to count to one billion.

Newton was only twenty-four when he gave general rules for the calculus.

The first time that an equals sign (=) was used was in 1557. Robert Recorde used the symbol in his book on algebra called *The Whetstone of Witte.*

The adoption of the Arabic numerals, which are the basis for our modern numerals, met with strong opposition from the business class in the Middle Ages, in particular from the powerful merchants of Florence.

The magic square from Albrecht Dürer's Melancholy
The total of each of the lines of numbers (vertical, diagonal and horizontal) and the numbers in the four corners is the same: 34. Try it and see . . .

$$
\begin{array}{cccc}
16 & 3 & 2 & 13 \\
5 & 10 & 11 & 8 \\
9 & 6 & 7 & 12 \\
4 & 15 & 14 & 1
\end{array}
$$

This magic square is referred to in the 3,000 year-old Chinese book of divination called the *I Ching.* The lines of numbers all add up to 15.

$$
\begin{array}{ccc}
8 & 1 & 6 \\
3 & 5 & 7 \\
4 & 9 & 2
\end{array}
$$

8

Earth & Weather

Pre-Science

'What is the world?' This is a question which must have been asked even by our remote cave-dwelling ancestors. It was natural for them to believe the Earth to be flat and to remain motionless with the sky rotating round it once a day. Nothing else would have seemed logical; after all, allowing for minor irregularities such as hills and valleys, the Earth does give the impression of being a flat plane.

Some of the ancient concepts sound bizarre today; they were of course bound up with ideas about the universe itself, and are discussed in the Astronomy section of this book. It was only with the Greeks that true science began to emerge, and even then progress was slow. The first of the great Greek philosophers, Thales of Miletus (c. 624–547 BC) certainly believed the Earth to be flat, while in the opinion of his younger contemporary, Xenophanes of Colophon (c. 571–478 BC), the upper side of the flat Earth touched the air, while its underside extended without limit. Even after it had been established that the Earth was a globe, it required a tremendous mental leap to dethrone our world from its proud central position, and this was a leap which few Greeks were prepared to take. Aristarchus of Samos was one, but he found few followers.

Earth as seen from space – Apollo 13 photographs
South America from a height of 22,000 miles

However, the Greeks did at least make a good measurement of the size of the Earth. This was done by Eratosthenes of Cyrene, about 250 BC. Incidentally, Eratosthenes' value was much more accurate than that used by Christopher Columbus in his voyage of discovery so many centuries later. Had Columbus put his faith in Eratosthenes, he would have known quite well that the land he reached could not possibly be India, and he would have come home with a far better idea of where he had been.

Mapping the world was a much more difficult problem, and early attempts depended solely upon reports from travellers who journeyed out from the Mediterranean. One of these was Pytheas, perhaps the earliest true geographer. Around 325 BC he passed through the Straits of Gibraltar and explored the coasts of Portugal, Spain, France and Britain; he may even have reached Norway. Only a few fragments of his writings have come down to us, but apparently he did comment that the thin ice-sheets formed in a cold sea were similar in appearance to the masses of jellyfish common in the Mediterranean. More importantly, he made at least an attempt to navigate by the stars. But the first world-map based upon truly scientific methods had to wait until the time of Ptolemy, the last great scientist of the Greek school of thought.

Exploring the Earth

Ptolemy of Alexandria (or, to give him his proper name, Claudius Ptolemæus) lived from about AD 120 to 180. We know nothing about his life or personality, but there can be no doubt about his skill; periodic attempts to discredit him, and to claim that he was a mere copyist, have been singularly unsuccessful. His work extended into all branches of science. He is probably best remembered as an astronomer, but one of his major achievements was to compile a map of the known world which was a vast improvement upon anything previously achieved.

Ptolemy based his map partly upon reports brought back by travellers and partly upon astronomical observations. Obviously his scope was limited, but he drew the Mediterranean region fairly accurately, together with Arabia and much of Europe and Western Asia – even though he did join Scotland on to England in a sort of back-to-front position. He showed part of North Africa, and put in a more or less recognizable representation of India, together with an enormously magnified Ceylon. It was a noble effort, even though Ptolemy was well aware that it took in only a small part of the entire globe.

Detailed maps had to await longer voyages of exploration. As time went by, travellers from Europe reached all parts of the world. There seems little doubt that the Vikings landed in North America more than a thousand years ago (incidentally, how many people know that the name 'America' was suggested in

1507 by a map-maker who had been translating the diaries of Amerigo Vespucci, whose main voyages were undertaken between 1499 and 1501?). The world was circumnavigated by 1522, by the *Vittoria* in the fleet of Magellan, and Australia and New Zealand were reached during the eighteenth century. Map-making was no longer dependent upon casual reports and hopeful guesswork.

In fact, the famous voyage of discovery by Captain James Cook began as a purely astronomical exercise. At known intervals the planet Venus passes directly between the Earth and the Sun, so that it appears in transit against the Sun's face. Transits occur in pairs; there are two, separated by eight years, after which there are no more for over a century. Thus there were transits in 1761, 1769, 1874 and 1882; the next will be in 2004. Before modern methods were developed, these transits provided the only reliable way of measuring the distance between the Earth and the Sun, known as the astronomical unit (now known to be approximately 93,000,000 miles). What had to be done was to measure the exact moment when the transit began and ended. The 1769 transit was expected to be seen well from the South Seas, and Cook was put in charge of an expedition to Tahiti, taking with him several eminent astronomers. The transit was successfully observed; and it was after leaving Tahiti that Cook sailed on to New Zealand and Australia.

Finally, in our own century, men managed to reach the most inaccessible parts of our globe. Peary went to the North Pole in 1909, Amundsen to the South Pole in 1911; and in 1953 Hillary and Tenzing climbed to the summit of Everest. Maps compiled by aircraft and by artificial satellites are now more or less complete. It is true that we lack precise knowledge of a few areas, such as the dense forests of South America, but by now it is fair to say that there is no part of the world which must be classed as 'unknown'.

The Age of the Earth

In 1656 a well-known Churchman, Archbishop Ussher of Armagh, made the categorical statement that the world was created at ten o'clock in the morning of 26 October, 4004 BC. He reached this remarkable conclusion by adding up the ages of the patriarchs and making some suitable adjustments. Religious leaders as a whole were well satisfied, and accepted Ussher's value readily; after all, it was in excellent accord with the account given in the Book of Genesis. Scientists were less impressed. In France, Baron Georges Cuvier (1769–1832) began studying fossils, the remains of long-dead organisms, and may be said to have founded the science of fossil study, or palæontology. All the evidence indicated that fossils were much more than a few thousands of years old. By the early part of the nineteenth century the evidence for a very ancient Earth had become overwhelming. The arguments now centred upon the question of how old it actually was.

Rocks might be expected to provide the main evidence, and here, too, there arose two very different schools of thought. The 'Neptunists', led by Abraham Werner (1750–1817) believed that all rocks had been formed by precipitation out of a solution of water. This was disputed by the 'plutonists', who eventually won the day. James Hutton (1729–1797) maintained that geological features were produced not by sudden catastrophes, but by a process of slow, continuous change; this doctrine of 'uniformitarianism' was supported by Sir Charles Lyell (1797–1875), whose most famous book, *Principles of Geology*, became a standard work. Lyell believed the Earth to be so old that for most practical purposes it could be regarded as infinitely ancient.

However, this view was questioned by the great physicist Lord Kelvin (1824–1907), whose opinions carried a great deal of weight. Kelvin calculated that if the Earth had originally been molten – as seemed almost certain – it would have cooled to its present state in only 100,000,000 years; later he reduced this estimate to between 20,000,000 and 40,000,000 years, which, the astronomers and geologists protested, was not nearly long enough.

The problem was finally solved by studies of radioactive elements. These elements are not stable; they decay spontaneously. The time taken for a radioactive element to decay by half is known as its 'half-life'; for instance radium itself ends up as lead. Therefore, comparing the amount of remaining radium with the associated lead gives a clue as to how long the process has been going on. In 1906 a radium mineral was found to be at least 2,000,000,000 years old, so that clearly the Earth itself must be more ancient than this. The method was refined by Arthur Holmes, whose classic book, *The Age of the Earth*, was published in 1913. Today we know of rocks which are well over 3,500,000,000 years old. Various other methods have also been developed, and all give much the same result; the Earth came into being, as an independent body, about 4,700,000,000 years ago. Analyses of rocks brought back from the lunar surface by the Apollo astronauts and the Russian automatic probes show that the age of the Moon is about the same.

According to modern theory, the Earth was built up by accretion from a 'solar nebula', a cloud of material associated with the youthful Sun. Other theories have been proposed; it was once thought that the Earth and the other planets were pulled off the Sun by the gravitational action of a passing star, and in 1878 George Darwin (son of Charles Darwin, the great naturalist) proposed that the Moon used to be part of the Earth, subsequently breaking away and becoming independent. But all these ideas have been found to have fatal mathematical weaknesses, and by now almost all authorities agree that the solar nebula idea is correct, though there is still considerable divergence of opinion over matters of detail.

We also know that the Earth will not last forever. In 1939 H.Bethe and G.Gamow developed the theory of the source of solar energy; the Sun radiates by means of nuclear transformations deep inside its globe, with hydrogen, the most abundant element in the universe, as the main 'fuel'. In perhaps 5,000,000,000 years from now the Sun will run short of available hydrogen, and will change its structure, swelling out to become a large, red star with a diameter of about 200,000,000 miles. Inevitably the Earth and the other inner planets will be destroyed. However, there is no immediate cause for alarm; the Sun will not change much in the foreseeable future. The only real danger to life on Earth comes from ourselves.

The Structure of the Earth

It is rather sobering to reflect that although we live on the Earth, we can make no direct investigations of what lies deep below our feet. No mine-shaft can penetrate for more than a few miles – and the diameter of the Earth is not far short of 8000 miles. For a long time it was not even known whether or not the Earth was hot inside, and some curious ideas were put forward. For instance, in 1823 Captain John Cleves Symmes, of the American Army, suggested that the Earth was made up of five concentric spheres, in each of which people lived; the way to the interior was through a wide opening at the North Pole. Symmes even tried to persuade Congress to send an expedition to test this remarkable theory.

Most of our present information comes from studies of earthquake waves. An earthquake is caused by compressed or stretched rocks suddenly 'snapping' along a fault in the Earth's surface, releasing tremendous amounts of energy and sometimes causing widespread devastation. Seismic or earthquake waves are sent through the globe, and are of two main types: primary or compressional waves (P-waves), in which the rock particles through which they pass shake back and forth in the direction of the wave, and shear or secondary waves (S-waves), in which the particles vibrate at right angles to the direction of the wave. (It is the surface or L-waves which cause the most damage, but these are less informative to geophysicists.) Both P- and S-waves can be transmitted through solids, but S-waves cannot pass through liquids. Seismic waves can be detected over great distances at velocities which depend upon the density of the material through which they pass. It was found that from some stations recording deep-seated earthquakes no S-waves were detected, and the clear inference was that the Earth's core is liquid. This core has a diameter of about 3400 miles.

The outermost region of the Earth is termed the crust. It is relatively thin; it goes down to less than five miles below the sea-floor, and not more than 30 miles below the continents. Beneath it comes the mantle, which is appreciably denser.

The boundary between the two was discovered in 1909 by the Jugoslav scientist A.Mohorovičić, and is therefore known as the Mohorovičić Discontinuity – or, more conveniently, as the Moho. It has never been reached; an American attempt to bore down to it through the ocean-floor had to be abandoned as too difficult, and the 'Mohole' has yet to be drilled.

The most disastrous earthquakes since 1960

Mag. stands for magnitude as measured on the Richter scale, in use since 1935.

Date	Place	Deaths	Mag
1960 Feb. 29	Morocco, Agadir	12,000	5.8
1960 May 21–30	Southern Chile	5,000	8.3
1962 Sept. 1	Northwestern Iran	12,230	7.1
1963 July 26	Yugoslavia, Skopje	1,100	6.0
1964 Mar. 27	Alaska	114	8.5
1966 Aug. 19	Eastern Turkey	2,520	6.9
1968 Aug. 31	Northeastern Iran	12,000	7.4
1970 Mar. 28	Western Turkey	1,086	7.4
1970 May 31	Northern Peru	66,794	7.7
1971 Feb. 9	Cal., San Fernando Valley	65	6.5
1972 Apr. 10	Southern Iran	5,057	6.9
1972 Dec. 23	Nicaragua	5,000	6.2
1974 Dec. 28	Pakistan (9 towns)	5,200	6.3
1975 Sept. 6	Turkey (Lice, etc.)	2,312	6.8
1976 Feb. 4	Guatemala	22,778	7.5
1976 May 6	Northwest Italy	946	6.5
1976 June 26	New Guinea, Irian Jaya	443	7.1
1976 July 28	China, Tangshan	800,000	8.2
1976 Aug. 17	Philippines, Mindanao	8,000	7.8
1976 Nov. 24	Eastern Turkey	4,000	7.9
1977 Mar. 4	Romania, Bucharest, etc.	1,541	7.5
1977 Aug. 19	Indonesia	200	8.0
1977 Nov. 23	Northwestern Argentina	100	8.2
1978 June 12	Japan, Sendai	21	7.5
1978 Sept. 16	Northeast Iran	25,000	7.7
1979 Sept. 12	Indonesia	100	8.1
1979 Dec. 12	Colombia, Ecuador	800	7.9

The upper mantle is made up of a thin, rigid layer going down to some 50 or 60 miles below the Moho; together with the crust it forms the 'lithosphere', which is divided into definite plates. Then comes a lower, still denser part of the mantle; this is bounded by the Gutenberg Discontinuity, discovered in 1914. Then comes the core itself, 4000 miles down. About the core we have only limited information, but it is certainly rich in iron, and has an estimated temperature of 5400° F. Its innermost part may well be solid.

We can at least study material from the upper mantle, because it is brought to the surface by volcanic activity. The hot, molten rock (magma) pours out, solidifying to become lava. Eruptions may be catastrophic. Probably the greatest outburst in near-historic times was that of Thera, in the Mediterranean, around 1500 BC; an island was virtually destroyed, and there seems little doubt that the waves set up swamped the shores of Crete, putting an abrupt end to the Minoan civilization there and giving rise to the legend of the sunken continent of Atlantis. In 1883 Krakatoa, in Indonesia, was similarly blown up, with the loss of 36,000 lives. Other volcanoes, such as Stromboli, are of different type, and less dangerous. And new volcanoes appear now and then, such as Paricutín, which burst forth in 1943 in a field belonging to an unsuspecting Mexican farmer.

A tornado approaching the Mississippi river, Kentucky USA

The worst storms since 1960   H – Hurricane   T – Typhoon

Date	Location	Deaths	Date	Location	Deaths
1960 Sept 4–12	H. *Donna*, Caribbean, E. U.S.	148	1970 July 30–		
1961 Oct 31	H. *Hattie*, Br. Honduras	400	Aug 5	H. *Celia*, Cuba, Fla., Tex.	31
1962 Feb 17	Flooding, German Coast	343	1970 Aug 20–21	H. *Dorothy*, Martinique	42
1962 Sept 27	Flooding, Barcelona, Spain	445	1970 Sept 15	T. *Georgia*, Philippines	300
1963 May 28–29	Windstorm, Bangladesh	22,000	1970 Oct 14	T. *Sening*, Philippines	583
1963 Oct 4–8	H. *Flora*, Cuba, Haiti	6,000	1970 Oct 15	T. *Titang*, Philippines	526
1964 Oct 4–7	H. *Hilda*, La., Miss., Ga.	38	1970 Nov 13	Cyclone, Bangladesh (est.)	300,000
1964 June 30	T. *Winnie*, N. Philippines	107	1971 Aug 1	T. *Rose*, Hong Kong	130
1964 Sept 5	T. *Ruby*, Hong Kong and China	735	1972 June 19–29	H. *Agnes*, Fla. to N.Y.	118
1964 Sept 14	Flooding, central S. Korea	563	1972 Dec 3	T. *Theresa*, Philippines	169
1964 Nov 12	Flooding, S. Vietnam	7,000	1973 June–Aug	Monsoon rains in India	1,217
1965 May 11–12	Windstorm, Bangladesh	17,000	1974 June 11	Storm *Dinah*, Luzon Is., Philip	71
1965 June 1–2	Windstorm, Bangladesh	30,000	1974 July 11	T. *Gilda*, Japan, S. Korea	108
1965 Sept 7–10	H. *Betsy*, Fla., Miss., La.	74	1974 Sept 19–20	H. *Fifi*, Honduras	2,000
1965 Dec 15	Windstorm, Bangladesh	10,000	1974 Dec 25	Cyclone levelled Darwin, Aus.	50
1966 June 4–10	H. *Alma*, Honduras, SE U.S.	51	1975 Sept 13–27	H. *Eloise*, Caribbean, NE U.S.	71
1966 Sept 24–30	H. *Inez*, Carib., Fla., Mex.	293	1976 May 20	T. *Olga*, floods, Philippines	215
1967 July 9	T. *Billie*, Japan	347	1977 July 25, 31	T. *Thelma*, T. *Vera* Taiwan	39
1967 Sept 5–23	H. *Beulah*, Carib., Mex., Tex.	54	1978 Oct 27	T. *Rita*, Philippines	c. 400
1967 Dec. 12–20	Blizzard, Southwest, U.S.	51	1979 Aug 30–		
1968 Nov 18–28	T. *Nina*, Philippines	63	Sept 7	H. *David*, Caribbean, E U.S.	1,100
1969 Aug 17–18	H. *Camille*, Miss., La	256			

Beneath the waves – ocean depths and locations

Name of area	Location		Metres	Depth Fathoms	Feet
Pacific Ocean					
Mariana Trench	11°21′N,	142°12′E	11,034	6,033	36,198
Tonga Trench	23°15.3′S,	174°44.7′W	10,882	5,950	35,702
Kuril Trench	44°15.2′N,	150°34.2′E	10,542	5,764	34,587
Philippine Trench	10°24′N,	126°40′E	10,539	5,763	34,578
Izu Trench	30°32′N,	142°31′E	10,374	5,673	34,033
Kermadec Trench	31°52.8′S,	177°20.6′W	10,047	5,494	32,964
Bonin Trench	24°30′N,	143°24′E	9,156	5,005	30,032
New Britain Trench	06°34′S				
Yap Trench	08°33′N,	138°02′E	8,527	4,662	27,976
Japan Trench	36°08′N,	142°43′E	8,412	4,597	27,591
Palau Trench	07°40′N,	135°04′E	8,138	4,449	26,693
Aleutian Trench	50°53′N,	176°23′E	8,100	4,429	26,574
Peru Chile Trench	23°18′S,	71°41′W	8,064	4,409	26,454
(Atacama Trench)	23°27′S,	71°21′W	8,064	4,409	26,454
New Hebrides Trench	20°36′S,	168°37′E	7,570	4,138	24,830
Ryukyu Trench	25°15′N,	128°32′E	7,507	4,105	24,629
Mid. America Trench	14°02′N,	93°39′W	6,669	3,642	21,852
Atlantic Ocean					
Puerto Rico Trench	19°35′N,	68°17′W	8,648	4,729	28,374
Cayman Trench	19°12′N,	80°00′W	7,535	4,120	24,720
So. Sandwich Trench	55°14′S,	26°29′W	8,252	4,512	27,072
Romanche Gap	00°16′S,	18°35′W	7,864	4,300	25,800
Brazil Basin	09°10′S,	23°02′W	6,119	3,346	20,076
Indian Ocean					
Java Trench	10°15′S,	109°E′ (approx.)	7,725	4,224	25,344
Ob Trench	(no position)		6,874	3,759	22,553
Vema Trench	(no position)		6,402	3,501	21,004
Agulhas Basin	(no position)		6,195	3,388	20,325
Diamantina Trench	35°00′S,	105°35′E	6,062	3,315	19,800
Arctic Ocean					
Eurasia Basin	82°23′N,	19°31′E	5,450	2,980	17,880
Mediterranean Sea					
Ionian Basin	36°32′N,	21°06′E	5,150	2,816	16,896

Source: Defence Mapping Agency Hydrographic/Topographic Center

The world's top twenty rivers

	Length (miles)		
1 Nile	4,150	11 Niger	2,600
2 Amazon	3,900	12 Mackenzie	2,500
3 Missouri-Mississippi-Red Rock	3,800	13 Parana	2,450
4 Yangtze	3,400	14 Volga	2,300
5 Ob-Irtysh	3,200	15 Yenisey	2,300
6 Hwang Ho	2,900	16 Madeira	2,100
7 Congo (Zaire)	2,900	17 Yukon	2,000
8 Amur	2,800	18 Arkansas	2,000
9 Lena	2,800	19 Colorado	2,000
10 Mekong	2,800	20 St Lawrence	1,800

Source: Whitaker's Almanack—1979

The world's top twenty mountains

		Height (feet)
1	Everest	29,028
2	K.2.	28,250
3	Kanchenjunga	28,208
4	Lhotse	27,923
5	Makalu I	27,824
6	Lhotse II	27,560
7	Dhaulagiri	26,810
8	Manaslu I	26,760
9	Cho Oyu	26,750
10	Nanga Parbat	26,660
11	Annapurna I	26,504
12	Gasherbrum	26,470
13	Broad	26,400
14	Gosainthan	26,287
15	Annapurna II	26,041
16	Gyachung Kang	25,910
17	Disteghil Sar	25,868
18	Himalchuli	25,801
19	Nuptse	25,726
20	Masherbrum	25,660

Source: (based on) The World Almanac and Book of Facts—1981

The world's top twenty lakes (freshwater and saltwater)

		Area (sq. miles)
1	Caspian Sea	143,244
2	Superior	31,700
3	Victoria	26,828
4	Aral Sea	24,904
5	Huron	23,000
6	Michigan	22,300
7	Tanganyika	12,700
8	Baykal	12,162
9	Great Bear	12,028
10	Malawi	11,150
11	Great Slave	11,031
12	Erie	9,910
13	Winnipeg	9,417
14	Ontario	7,550
15	Ladoga	6,835
16	Balkhash	7,115
17	Chad	6,300
18	Maracaibo	5,217
19	Onega	3,710
20	Volta	3,276

Source: The World Almanac and Book of Facts—1981

The world's top twenty oceans and seas

		Area (sq. miles)	Average depth (feet)
1	Pacific Ocean	64,186,300	13,739
2	Atlantic Ocean	33,420,000	12,257
3	Indian Ocean	28,350,500	12,704
4	Arctic Ocean	5,105,700	4,362
5	South China Sea	1,148,500	4,802
6	Caribbean Sea	971,400	8,448
7	Mediterranean Sea	969,100	4,926
8	Bering Sea	873,000	4,893
9	Gulf of Mexico	582,100	5,297
10	Sea of Okhotsk	537,500	3,192
11	Sea of Japan	391,100	5,468
12	Hudson Bay	281,900	305
13	East China Sea	256,600	620
14	Andaman Sea	218,100	3,667
15	Black Sea	196,100	3,906
16	Red Sea	174,900	1,764
17	North Sea	164,900	308
18	Baltic Sea	147,500	180
19	Yellow Sea	113,500	121
20	Persian Gulf	88,800	328

Source: The World Almanac and Book of Facts—1981

The world's top twenty islands

		Area (sq. miles)
1	Greenland	840,000
2	New Guinea	305,000
3	Borneo	290,000
4	Madagascar	228,000
5	Baffin Island (Canada)	190,000
6	Sumatra	163,000
7	Honshu	88,839
8	Great Britain	88,745
9	Victoria Island (Canada)	80,000
10	Ellesmere Island (Canada)	77,000
11	Celebes	69,000
12	South Island, New Zealand	58,093
13	Java	48,800
14	North Island, New Zealand	44,281
15	Cuba	44,000
16	Newfoundland	42,750
17	Luzon	40,400
18	Iceland	40,000
19	Mindanao	36,500
20	Ireland	32,600

The Ancient Earth

Our ideas about the long-term changes in the outlines of the Earth's continents and oceans have been dramatically altered in modern times. The major breakthrough was made in 1915 by a German meteorologist named Alfred Wegener, who put forward the idea of 'continental drift'. Wegener was largely ignored at the time, and indeed for years after his death in 1930; it was only in the 1960s that his ideas were refined, improved and extended to make up the new study of 'plate tectonics'.

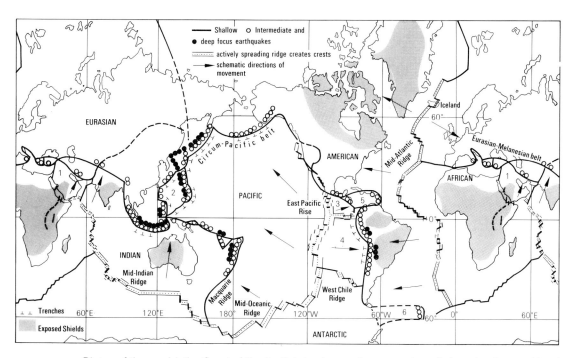

Plates of the world: the Crust of the Earth is broken up into a number of plates by the combined action of oceanic ridges which cause sea-floor spreading, faults which dislocate crustal fragments over hundreds of miles, and Benioff zone/island arc trenches where excess crustal material is destroyed and recirculated. There are six major plates and six smaller ones as indicated here. The innumerable micro plates are omitted from this diagram.
    1 – Arabian Plate, 2 – Philippine Plate, 3 – Cocos Plate, 4 – Nazca Plate, 5 – Caribbean Plate, 6 – Scotia Plate.

Basically, it seems that the Earth's continents 'drift around', very slowly. Wegener noticed that the bulge of South America fits into the 'dip' of Africa, and this was only one of many examples – as was shown even more forcefully in 1958 by S.W.Carey, in America, who fitted representations of the continents together on the surface of a Pyrex globe. On its own, this might possibly be dismissed as coincidental, but there was much additional evidence. Fossils were most informative, and so was what is known as palæomagnetism. The Earth is a giant magnet, due to the large quantities of iron and other magnetic materials inside it. Heated rocks lose their magnetism, but when they cool they are re-magnetized, and the resulting 'remnant magnetism' lies parallel to the direction of the main field at the time when the rocks were formed. We can therefore work out the magnetic conditions which prevailed in very ancient times. It seems that the direction of the field changes slowly; in fact, the magnetic poles 'wander'. If we assume that the continents also have wandered around, the whole jigsaw falls neatly into place; and this is one of the most important pieces of evidence in favour of continental drift.

The fit of North America, Greenland and Europe at the 500–fathom contour (Source: Understanding the Earth, Artemis Press, 1972)

Obviously we have only very incomplete evidence about the distribution of land and sea early in the Earth's history, but it is generally thought that about 500,000,000 years ago there were three vast land-masses. These persisted until about 275,000,000 years ago, when they collided to form a single huge mass, known as Pangæa. Then, about 100,000,000 years ago, Pangæa started to break up, and this led on to the distribution we know today; for instance, Africa separated from South America, and by 50,000,000 years ago the Indian, Pacific and Atlantic Oceans existed in recognizable form. Also, Australia has broken away from Antarctica. Of course there have been many minor modifications; for instance Britain is no longer joined on to the mainland of Europe, the result of the flooding of what is now the North Sea, at the end of the last Ice Age only about 10,000 years ago.

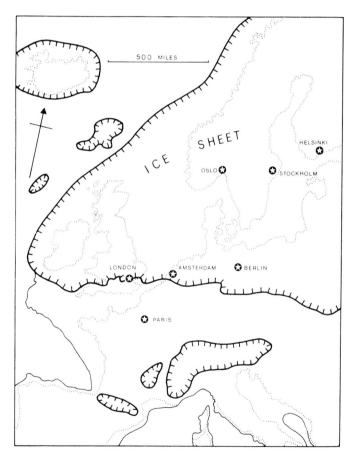

Glaciation hazard: Europe. Because of its latitudinal extent Europe would suffer under the return of glaciation to a greater extent than North America. Most of the EEC capitals would fall before the onslaught of an expanding polar ice cap as winter snow falls exceed the summer thaws. The associated withdrawal of the sea to near the edge of the continental shelf would expose both the sea floor and lowland south of the ice cap to harsh tundra conditions and destroy valuable agricultural land.

The concept of an Ice Age was first proposed in the earlier part of the nineteenth century. In fact there have been periodical Ice Ages throughout the Earth's history, and it is generally thought that the root cause lies in slight changes in the output of energy from the Sun, though again there are differences of opinion. To be accurate, the last Ice Age was made up of four 'cold periods' separated by warmer spells or 'interglacials'. It may even be that we are now in the midst of another interglacial, and that in thousands of years' time the cold will return. This could well be correct – but at least we will have plenty of warning.

The Evolution of Life

We cannot claim to be at all certain about the origin of life on Earth. Early in our own century the Swedish scientist, Svante Arrhenius, put forward his 'panspermia' theory, according to which life was first brought here by way of a meteorite from outer space, and a different version of the same basic idea has been supported as recently as 1978 by Sir Fred Hoyle and Chandra Wickramasinghe; but it is more generally believed that Earthly life began here in Pre-Cambrian times – that is to say, more than 600,000,000 years ago. It also seems that life began in the sea.

The world in those days would have seemed a very unfamiliar place. For instance, the atmosphere was different. The original atmosphere had been lost, and a secondary atmosphere had been produced from material sent out from inside the Earth, but it was poor in free oxygen, and rich in carbon dioxide. It was not until later that plants spread on to the land, and caused a dramatic change. By the process of photosynthesis, they removed much of the carbon dioxide, and replaced it with oxygen. If we could enter a time machine and send ourselves back to the early period of the Earth's history, we would find ourselves totally unable to breathe.

With the start of the so-called Palæozoic era, around 570,000,000 years ago, we come to the 'record of the rocks', and studies of fossils have enabled us to build up a good picture of the evolution of life. During the Palæozoic era, which ended about 225,000,000 years ago, the primitive marine organisms developed into fishes, amphibians and reptiles. The Mesozoic era (225,000,000 to 70,000,000 years ago) was the age of the great reptiles – who has not heard of the ichthyosaur, the plesiosaur, the tyrannosaurus and the other vast, almost brainless dinosaurs? But then, at the end of the Mesozoic era, the dinosaurs died out comparatively suddenly. There have been all sorts of theories about their abrupt extinction, ranging from a solar outburst to a violent climatic change or even a surge of deadly radiation from a nearby supernova. We have to confess that we simply do not know. At any rate, their disappearance left mammals free

Geological time scale

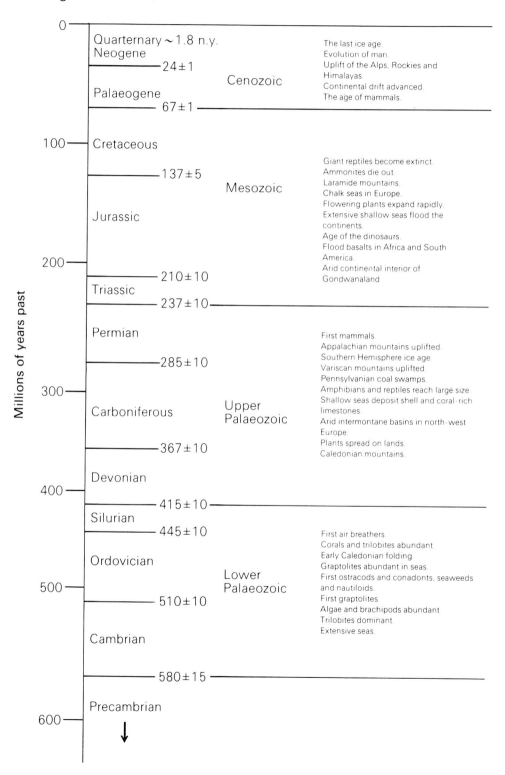

Millions of years past

0		
	Quarternary ~ 1.8 n.y.	The last ice age.
	Neogene	Evolution of man.
	24±1	Uplift of the Alps, Rockies and
		Himalayas.
	Palaeogene	Cenozoic	Continental drift advanced.
	67±1	The age of mammals.
100	Cretaceous	
		Giant reptiles become extinct.
	137±5	Ammonites die out.
		Laramide mountains.
	Jurassic	Mesozoic	Chalk seas in Europe.
		Flowering plants expand rapidly.
		Extensive shallow seas flood the
		continents.
200		Age of the dinosaurs.
	210±10	Flood basalts in Africa and South
		America.
	Triassic	Arid continental interior of
	237±10	Gondwanaland
	Permian	First mammals.
		Appalachian mountains uplifted.
	285±10	Southern Hemisphere ice age.
		Variscan mountains uplifted.
300		Pennsylvanian coal swamps.
	Carboniferous	Upper Palaeozoic	Amphibians and reptiles reach large size.
		Shallow seas deposit shell and coral-rich
		limestones.
		Arid intermontane basins in north-west
	367±10	Europe.
		Plants spread on lands.
	Devonian	Caledonian mountains.
400		
	415±10	
	Silurian	
	445±10	First air breathers.
		Corals and trilobites abundant.
		Early Caledonian folding.
	Ordovician	Graptolites abundant in seas.
		First ostracods and conadonts, seaweeds
500	Lower Palaeozoic	and nautiloids.
	510±10	First graptolites.
		Algae and brachipods abundant.
		Trilobites dominant.
	Cambrian	Extensive seas.
	580±15	
	Precambrian	
600	↓	

to develop, and we can trace their story through the Cenozoic era, from the small, tree-living primates through to *homo sapiens.*

The theory of 'natural selection' was proposed in 1858 by Charles Darwin (and also by Alfred Russel Wallace). Broadly, Darwin assumed that species develop through what may be termed the survival of the fittest – as distinct from the older ideas of Jean Lamarck (1744–1829), who had believed that species will adapt themselves to survive in their particular environment. Darwin's theory caused a violent controversy – every whit as violent, in fact, as that which had greeted Copernicus' theory that the Earth moves round the Sun. Churchmen were strongly opposed to it, mainly because it was tacitly assumed that, according to Darwin, men were descended from apes. In fact Darwin said nothing of the kind; all he claimed was that men and apes have common ancestry, which is certainly true. Yet even in modern times the old prejudice has not entirely died out. In 1925 Thomas Scropes was brought to trial in the State of Tennessee for daring to teach Darwinism to his pupils in contravention of the Act making it 'unlawful for any teacher to teach any theory that denies the story of the divine creation of Man as taught in the Bible, and to teach instead that Man has descended from a lower order of animals'. Scropes was actually fined a hundred dollars. And Darwinism is still officially frowned upon by the Dutch Reformed Church in South Africa. . .

It is not known for certain when the first men appeared on Earth. Between 1960 and 1963 Louis Leakey found primitive stone implements in the Olduvai Gorge in Tanzania which can be dated back 1,780,000 years, and it now seems that true men may extend back much further than this. But the story of true civilization is essentially 'modern'. The interval between the Stone Age and the Space Age is very short indeed by geological standards.

The Earth's Atmosphere and Weather

The Earth's atmosphere is unique in the Solar System. It is made up principally of oxygen and nitrogen, and it alone is 'breathable', so far as we know. Other planets and some satellites have atmospheres; that of Venus, for instance, is made up principally of carbon dioxide, with sulphuric acid clouds, while that of Saturn's largest satellite, Titan, has proved to be chiefly nitrogen at a very low temperature. But no other atmosphere is at all similar to that of the Earth.

The reason for the Earth's particular kind of atmosphere lies partly in its distance from the Sun, and partly in its escape velocity of seven miles per second. If the Earth were more massive, it would have retained more of the lighter gases which presumably once existed; if it were much less massive, the atmosphere would have leaked away – as has indeed happened with the Moon, and to a large extent with Mars also.

The clouds

Genus	Ht. of base (ft.)	Temp. at base level (°C.)	Official description
Cirrus (Ci)	16,500 to 45,000	−20 to −60	Detached clouds in the form of white, delicate filaments, or white or mostly white patches or narrow bands. They have a fibrous (hair-like) appearance on a silky sheen, or both
Cirrocumulus (Cc)	16,500 to 45,000	−20 to −60	Thin, white patch, sheet or layer of cloud without shading, composed of very small elements in the form of grains, ripples, etc., merged or separate, and more or less regularly arranged.
Cirrostratus (Cs)	16,500 to 45,000	−20 to −60	Transparent, whitish cloud veil of fibrous or smooth appearance, totally or partly covering the sky, and generally producing halo phenomena.
Altocumulus (Ac)	6,500 to 23,000	+10 to −30	White or grey, or both white and grey, patch, sheet or layer of cloud, generally with shading, composed of laminae, rounded masses, rolls, etc., which are sometimes partly fibrous or diffuse, and which may or may not be merged.
Altostratus (As)	6,500 to 23,000	+10 to −30	Greyish or bluish cloud sheet or layer of striated, fibrous or uniform appearance, totally or partly covering the sky, and having parts thin enough to reveal the sun at least vaguely.
Nimbostratus (Ns)	3,000 to 10,000	+10 to −15	Grey cloud layer, often dark, the appearance of which is rendered diffuse by more or less continually falling rain or snow which in most cases reaches the ground. It is thick enough throughout to blot out the sun. Low, ragged clouds frequently occur below the layer with which they may or may not merge.
Stratocumulus (Sc)	1,500 to 6,500	+15 to −5	Grey or whitish, or both grey and whitish, patch, sheet or layer of cloud which almost always has dark parts, composed of tessellations, rounded masses, rolls, etc., which are non-fibrous (except for virga) and which may or may not be merged.
Stratus (St)	surface to 1,500	+20 to −5	Generally grey cloud layer with a fairly uniform base, which may give drizzle, ice prisms or snow grains. When the sun is visible through the cloud its outline is clearly discernible. Stratus does not produce halo phenomena (except possibly at very low temperatures). Sometimes stratus appears in the form of ragged patches.
Cumulus (Cu)	1,500 to 6,500	+15 to −5	Detached clouds, generally dense and with sharp outlines, developing vertically in the form of rising mounds, domes or towers, of which the bulging upper part often resembles a cauliflower. The sunlit parts of these clouds are mostly brilliant white; their bases are relatively dark and nearly horizontal.
Cumulonimbus (Cb)	1,500 to 6,500	+15 to −5	Heavy and dense cloud, with a considerable vertical extent, in the form of a mountain or huge towers. At least part of its upper portion is usually smooth, or fibrous or striated, and nearly always flattened; this part often spreads out in the shape of an anvil or vast plume. Under the base of this cloud, which is often very dark, there are frequently low ragged clouds either merged with it or not, and precipitation.

The Arab astronomers of a thousand years ago knew quite well that the atmosphere is limited in extent, and they also knew that atmospheric pressure decreases with altitude. A great advance was made in 1643 by Evangelista Torricelli, a pupil of the great Italian scientist, Galileo, who invented the barometer, which in effect measures air-pressure by balancing it against a column of liquid. Torricelli used alcohol, but in 1657 the first mercury barometers were made in Florence – and even today there are countless 'household' barometers which work in precisely the same way. The aneroid barometer, which depends upon the varying pressure exerted upon a partly-evacuated capsule, came along later; the first aneroid was made by Lucien Vidie in 1843.

Obviously it was desirable to study conditions in the upper atmosphere, and equally obviously this was not possible before the development of flying machines. So far as is known, the first attempts were made in 1749 by Alexander Wilson, who sent up recording instruments in kites, but it was only in 1783–4 that the first truly 'meteorological' flights were made – first by Jacques Charles and then by John Jeffries and Jean Blanchard, who entrusted their lives to those newly-invented contraptions known as balloons. Jeffries and Blanchard succeeded in obtaining temperature and humidity measurements up to a height of 9000 feet.

Naturally, all our 'weather', in the accepted sense of the term, occurs in the lowest and densest part of the atmosphere – the region known as the troposphere, which extends up to less than ten miles on average. It is here that we see all our familiar clouds. In 1804 Luke Howard devised a system of cloud classification which has been retained and extended. Howard divided the clouds into four main types: cirrus (thread cloud), cumulus (heap cloud), stratus (flat cloud) and nimbus (rain cloud). Today we use a modified form of this system and classify clouds according to shape and height. There are the high clouds: cirrus, cirrostratus and cirrocumulus. Medium clouds are altocumulus and altostratus. The low clouds are stratocumulus, nimbostratus, cumulus, cumulonimbus and stratus.

It became clear that weather forecasting must depend upon a good knowledge of the prevailing conditions over wide areas (the term 'weather forecast' was first used in 1850 by the American pioneer of meteorology, Admiral Fitzroy). This means compiling a synoptic chart. One major feature of such a chart is the system of isobars, an isobar being a line joining places of equal barometric pressure. In an anticyclone or 'high', there is a region of high pressure surrounded by areas in which the pressure falls steadily away. Winds are due essentially to pressure-differences, and one would expect the winds to blow straight away from high-pressure centres; but we have to take into account the rotation of the Earth, which produces the so-called Coriolis effect, so that in the northern hemisphere the winds in an anticyclonic system blow clockwise and make up roughly circular isobars. With a 'low', with pressure rising all round the centre of the system, the winds tend to blow anti-clockwise. In the southern hemisphere of the Earth these conditions are reversed.

The first weather-maps issued to the public were produced in 1851, in connection with the Great Exhibition in London, and the first forecasts given regularly to the British press date from 1861. By then, meteorology was becoming a true science rather than a medley of intuition and guesswork. Thermometers, pioneered in 1641 by Ferdinand II, Grand Duke of Tuscany, had been perfected. The two principal scales in use were those of Gabriel Fahrenheit (freezing-point of water at standard temperature and pressure 32°, boiling-point 212°) and Anders Celsius (freezing point 0°, boiling point 100°). Both these systems are still in use, but in most countries, and in all science, the

Celsius or Centigrade scale is preferred. (There is also the Kelvin scale, beginning at absolute zero or minus 273° Centigrade.) In 1840 Thomas Stevenson, father of the famous novelist, developed the now-familiar Stevenson screen, which has louvred sides to regulate the airflow passing over the thermometers inside.

Windspeeds were carefully measured with instruments known as anemometers; the cup anemometer, in which hemispherical cups are whirled around on the ends of rods fastened to a central rotatable pole, was invented in 1846 by Romney Robinson, Director of the Armagh Observatory in Northern Ireland. Much earlier, in 1805, Admiral Beaufort had produced his famous 'wind scale', ranging from 0 (absolute calm) to 12 (hurricane).

The development of meteorology was also associated with the precautions which could be taken against natural disasters. Lightning is probably the worst of the common dangers; it is associated with massive cumulonimbus clouds of great vertical development. Lightning conductors were invented in 1752 by the American pioneer Benjamin Franklin, and only eighteen years later a lightning conductor was fitted to the top of St Paul's Cathedral. Yet lightning still causes many deaths per year, and unfortunately there is no absolute safeguard.

Up to near-modern times, the meteorologist was hampered by two limiting factors. First, he had to depend upon information received from scattered weather stations, and the coverage was often very unsatisfactory; for instance it would be over-optimistic to hope for many stations in the Arctic and Antarctic zones of the Earth, which are very important indeed, meteorologically. Secondly, nothing positive was known about the upper part of the atmosphere. There could be no doubt that some 'air' existed at great heights, and this had been demonstrated in 1796 by two German students, Brandes and Benzenberg, who measured the heights of meteors – tiny particles dashing into the upper atmosphere and burning away by friction. (We now know that the average meteor burns out by the time it has penetrated to within 40 miles above sea-level.) But conditions at those altitudes were still largely unknown.

The problem was tackled energetically by a Frenchman, Teisserenc de Bort, near the end of the nineteenth century. His method was to use high-altitude balloons. In measuring temperatures and pressures, he made a surprising discovery. At the top of the troposphere comes a thin layer called the tropopause; above this is the stratosphere (a name introduced by de Bort), in which the temperature no longer falls, but remains more or less constant. The 'lapse-rate', 5.4° Fahrenheit per thousand feet, is suspended. Up to 19 miles or so, the temperature in the stratosphere is approximately −68° Fahrenheit. This is above the region of normal clouds, though there are occasional nacreous or mother-of-pearl clouds whose precise nature is still rather obscure.

Subsequent experiments, both with balloons and with rockets, have shown that the structure of the atmosphere is much more complex than had been originally thought. The stratosphere is succeeded by an even more rarefied

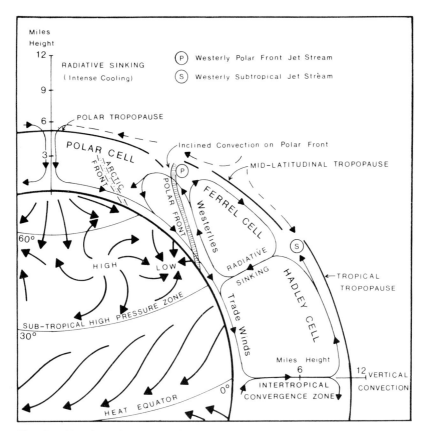

The Earth's climatic engine: here, in a diagrammatic section of part of the Northern Hemisphere, the airflow pathways of the world clearly demonstrate how the climatic zones of our planet are interrelated. In equatorial regions, moisture-laden air rises rapidly along the Intertropical Convergence Zone into the cooler zones of the upper atmosphere. The cooling effect in this zone of vertical convection causes towering masses of cumulonimbus thunderclouds to develop; this accounts for the heavy rains experienced in tropical regions. The circulation of this, now dry, air of the Hadley Cell just below the tropical tropopause meets a similar air stream from the Ferrel Cell and the combined, cooled, airstreams undergo radiative sinking to produce the sub-tropical high pressure zone at the Earth's surface. The air streams separate here; one flows south as the trade winds, while the other flows north as the westerlies. The coriolis effect of the rotating Earth deflects these airstreams in the direction opposite to that of the Earth's rotation.

The polar front is caused by the cold air of the Polar Cell forming a wedge beneath the warmer northern margin of the Ferrel Cell. The warmer air rises over the cold wedge in a zone of disturbed westerlies marked by an alternating pattern of high and low pressure anticyclones and cyclones, the position of which is closely determined by the position of the westerly polar front jet stream. Complex airflow patterns which are associated with the polar front are responsible for the vagaries in the weather of the Northern Hemisphere. The Arctic front (and corresponding Antarctic front) demark the junction between the intensely cooled polar airflow and the disturbed southerly wedge of the Polar Cell. (In the case of the southern hemisphere the compass directions are, of course, reversed.)

region, the ionosphere; it is here that we find the reflecting layers which 'bounce back' some kinds of radio waves, and make long-range wireless communication possible. Here, too, occur the lovely polar lights or auroræ, which are caused by electrified particles coming from the Sun. These particles enter zones of radiation surrounding the Earth (the van Allen zones), and overload them; the particles cascade downward into the ionosphere, and auroræ are seen. Because the particles are electrically charged, they tend to move toward the magnetic poles, and auroræ are commonest at high latitudes. In the equatorial regions of the Earth they are very rare, though it is on record that one auroral display was seen in historical times as close to the equator as Singapore.

Beyond the ionosphere comes the exosphere. This is the outermost part of the Earth's atmospheric shell, and the density is so low that it corresponds to what we usually call a laboratory vacuum. The exosphere has no definite boundary, but gradually thins out until its density is no greater than that of the material in interplanetary space.

Temperature measurements of these outer layers proved to be somewhat puzzling, because there was a high-temperature region well above the densest part of the atmosphere. However, 'temperature' in its scientific sense does not correspond to what we normally term 'heat'. Temperature depends upon the speeds at which the atoms and molecules fly around. In the upper air there is a region where these velocities are very great, and so the 'temperature' is high; but there are so few of the particles that there is very little 'heat'. The situation may be compared with that of a red-hot poker and a firework sparkler. Each spark of the firework is white-hot, but the masses of the sparks are so slight that the firework may be held in the hand without causing injury – though it would be distinctly unwise to grip a red-hot poker.

The various layers in the upper atmosphere are of vital importance inasmuch as they block out most of the radiations coming from space; were it not so, life on Earth could never have developed. Visible light is only a very small part of the total range of wavelengths or 'electromagnetic spectrum'. It extends from a wavelength of 7600 ångströms for red light down to 3900 ångströms for violet. To the shortwave end of the visible band come ultra-violet, X-rays and gamma-rays; to the longwave end of red light come infra-red and then radio waves. Only visible light and some of the radio waves can pass through the screening layers, making up what are termed the 'optical' and 'radio' windows. To study the rest of the electromagnetic spectrum means sending up equipment to heights of over 70 miles or so – even above the highest clouds, the strange noctilucent clouds of the ionosphere, which may be due to dust associated with meteor trails. Balloons cannot fly high enough, so that the only answer is to use the rocket.

Rockets were developed by the Chinese long ago, but it is only in our own time that they have become powerful scientific research tools. The first liquid-propellant rocket was fired in 1926 by Robert Hutchings Goddard in

America. Before and during the war, in the period following 1933, rockets were developed by the Germans for military purposes; the V2 weapons sent against London in 1944 and 1945 led on to the space-rockets and artificial satellites of today, and the Space Age opened on 4 October 1957 with the launching of the first man-made moon, Russia's Sputnik 1. Yet the first real discovery was made in 1958 by the midget-sized American satellite, Explorer 1. Instruments carried in it detected zones of intense radiation surrounding the Earth, now known as the van Allen zones in honour of James van Allen, the scientist involved.

In 1959 came the first satellite to send back meteorological data: Explorer 7. Then, in 1960, came Tiros 1, which was purely a 'weather satellite'. It has been followed by many others, and by 1980 a world-wide satellite network had been established by using what are termed synchronous satellites, which enables us to study the behaviour of whole air-masses.

The first radio weather forecast had been broadcast by the BBC, from London, as early as 14 November 1922, and the first television synoptic chart was shown on 1 November 1936; but the development of weather satellites has made all the difference. So far as Britain is concerned, the main receiving station is at Lasham in Southern England, and all the information is sent through to the Meteorological Office at Bracknell in Berkshire, where the official forecasts are compiled and issued. Though we cannot yet pretend to have a complete understanding of the way in which the air-masses behave, we do at least know far more than would have seemed possible a few years ago.

Will we ever be able to control the weather? Various suggestions have been made, but so far rain-making experiments have not been very successful, and neither can we disperse clouds which have been all too liberal in producing rain or snow. Moreover, it is still difficult to make predictions accurate for more than a few days ahead at most, and not a great deal of reliance can be placed on the long-range forecasts issued by the various Meteorological Offices, since they depend more upon statistical analyses of the weather over past years than on the current situation. In the future we will undoubtedly be more successful; meanwhile we must accept the weather as it is – predictable in some areas of the world, wildly erratic in others. At least we know that we owe our very existence to the layers of atmosphere encircling the Earth. Without them, our world would be barren and lifeless.

The story of the Earth is a long one, and it is a story of continuous activity. Tectonic plates shift and jostle against each other; mountains are uplifted, only to be eroded away by wind and water; volcanoes burst forth, devastating wide areas; the oceans change in shape and depth; the climates alter, with warm periods and ice ages; even the magnetic field is variable. Yet all in all, we are fortunate in our home planet. In our experience it is unique in its ability to support advanced life-forms. No doubt other 'Earths' exist in the systems of other stars, but in the Sun's family we are alone.

Nearly one eighth of the earth's land surface receives under 10 inches of rain in a year.

The earth's equatorial circumference is almost 42 miles longer than its polar circumference.

Less snow falls in the Arctic lowlands than falls in the State of Virginia.

We are standing about 4000 miles above the centre of the earth.

As the earth revolves on its axis a point on the equator moves at over 1,000 mph.

A heavy object dropped into the water over the 6.77 mile-deep Mariana Trench, in the Pacific, would take over an hour to sink to the bottom.

The USSR is larger than the whole continent of South America.

More than 70 per cent of the earth's surface is covered by sea.

The continent of Asia, excluding Europe, covers over one quarter of the earth's land surface.

The volume of water in the river Amazon is greater than the combined total volume in the next eight largest rivers on earth.

If the world's twenty highest mountains were laid end to end they would stretch for 103 miles – almost the distance from London to Gloucester.

The hottest place in the world is Dallol in Ethiopia, with an annual average temperature of 94°F. The coldest place is Polus Nedostupnostif in Antarctica, where it is −72°F.

9

Astronomy

Early Theories

Originally, the Earth was thought to be flat and motionless, with the entire sky rotating round it once a day; when the Earth was found to be a globe, it was still regarded as occupying a central position, and not until less than five hundred years ago was it definitely relegated to the status of a planet moving round the Sun. Then the Sun itself was found to be an unimportant star, and in our own century it has been established that our star-system or Galaxy is one of many. Today we have landed men on the Moon, and sent automatic spacecraft into the depths of the Solar System. Even as I write [PM] the Americans have successfully launched their space-shuttle, the world's first reusable spacecraft. What man has not done, so far, however, is to establish the existence of life anywhere except on Earth.

In looking at the chronological development of astronomy and space-research we have to start with the Egyptians who, so far as we know, were among the very earliest of serious stargazers. It is said that Egypt was unified around 4000 BC by King Menes, who founded the city of Memphis and reigned for 62 years before being killed by a hippopotamus, the only monarch known to have died in this alarming manner. The Egyptians were certainly interested in the sky, but they made the initial mistake of supposing that the universe is shaped like a rectangular box, with a flat ceiling supported by four pillars at the cardinal points. In the Nile Delta it was even thought that the heavens were formed by the body of a goddess with the appropriate name of Nut, who was permanently suspended in what must have been an uncomfortable as well as an inelegant position. Egypt lay in the centre of the flat Earth, and was surrounded on all sides by a vast ocean. However, the Egyptians divided up the stars into groups or constellations, and they were excellent builders; there is no doubt that the famous Pyramids are astronomically aligned. The ancient Chinese were also sky-minded, and left records of phenomena such as comets and eclipses.

True astronomy, however, begins with the Greeks; the first great Greek philosopher was Thales of Miletus (c. 636–c. 546 BC). He knew that a solar eclipse is liable to be followed by another after a definite time-interval, and he is said to have made a successful prediction of the eclipse of 585 BC. At this moment a battle was in progress between the Lydians and the Medes, but both armies were so alarmed by the sudden darkness that they concluded a hasty peace.

The Greeks also divided up the stars into constellations. It is true that the origin of the constellations we know today is somewhat obscure, but at any rate they are different from those of the Egyptians or the Chinese; for instance, our Great Bear and Cassiopeia were represented by the Egyptians as a hippopotamus, while our Great Dog was their Cow. Not until much later was it realized that the stars are at very different distances from us, so that the constellations are nothing more than line-of-sight effects, and have no real significance. If we could observe the universe from a different vantage-point, the star-patterns would be quite unfamiliar.

The famous geometer, Pythagoras (fl. c. 540–c. 510 BC), discussed the movements of the planets. It had become known that there were five star-like points which behaved in a most unstarlike way, inasmuch as they wandered around the sky from one constellation to another; the word 'planet' means 'wanderer'. The five naked-eye planets are those we now call Mercury, Venus, Mars, Jupiter and Saturn. Pythagoras reasoned that they must be much closer than the stars, and probably he also believed that the Earth itself was a globe.

Anaxagoras of Clazomenae (born about 500 BC) maintained that the Moon shines by reflected sunlight, and that he knew the causes of lunar and solar eclipses. His insistence that the Sun was a red-hot stone larger than the Peloponnesus led to his being accused of impiety, and he was expelled from Athens; but for his friendship with Pericles, the ruler of the city, he might have fared even worse.

The first scientific proofs that the Earth is not flat came from Aristotle, the Greek philosopher (384–322 BC). For instance, he pointed out that when the Earth's shadow falls on the Moon, during a lunar eclipse, the shadow is curved. Also, the view of the sky alters according to one's position on the Earth; thus the brilliant star Canopus can be seen from Alexandria, but never rises from Athens. Phenomena of this sort could be explained only on the assumption that the Earth was a globe.

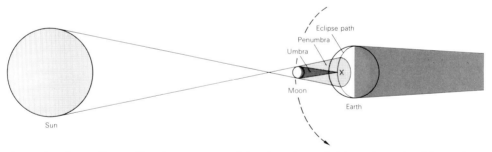

A total solar eclipse. The longest possible duration of this, when the Moon is at perigee and is eclipsed at noon over the equator, is 7 minutes 40 seconds

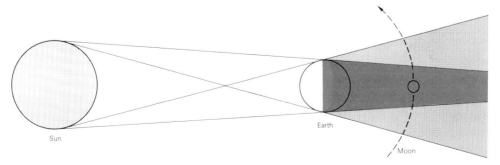

A lunar eclipse, simultaneously visible from all places on the dark side of the Earth

Aristarchus of Samos, one of the most far-sighted of all the Greeks, believed that the Earth moves round the Sun, not vice versa. However, he could give no positive proofs, and met with little support. Yet he also wrote a treatise about the relative distances of the Moon and Sun which was a great advance on any previous work.

The first measurement of the Earth's size was made about 250 BC by Eratosthenes of Cyrene, who was in charge of the great Alexandrian Library (afterwards destroyed, to the everlasting regret of all scholars). He found that at noon in midsummer the Sun was overhead at Alexandria, but 7 degrees from the vertical at the town of Syene (the modern Aswan), some way up the Nile. A full circle contains 360 degrees, and 7 is about 1/50 of 360, so that if the Earth was a globe its circumference must be fifty times the distance from Alexandria to Syene. His figure came remarkably close to the actual value and was far more accurate than the value adopted by Christopher Columbus on his voyage to the New World so long afterwards.

Perhaps the greatest astronomer of antiquity was Hipparchus of Nicaea (c. 190–120 BC). He compiled a good star-catalogue, and made the first systematic use of trigonometry. He also discovered precession, the apparent shift of the pole of the sky. Today, the north polar star is Polaris in Ursa Minor (the Little Bear); in Egyptian times it was the fainter star Thuban in Draco (the Dragon). The reason for the shift is that the Earth is not a perfect sphere; it bulges slightly at the equator, so that the equatorial diameter is about 26 miles greater than the diameter as measured through the poles. The Sun, Moon and planets pull on its bulge, and the Earth's axis of rotation 'wobbles' slowly, in the manner of a toppling gyroscope. The motion is very slight (it takes 26,000 years for the pole to describe a full circle in the sky), and the fact that Hipparchus was able to detect it is adequate testimony to his skill. In 12,000 years from now we will have a really brilliant north polar star, Vega in Lyra (the Lyre).

Bright stars in the ancient world invite a consideration of 'the Star of Bethlehem'. It is mentioned only once in the Bible, and nowhere else, so that our information is decidedly scanty. It has been attributed to Venus, to a conjunction or close approach of two planets, to a new star or nova, to a bright comet, and so on. Alas, none of these theories seems to be satisfactory. It is best to admit that we simply do not know, and probably never will.

The last great astronomer of classical times was Claudius Ptolemaeus (Ptolemy), of Alexandria. He is thought to have lived between about AD 120 and 180. His great work, the *Syntaxis*, has come down to us by way of its later Arab translation, and we know it by its Arab name of the *Almagest*. In it, Ptolemy summarized not only the astronomy of the time, but also many other branches of science, and he drew up the first map of the Earth which was based upon scientific principles rather than guesswork. He believed the Earth to be the centre of the universe, with the Moon, Sun and planets moving round it; beyond the planets came the sphere of the fixed stars. All paths or orbits had to

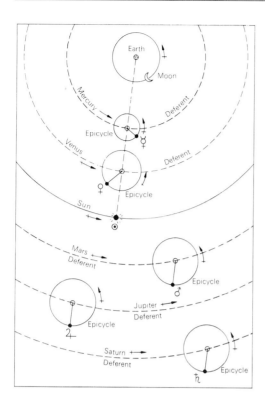

The Earth-centred, Ptolemaic system of astronomy

be circular, because the circle is the 'perfect' form, and nothing short of perfection can be allowed in the heavens. Yet Ptolemy was an excellent observer, and he knew that the planets do not move across the sky with absolute regularity; therefore he adopted a system according to which each planet moved in a small circle or epicycle, the centre of which (the deferent) itself moved round the Earth in a perfect circle. Various epicycles had to be introduced to account for the observed movements of the planets, and the whole system was hopelessly clumsy and artificial, but at least it fitted the facts as Ptolemy knew them, and his system – always known as the Ptolemaic, though Ptolemy himself did not invent it – remained 'official' for well over a thousand years after his death. Periodic attempts to discredit Ptolemy, and to claim that his star-catalogue was copied from that of Hipparchus, are not very convincing, and he merits his nickname of 'the Prince of Astronomers'.

The first known science fiction story was written by a Greek satirist, Lucian of Samosata, about AD 150. It was called the *True History* (*Vera Historia*), because, in Lucian's own words, it was made up of nothing but lies from beginning to end. It described a voyage to the Moon, undertaken involuntarily by some sailors whose ship was caught up in a waterspout and hurled moonward. On arrival, the sailors found that they had arrived at an opportune moment, because the King of the Moon was about to wage war against the King of the Sun with regard to who should have first rights on Venus (the planet, not the goddess). At least it was already certain that the Moon has no light of its own, and Pliny, in his essay *On the Face in the Orb of the Moon* (around AD 80) had maintained that it was 'earthy', with mountains and ravines.

It was around the year AD 570 that the first clear distinction was drawn between astronomy and astrology, by Isidorus, Bishop of Seville. It is remarkable that even today there are some people who still confuse the two. In fact they are quite unrelated. Astronomy is an exact science, while astrology tries to link human fortunes and characters with the apparent positions of the Sun, Moon and planets against the constellation patterns. This is quite irrational; the planets are much closer than the stars, and to say that a planet is 'in' a constellation is as absurd as holding up your finger against a cloud background and claiming that your finger is 'in' the cloud. Moreover, the constellation patterns are both artificial and meaningless. To give just one example: Pisces, the Fishes, is said to be a 'watery' sign – yet it is marked merely by some faint stars which are unrelated to each other, and do not resemble the outline of fishes or anything else. The best that can be said of astrology, ancient or modern, is that it is fairly harmless so long as it is confined to seaside piers and circus tents.

In 813 a major astronomical observatory was set up at Baghdad by Al-Mamun, son of Harun al-Rashid, of *Arabian Nights* fame. It was quite unlike a modern observatory, and telescopes lay far in the future, but it contained measuring instruments as well as a fine library.

It was the Arabs, in fact, who were responsible for the rebirth of astronomy after the 'Dark Ages' following the end of Classical times. They translated Ptolemy's great book into Arabic, and drew up star-catalogues which were far better than those of the Greeks. True, they were concerned largely with astrology, for which they needed to know the star-positions as well as the movements of the planets, but they were excellent observers. The last famous astronomer of the Arab school was a Mongol, Ulugh Beigh, grandson of the oriental conqueror, Tamerlane. Ulugh Beigh set up a magnificent observatory at his capital, Samarkand, and equipped it with the best instruments of the time. The observatory was complete by 1433. Unfortunately Ulugh Beigh was a firm believer in astrology; he cast the horoscope of his eldest son Abdallatif, and found to his dismay that the boy was destined to kill him. He therefore dismissed him from Court and sent him into exile. Abdallatif was not to be set aside; he raised a rebellion, and had Ulugh Beigh murdered. That was one astrological prediction which came true!

During these 'Arab times' two brilliant exploding stars or supernovae appeared, one in 1006 in the southern constellation of Lupus (the Wolf) and the other in 1054 in Taurus (the Bull). The Taurus star has produced the gas-patch which we now know as the Crab Nebula, about which more will be said below.

The Age of Discoveries

In the period of the late Renaissance in the West, the year 1543 saw the publication of a book by a Polish canon, Mikołaj Kopernik (usually known by his Latinized name of Copernicus), which caused a complete revolution in human thought. Copernicus was born at Toruń, on the River Vistula in 1473. He studied in Poland and then in Italy, after which he returned home and became Canon of Frombork, one of the remoter areas of the country. He was a politician, a medical practitioner and an administrator, but his main interest was astronomy, and he became dissatisfied with Ptolemy's theory of the universe. He saw that many of the complexities could be removed by the simple expedient of removing the Earth from its proud central position and putting the Sun there instead. He realized that this would be regarded as heresy, and he had no wish to become involved in a clash with the Church; accordingly he deferred publication of his book, *De Revolutionibus Orbium Cælestium* (on the Revolutions of the Celestial Bodies) until he was dying.

It must be admitted that he made many errors, and his final system was faulty; in particular he retained perfectly circular orbits, and was even reduced to bringing back epicycles. But he had taken the essential step, and the 'Copernican system' became a serious rival to the Ptolemaic.

His misgivings had been well-founded. The Church was fiercely hostile to the new ideas, and Martin Luther described Copernicus as 'a fool' who wanted to turn the universe upside-down. Persecutions followed; in 1600 Giordano

Copernicus (1473–1543), the Polish astronomer, who challenged the Ptolemaic theory

Bruno was burned at the stake in Rome, one of his crimes being that he persisted in teaching Copernicanism. Not for well over a century after Copernicus's death was the Earth-centred system of the universe finally discarded.

In 1572 a cataclysmic stellar outburst became bright enough to be visible with the naked eye in broad daylight, and lasted for months before fading back to invisibility. It was a supernova, in which a massive star literally blew itself to pieces. It was studied by Tycho Brahe, an eccentric Danish nobleman, who thereafter drew up much the best star-catalogue of pre-telescopic times, even though he could never bring himself to believe that the Earth could be in motion round the Sun.

Tycho was nothing if not colourful. In his infancy he was kidnapped by his uncle, who brought him up; as a student he had part of his nose sliced off in a duel, and made himself a new one out of gold, silver and wax. When he set up his observatory at Uraniborg, 'the City of the Heavens', on the Baltic island of Hven, he equipped it not only with scientific instruments, but also with a prison, in which he incarcerated those tenants who refused to pay their rents. His retinue included a pet dwarf, who used to entertain his visitors (one of whom was James, King of Scotland, afterwards James I of England). Finally Tycho quarrelled with the Danish court, and retired to Bohemia, where he died in 1601. His observations, both of the stars and of the movements of the planets (particularly Mars) came into the possession of his last assistant, a young German named Johannes Kepler, who used them well.

Kepler had implicit faith in the accuracy of Tycho's observations, and when studying the motions of Mars he realized that no circular orbit would fit the facts. After years of work he found the answer. The planets did indeed move round the Sun, but they travelled in ellipses, not in circles. He was then able to draw up his Laws of Planetary Motion, of which the first two were published in 1609 and the third in 1618. Kepler also wrote a story, the *Somnium* (Dream), describing a voyage to the Moon; his hero was transported there by obliging demons. However, there was a serious side to the story, and Kepler's description of the lunar world was very much in accord with the science of the time.

While Kepler was at work in Germany, telescopes were invented in Holland. The year was 1608 and while they may have been known earlier, there is no positive proof. News of the invention reached Galileo Galilei, Professor of Mathematics at the Italian university of Padua, who made a telescope for himself and turned it skywards. He was not the first to do so (he had been anticipated by, among others, Thomas Harriott, one-time tutor to Sir Walter Raleigh), but he was the first great telescopic observer, and in a few months early in 1610 he made a series of spectacular discoveries. The Moon was mountainous and cratered; the planet Venus showed lunar-type phases, which according to the Ptolemaic system was impossible; the giant planet Jupiter was attended by four moons or satellites; Saturn was curiously-shaped (though

Galileo Galilei (1564–1642), whose astronomical discoveries led him to support the Copernican system of the universe

Galileo was unable to see a distinct ring); and the Milky Way was made up of stars. Slightly later, Galileo also observed spots on the surface of the Sun.

Galileo published his observations, and used them to support the Copernican system of the universe. Unfortunately he was not tactful and he incurred the ire of the Church. The Pope was infuriated (he believed that Galileo had ridiculed him in his major book, the *Dialogues*, published in 1632), and the luckless scientist was summoned to Rome to stand trial for heresy. He saved himself only by a public recantation of the 'false theory' that the Earth moves round the Sun, after which he was kept under close guard until the end of his life in 1642.

Isaac Newton was born at Woolsthorpe, in Lincolnshire in 1642, the year of Galileo's death. He went to Cambridge University, but in 1665 the University was temporarily closed because of the danger from Plague, and Newton spent some time in his home village, where he made discoveries of fundamental importance. In particular, he drew up the laws of universal gravitation. According to a story which is probably true, he saw an apple fall from a tree, and realized that the force pulling on the apple was the same as that which keeps the Moon in its path – and, for that matter, keeps the Earth in its orbit round the Sun. His greatest work, known generally as the *Principia*, was published in 1687, and has been described as the greatest mental effort ever made by one man. It certainly sounded the death-knell of the Ptolemaic system.

Newton also split up the Sun's light by means of a glass prism, and found that it was composed of all the colours of the rainbow, from violet to red; this was the true beginning of the science we now call spectroscopy. In or around 1668 he built the first reflecting telescope, which collects its light by means of a curved mirror instead of a lens. It was a tiny thing, with a mirror only one inch in diameter, but has led on to the giant reflectors of today, such as the 200-inch Hale telescope at Palomar in America, and the Russian 236–inch telescope which has been set up in the Caucasus Mountains.

By the latter part of the seventeenth century telescopes had been much improved, and they made it possible to compile much more accurate star-catalogues. England has always been a seafaring nation, and at that time sailors out of sight of land had great difficulty in finding out just where they were – with results which were sometimes disastrous. The best method of position-fixing involved observations of the celestial bodies. The best available star-catalogue, Tycho's, was pre-telescopic, and not sufficiently accurate; so King Charles II ordered the setting-up of a new observatory, so that a better catalogue could be produced. (Typically, Charles paid the initial cost by selling 'old and decayed gunpowder' to the French!) Greenwich Observatory was established in 1675; the original buildings were designed by Sir Christopher Wren, who had been Professor of Astronomy at Oxford before turning to

The Royal Observatory, Greenwich, in the Rev John Flamsteed's time (1646–1719), showing observers with quadrant and telescope

architecture. The Rev John Flamsteed was put in charge, afterwards becoming the first Astronomer Royal. His conditions of employment were not ideal. He had to provide his own telescopes, and as assistant he had only a 'silly, surly labourer' who rejoiced in the name of Cuthbert, and who was more interested in the local taverns than in the stars. The catalogue was eventually completed, though it was not published until 1725, after Flamsteed's death. Greenwich has always remained the 'timekeeping centre' of the world, and the zero for longitudes passes through the Observatory, though in the 1950s the main instruments were removed to a new site at Herstmonceux in Sussex, away from the glare of London lights.

Of all celestial bodies, comets are those which have caused the most alarm over the ages. They may become brilliant, with long tails stretching across the sky, and so have often been regarded as forerunners of disaster. The Roman author, Pliny, who was killed during the eruption of Vesuvius in AD 79, went so far as to write that 'we have in the war between Caesar and Pompey an example of the terrible effects which follow the apparition of a comet . . . that fearful star which overthrows the powers of the Earth, showing its terrible locks'. As late as 1681, when a comet with a long tail was seen, the Town Council of Baden in Switzerland ordered that 'all are to attend Mass and Sermon every Sunday and Feast Day, not leaving the church before the sermon, or staying away without good reason; all must abstain from playing or dancing; none must wear unseemly clothing, not swear nor curse'. Comets were regarded as intruders into the Sun's system, and their nature was unknown.

In 1682 a comet was observed by Edmond Halley, who afterwards succeeded Flamsteed as Astronomer Royal. Halley calculated its path, and by 1705 he had found that it moved in much the same way as comets seen previously in 1607 and 1531. He believed that the three comets were one and the same, and that the comet moved round the Sun in a period of 76 years, so that it

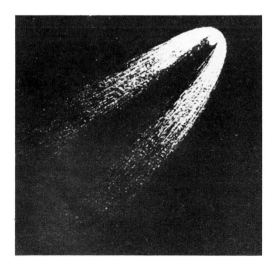

A photograph of a Comet.

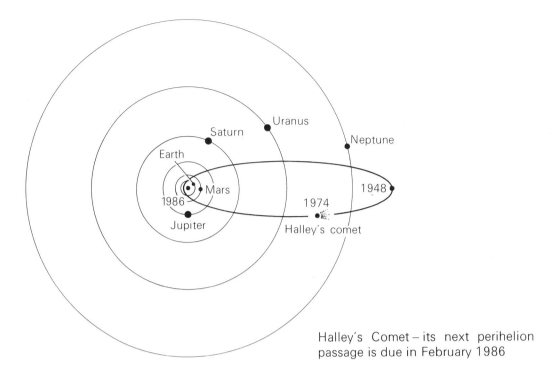

Halley's Comet – its next perihelion
passage is due in February 1986

would return once more in 1758. By then Halley was long dead, but the comet
did indeed come back; it was observed on Christmas Night 1758 by the German
amateur astronomer Palitzsch. Since then it has returned in 1835 and 1910, and
we may confidently expect it once more in 1986. It has a long history; it has been
traced back well before the Christian era, and it was also visible in 1066, just
before the Battle of Hastings. A scene in the Bayeux Tapestry shows the comet
high in the sky, with King Harold tottering on his throne. (*En passant*: when
Halley's Comet last returned, in 1910, an enterprising gentleman in the United
States made a large sum of money by selling was he called anti-comet pills,
though it is not clear just what they were meant to do!)

A century later than Halley's discovery we come to another momentous
year. Probably the year 1781 will always be best remembered because of the
discovery of a new planet by a then-unknown Hanoverian musician, William
Herschel, who had come to England and had become organist at the Octagon
Chapel in the city of Bath. He became interested in astronomy, and set to work
to make himself telescopes which would be powerful enough for his 'reviews of
the heavens', with the ultimate aim of finding out the distances and distribution
of the stars in our Milky Way system. After two hundred initial failures he was
able to make reflecting telescopes which were the best of their time, and when
using one of these, on 13 March 1781, he made the discovery by which he
became famous almost overnight.

He was examining parts of the constellation of Gemini, the Twins, when he came across an object which was certainly not a star. It showed a small disk, which no star can do, and it moved against the starry background – not visibly, but enough to show a distinct shift in position after only a few hours. Herschel believed it to be a comet, which would be interesting but not sensational (faint telescopic comets are common enough). However, as soon as its orbit was calculated, its true nature became clear. The object was a new planet, moving well beyond the orbit of Saturn, the outermost of the planets known in ancient times.

It was already known that the Solar System is divided into two main parts. There are four inner planets, Mercury, Venus, the Earth and Mars, which are relatively small, with solid surfaces; then comes a wide gap, and then there are the giants, of which Jupiter and Saturn are bright, naked-eye objects. The giants are quite unlike the Earth; they have gaseous surfaces, and are now believed to be mainly liquid inside, with comparatively small solid cores. Nobody had given serious thought to the possibility of a new planet still further out, but there it was, and it too was a giant, with a diameter of around 30,000 miles (rather less than half that of Saturn). It was named Uranus, in honour of the original ruler of Olympus. Subsequently Herschel discovered two of its satellites; three more have been found since.

Sir William Herschel, the discoverer in 1781 of the planet Uranus

That discovery altered Herschel's whole life. He was given a pension of £200 a year by King George III, and was able to give up music as a career, devoting all his time to astronomy. With his sister, Caroline, as assistant, he undertook a programme of observation which called for the utmost skill as well as dedication. He also built larger telescopes; the greatest of all had a mirror 49 inches across, though admittedly it was clumsy to use and never really came up to expectations.

Over the years, Herschel explored the whole of the sky visible from England. He discovered hundreds of double stars, star-clusters and the hazy patches known as nebulae; in 1803 he proved that many of the double stars are 'binary' systems, in which the components are genuinely associated and are moving round their common centre of gravity, much as the two bells of a dumb-bell will do when twisted by the arm joining them; and he was the first to draw up a reasonably good picture of the shape of the star-system or Galaxy, which he found to be a flattened system. This explains the appearance of the Milky Way; when we look along the main plane of the system we see many stars in almost the same direction, giving a false impression of crowding in a definite band. Herschel also split up the Sun's light by using a prism, as Newton had done before him, and found 'heating' effects beyond the red or long-wave end of the spectrum; he had discovered what we now call infra-red radiation. As an observer, Herschel has probably never been equalled. Yet some of his ideas sound curious today; to the end of his life, in 1822, he believed that the Moon must be inhabited, and he also thought that there were inhabitants in a dark, cool region beneath the glowing clouds of the Sun.

In the very same year as Herschel's discovery of Uranus, the first major catalogue of star-clusters and nebulae was drawn up by the French observer, Charles Messier. Messier was interested mainly in comets, and searched the skies for them persistently; but he found himself misled by hazy patches which were non-cometary, and were either star-clusters or nebulae. Finally he decided to list them, as 'objects to avoid', and he catalogued more than one hundred of them. Ironically, it is for this list that we remember him today; most people have forgotten his cometary discoveries. We still use his numbers; thus the Great Nebula in Orion is Messier 42 (M.42), the Andromeda Spiral is M.31, and the Crab Nebula, the remnant of the 1054 supernova, is M.1.

The catalogue contains objects of various kinds. There are open star-clusters, such as the Pleiades or Seven Sisters (M.45); gaseous nebulae such as M.42; globular clusters, such as M.13 in the constellation of Hercules; and objects which we now know to be independent galaxies, so far away that their light, travelling at 186,000 miles per second, takes millions of years to reach us. The best-known of these galaxies is the Andromeda Spiral, M.31, which is just visible with the naked eye on a dark, clear night.

By the end of the eighteenth century it has been firmly established that the stars are suns, and that our Sun is nothing more than a run-of-the-mill star. The planets are related to the Sun – but how were they formed? Pierre Simon de Laplace produced what was called the Nebular Hypothesis. He believed, correctly, that the Sun condensed out of a cloud of dust and gas in space. He went on to suggest that as the youthful Sun shrank, under the influence of gravitation, it threw off rings of material, each ring subsequently condensing into a planet.

The original Nebular Hypothesis could not withstand the attacks of mathematicians, and was discarded. Other theories replaced it; for instance, it was suggested that the planets might have been pulled off the Sun by the action of a passing star. This idea was championed in the 1920s and 1930s by the famous English astronomer Sir James Jeans, but it, too, was later rejected on mathematical grounds. Current theories assume that the planets built up by accretion from a cloud of material once associated with the Sun; the process is not the same as that proposed by Laplace, but there are points of similarity. We do at least now know the age of the Earth and Moon, both of which came into existence between 4,500,000,000 and 5,000,000,000 years ago. Presumably the other planets were born at the same time.

Yet another member of the Solar System was discovered in 1801. This was Ceres, first of the minor planets or asteroids. In 1772 Johann Elert Bode, in Germany, drew attention to a strange mathematical relationship linking the distances of the planets from the Sun; it is always called Bode's Law, though actually it was discovered by Titius of Wittemberg. Whether or not it has any real significance is highly doubtful, but extra credence was given to it when Uranus, discovered in 1781, was found to fit well into the general pattern. Bode's Law predicted an extra planet between the orbits of Mars and Jupiter, and in 1800 there was a meeting of astronomers at Lilienthal near Bremen, to investigate the problem. The 'Celestial Police', as they called themselves, decided to conduct a systematic search for the expected planet. Ironically, they were forestalled; on 1 January 1801 – the first day of the new century – Ceres was discovered from Palermo by G.Piazzi, who had been drawing up a new star catalogue.

Ceres orbited the Sun at the correct 'Bode distance', but it proved to be very small, with a diameter of less than 700 miles – much smaller than the Moon. The Celestial Police continued their efforts, and within a decade three more small worlds had been found: Pallas, Juno and Vesta. No more seemed to be forthcoming, and the search was given up, only for it to be later started again by another amateur, Hencke (postmaster of the village of Driessen), who hunted patiently for fifteen years before discovering Asteroid No. 5, Astræa, in 1845. Several thousands of asteroids are now known, but Ceres remains much the largest member of the swarm, and only Vesta is ever visible with the naked eye. It is likely that the asteroids represent material 'left over', so to speak, when the main planets were formed. Very few are over 150 miles in diameter, and many are mere chunks of rocky material. Even if lumped together, they would not make up one body as massive as the Moon. Needless to say, no asteroid can retain any trace of atmosphere.

Some asteroids move away from the main swarm, and may approach the Earth. The most famous of these is Eros, discovered in 1898, which can come within 16,000,000 miles of us, as last happened in 1975. It is an irregularly-shaped body, 18 miles wide and only 9 broad, so that it has been likened to a cosmic sausage. The present holder of the 'approach record' is Hermes, only about a mile in diameter, which by-passed the Earth in 1937 at a distance of only 485,000 miles – less than twice the distance of the Moon. (The London *Daily Mirror* published a sensational headline: 'World Disaster Missed by Five Hours as Tiny Planet Hurtles Past!') One asteroid, the dwarf Icarus, has an orbit which carries it inside that of Mercury; on the other hand the Trojan asteroids move in the same path as Jupiter, about 483,000,000 miles from the Sun, and Asteroid No. 944, Hidalgo, travels out almost as far as Saturn. There is also Chiron, discovered by Charles Kowal in 1977, which moves between the orbits of Saturn and Uranus. It may be as much as 400 miles across, but its nature is rather uncertain.

Most people are familiar with shooting-stars or meteors. A meteor is a small body, usually smaller than a pin's head, moving round the Sun; if it dashes into the upper air, at a height of less than about 120 miles above the ground, it is heated by friction against the air-particles, and destroys itself in the streak of radiance which we call a shooting-star. Many meteors move round the Sun in shoals, and each time the Earth passes through a shoal we see a shower of shooting-stars. The most reliable yearly shower is that of August, known as the Perseids, because the meteors seem to come from the direction of the constellation Perseus, but now and then the November meteors, the Leonids (from the constellation Leo, the Lion) may produce really spectacular displays. This happened in 1799, and was described by the famous explorer Humboldt; it seems that the meteors rained down as thickly as snowflakes, in a display lasting several hours. Other brilliant Leonid displays were seen in 1833, 1866 and 1966. A few Leonid meteors are seen every year, but for a major display we shall have to wait until the Earth passes through the thickest part of the swarm.

Meteor shoals move in the same paths as comets, and it may be said that meteors are simply cometary débris. They end their journey to the ground in the form of very fine 'dust'. There are also the so-called sporadic meteors, which do not belong to showers, and may appear from any direction at any moment.

The Earth may also encounter larger bodies, which survive the complete drop to the ground and are then known as meteorites. For many years the existence of 'stones from the sky' was doubted, but in 1803 a whole shower of meteorites fell on the French village of L'Aigle; they were investigated by a well-known astronomer, J.B.Biot, who proved without doubt that they did indeed come from space. Many older specimens have been found; for instance,

Space bombardment – objects that penetrate our atmosphere

Weight of objects before entry into the Earth's atmosphere	Approximate average frequency
space 'dust'	over a million tons filters down to the surface of the Earth each year
meteors only visible with telescopes (burnt up in the atmosphere)	over 1,000,000,000 every day
meteors visible to the naked eye (burnt up in the atmosphere)	over 500,000 every day
small meteorite c. 10 lb (only a few ounces reach the ground)	3 or 4 every day, but very irregular, often arriving in swarms composed of considerable numbers
5 tons (not more than about 1000 lb reaches the ground)	1 every month
50 tons	1 every 30 years
250 tons	1 every 150 years
50,000 tons	1 every 100,000 years
small planets (asteroids) with diameters measurable in miles	1 every 1–50 million years.

the Sacred Stone in the city of Mecca is certainly a meteorite.

Some meteorites may produce craters. There is no doubt, for instance, that the Arizona Crater in the United States, nearly a mile wide, was produced by a meteoritic fall about 22,000 years ago. Fortunately, major falls are rare, and during the present century there have been only two. In 1908 a missile hit the Tunguska region of Siberia, and blew pine-trees flat for a wide area; luckily there were no inhabitants. No crater was produced, and it is probable that the object was the icy nucleus of a small comet. In 1947 there was another impact, this time in the Vladivostok area of Siberia, which scattered meteoritic fragments over a wide area. Minor falls are comparatively common, and as a result most museums have meteorite collections.

It is important to remember that a meteorite is not simply a large meteor. The two are quite distinct, and meteorites are more nearly related to the minor planets or asteroids; it may well be that there is no real difference between a large meteorite and a small asteroid. It is also worth noting that there is no known case of anyone having been killed by a plunging meteorite.

But we are running ahead of the story. In the context of astronomical discoveries we have noted that both Newton and Herschel split up the Sun's light by means of a prism, and studied the rainbow spectrum. In 1801 an Englishman, W.H.Wollaston, repeated the experiment, using a slit to admit the sunlight, and detected dark lines across the rainbow; but he believed them to be merely the demarcation points between the various colours, and so missed the chance of making a major discovery.

The real 'father of solar spectroscopy' was Joseph von Fraunhofer, born at Straubing in Bavaria in 1787. Both his parents died when he was a boy, and he was apprenticed to a glassmaker; one day the tumbledown house in which he was living collapsed, and he was rescued by no less a person than the Elector of Bavaria, who was driving past. The Elector befriended Fraunhofer, who became the leading optical worker of his time.

Examining the solar spectrum, Fraunhofer realized that the dark lines crossing it were permanent in both position and intensity. He mapped them, and believed them to be extremely significant. Unfortunately he died at the early age of 39, and the correct interpretation of the 'Fraunhofer lines' was left to two of his countrymen, Kirchhoff and Bunsen, in 1859.

Kirchhoff, who played the major role in the work, found that each line was due to some particular element or group of elements, and could not be duplicated by any other substance. It therefore became possible to tell which elements were present in the Sun. For instance, there are two prominent dark lines in the yellow part of the rainbow band; these are trademarks of the element sodium, and sodium must consequently exist in the Sun. Iron alone produced thousands of spectral lines.

Kirchhoff then drew up his Laws of Spectroscopy. An incandescent solid, liquid or gas at high pressure will produce a rainbow or continuous spectrum, while a gas under lower pressure yields an emission spectrum of isolated bright lines. With the Sun, the bright surface of photosphere produces a continuous band. Surrounding the photosphere are layers of gases at lower pressures; on their own, these gases would yield bright lines, but against the background rainbow the lines are 'reversed', and appear as dark or absorption lines. By now, over 70 of the naturally-occurring elements have been identified in the Sun. The most plentiful substance is hydrogen; next in abundance comes helium. These are the two lightest elements. In the universe, hydrogen atoms are more numerous than the atoms of all other elements put together.

Herschel, we have seen, had made unsuccessful attempts to measure the distances of the stars. In 1838 the problem was then attacked by Friedrich Bessel, of Königsberg, using the same method. If a comparatively nearby star is observed at an interval of six months, it will be seen from opposite sides of the Earth's orbit, and will appear to shift slightly against the background of more remote stars. Bessel selected a dim naked-eye star, 61 Cygni in the Swan, because it was a wide binary and showed appreciable proper or individual motion. He found that its parallax was about 0.3 seconds of arc, corresponding to a distance of about 11 light-years. Soon afterwards the Scottish astronomer, Thomas Henderson, announced a greater parallax for the brilliant southern star Alpha Centauri. The faintest member of the triple Alpha Centauri system,

(a) The brightest stars

Name	RA (2000) (h)	(min)	Dec. (°)	(')	Sp		V	B–V	d l.y.	PM (")	RV (km/s)	M_V
Sun					G2	V	−26·7	+0·63				+4·8
Sirius	06	45	−16	43	A1	V	−1·42	0·00	8·6	1·32	−8	+1·4
Canopus	06	24	−52	41	F0	II	−0·72	+0·16	185	0·02	+21	−4·5
Alpha Centauri	14	40	−60	50	G2	V	−0·28	+0·72	4·3	3·68	−24	+4·7
Arcturus	14	16	+19	11	K2	III	−0·06	+1·24	36	2·28	−5	−0·3
Vega	18	37	+38	47	A0	V	0·00	0·00	26	0·34	−14	+0·5
Capella	05	17	+46	00	G8	III	+0·06	+0·81	32	0·44	+30	+0·1
Rigel	05	15	−08	12	B8	Ia	+0·18	−0·03	680	0·00	+21	−6·4
Procyon	07	39	+05	14	F5	IV	+0·36	+0·42	11	1·25	−3	+2·7
Achernar	01	38	−57	15	B5	IV	+0·48	−0·16	140	0·10	+19	−2·6
Beta Centauri	14	04	−60	22	B1	II	+0·62	−0·24	180	0·04	−11	−3·1
Betelgeuse	05	55	+07	24	M2	Iab	+0·7	+1·86	170	0·03	+21	−2·9
Alpha Crucis	12	27	−63	06	B1		+0·76	−0·25	200	0·04		−3·2
Altair	19	51	+08	52	A7	V	+0·78	+0·22	16	0·66	−26	+2·3
Aldebaran	04	36	+16	30	K5	III	+0·8	+1·55	68	0·20	+54	−0·8
Antares	16	29	−26	26	M1	I	+0·9	+1·83	590	0·03	−3	−5·4
Spica	13	25	−11	09	B1	V	+0·98	−0·23	160	0·05	+1	−2·4
Pollux	07	45	+28	01	K0	III	+1·13	+1·00	35	0·62	+3	+1·0
Fomalhaut	22	58	−29	37	A2	V	+1·16	+0·09	22	0·37	+6	+2·0
Deneb	20	41	+45	16	A2	Ia	+1·25	+0·09	530	0·00	−5	−3·5
Beta Crucis	12	48	−59	42	B0	IV	+1·25	−0·24	290	0·05	+20	−4·8
Regulus	10	08	+11	58	B7	V	+1·35	−0·12	84	0·25	+4	−0·7

(b) The nearest stars

Name	RA (2000) (h)	(min)	Dec. (°)	(')	Sp		V	B–V	d l.y.	PM (")	RV (km/s)	M_V
Sun					G2	V	−26·7					+4·8
Alpha Centauri A	14	40	−60	50	G2	V	+0·1		4·3	3·68		+4·5
Alpha Centauri B	14	40	−60	50	K5	V	+1·5		4·3	3·68		+5·9
Proxima Centauri	14	29	−62	41	M5e	V	+11		4·3	3·68		+15·4
Barnard's Star	17	58	+04	33	M5	V	+9·5		5·9	10·30		+13·2
LFT 750	10	57	+07	03	M6e	V	+13·5		7·6	4·84		+16·7
LFT 756	11	04	+36	02	M2	V	+7·5		8·1	4·78		+10·5
Sirius A	06	45	−16	43	A1	V	−1·5		8·6	1·32		+1·4
Sirius B	06	45	−16	43	wd		+7·2		8·6	1·32		+10·1
UV Ceti A	01	38	−17	58	M6e	V	+12·5		8·9	3·35		+15·3
UV Ceti B	01	38	−17	58	M6e	V	+13·0		8·9	3·35		+15·8
LFT 1437	18	50	−23	50	M5e	V	+10·6		9·4	0·74		+13·3

A star's apparent magnitude is a measure of its brightness in the sky, and works in the same way as a golfer's handicap, with the more brilliant performers having the lower values. Bright stars are of magnitude 1, or even, in a few cases, zero or minus values; the faintest stars normally visible with the naked eye are of magnitude 6, and modern telescopes can reach down below magnitude 20. Sirius, the brightest star, has an apparent magnitude of −1.42; of the planets, Venus can reach −4.

Note that apparent magnitude is no certain clue as to a star's real luminosity, since the stars are at very different distances from us. Sirius, 8.6 light-years away, is – as we have noted – 26 times as luminous as the Sun. Rigel in Orion is of apparent magnitude +0.18, much fainter than Sirius; but it is much further away, and is far more powerful, with a luminosity of about 60,000 times that of the Sun.

The successive columns above give the star's name; its right ascension (*RA*) and declination (*Dec.*) for AD 2000 which give its position in the sky; its visual magnitude (*V*); its colour (*B–V*); its distance (*d*) in light years (*L.Y.*); its proper motion in seconds of arc per year (*PM*); its radial velocity in kilometres per second (*RV*); and its absolute visual magnitude (*Mv*). Many of the quantities given in table 1 are not known exactly, being subject to 'observational uncertainty' even for the brightest stars.

It is not possible to give an exact answer to the question which is frequently asked, 'How many stars in the Galaxy?' All that can be said is that the estimated mass of the Galaxy is 200,000 million times that of the Sun. If most of this is condensed into stars, and if the greater number of these are like the stars near the Sun with an average mass of only 0.2 that of the Sun, the number of stars in the Galaxy may well be of the order of a million million.

Proxima, is now known to be 4.3 light years away, corresponding to about 24,000,000,000,000 miles; it is the nearest star beyond the Sun.

The method is reliable for close stars, but becomes useless beyond distances of a few hundred light-years, because the parallax shifts become swamped by errors of observation. Less direct methods have to be used, generally involving an estimate of the star's real luminosity from studies of its spectrum; the distances are 8.6 light-years (Sirius), 27 light-years (Vega), 68 light-years (Aldebaran), 520 light-years (Antares) and about 900 light-years (Rigel).

Distances like these almost seem beyond comprehension. The Moon is much the closest natural body in the sky. Its mean distance from us is less than 250,000 miles, so that surface details are easy to make out. Early maps of the moon were produced by Thomas Harriott and by Galileo. A better map was produced by the Danzig astronomer, Hevelius, in 1645 (unfortunately the original copperplate has not survived: apparently it was melted down after Hevelius' death and made into a teapot). Then, in 1651, the Jesuit astronomer Riccioli drew another map, and named the chief craters after famous people, generally – though not always – astronomers. The system has survived, though of course it has been extended. Copernicus, Newton, Tycho Brahe and others have their lunar craters; and, rather naturally, Riccioli named a large and important walled plain after himself.

The Moon's surface is very rough. There are the great grey plains still miscalled seas even though there has never been any water in them; there are mountains, valleys, and of course the all-important craters, which are found

Landing on the Moon

The path of a rocket to the Moon, or any other planet, is not an easy or direct one. In order for a satellite to orbit the Earth it must travel at almost exactly 18,000 mph. If slower that this it will fall; faster, it will shoot off into space. But to hit the Moon, apart from the complexities of the rocket and launching, there are many natural physical phenomena to consider.

The rocket, soon after launching, must reach a minimum speed of 24,820 mph in order to escape from the Earth's gravity and then vary its speed so as to reach the Moon at about 740 mph. Whilst the rocket is travelling at this enormous speed the Moon is orbiting the Earth at an average speed of 2,270 mph. This speed varies, sometimes more, sometimes less, and the path of the Moon is elliptical with a difference of 31,247 miles between its nearest and farthest approaches to the Earth. For the last 20,000 miles or so of its journey the rocket's speed must be carefully controlled as it becomes more strongly affected by the gravitational pull of the Moon.

Some idea of the precision required in such a project may be gathered from the fact that a variation of less than 1° from its planned route would cause the rocket to arrive at the estimated position of the Moon perhaps 7 hours too soon or too late. A variation of maximum speed of only 1 mph would result in the Moon being missed by about 1,000 miles.

everywhere. These craters range from huge walled plains, over 150 miles in diameter, down to tiny pits. Even today we are not certain how they were formed; some astronomers believe them to be of internal (volcanic) origin, while others attribute them to the impacts of meteorites. No doubt both types of craters exist.

The first really good lunar map was the work of two Germans, Wilhelm Beer and Johann von Mädler. Using the $3\frac{3}{4}$ inch Fraunhofer refractor at Beer's private observatory, near Berlin, they produced a chart which was a master-piece of careful observation. It was published in 1838, and remained the best for over forty years. Beer and Mädler knew that the Moon has virtually no atmosphere, and they believed – correctly – that the surface must be to all intents and purposes changeless.

In 1840 J.W.Draper took the first photographs of the Moon – the first use of photography in astronomy. As techniques improved, photography began to supersede visual observation, and within a hundred years of Draper's pioneer attempts almost all astronomical researches were carried out photographically. Today, photography is itself being superseded by electronic devices.

The third Earl of Rosse, Irish nobleman and amateur astronomer, built a reflector in 1845 with a mirror 72 inches in diameter – far larger than any previous telescope. It was cumbersome, since it was mounted between massive stone walls and could reach only a limited area of the sky, but Lord Rosse used it to study the 'starry nebulae', and made a discovery of vital importance. Some of the objects were spiral in form, like catherine-wheels; among these is the Great Nebula in Andromeda, M.31, though it is placed at a narrow angle to us and the full beauty of the spiral is lost. Other nebulae, however, could not be resolved into stars, and in 1864 the English spectroscopist William Huggins showed that they are gaseous in nature. It is now known that the gaseous nebulae are members of our Galaxy, while the spirals are independent galaxies in their own right. (Note, however, that by no means all external galaxies are spiral.) Lord Rosse's reflector, set up at Birr Castle in Central Ireland, remained the largest in the world until 1917, when the 100-inch telescope at Mount Wilson in California was completed.

A year after Lord Rosse built his then vast telescope, the planet Neptune was discovered. This was a triumph of mathematical astronomy. Uranus, discovered by Herschel in 1781, was not moving as it had been expected to do; something was pulling it out of position. Two mathematicians, J.C.Adams in England and U.J.J. Le Verrier in France, realized that the perturbing body must be an unknown planet. Adams finished his calculations first, but the new world, now called Neptune, was first identified by J.Galle and H.D'Arrest, at the Berlin Observatory, from Le Verrier's results.

Neptune proved to be very similar to Uranus. It is slightly smaller, somewhat more massive, and much further away; its mean distance from the Sun is 2,793,000,000 miles, and its revolution period is $164\frac{3}{4}$ years. It is too faint to be seen with the naked eye, but binoculars will show it. It has two satellites, one of which, Triton, is considerably larger than our Moon. A third satellite has recently been suspected.

Even then there were still slight, unexplained irregularities in the movements of the outer planets. In the early twentieth century the American astronomer Percival Lowell returned to the problem, and predicted the position of yet another planet. In 1930, fourteen years after Lowell's death, the planet Pluto was found by Clyde Tombaugh at the observatory which Lowell had founded at Flagstaff in Arizona.

Pluto is very much a puzzle. It is much smaller than the Earth, and is probably icy in composition (with a 'surface' temperature of nearly −400°F); it has a relatively large satellite, Charon. Pluto takes 248 years to go once round the Sun, and at perihelion (its closest point to the Sun), it comes within the orbit of Neptune. The next perihelion is due in 1989, so from now until 1999 Neptune, not Pluto, will rank as the outermost planet.

Yet is Pluto worthy to be ranked as a proper planet at all? This now seems doubtful. Moreover, its low mass means that it could not possibly pull Uranus or Neptune measurably out of position, and it may well be that Lowell's correct prediction was due to sheer luck. There could still be another planet beyond Pluto, but if it exists it will be very faint, and extremely difficult to find.

During a total eclipse of the Sun, when for a few fleeting minutes the Moon hides the brilliant solar disk completely, the Sun's 'atmosphere' flashes into view; we see the prominences, which are masses of glowing hydrogen, and also the pearly mist known as the corona, made up of very thin gas spreading outwards for vast distances. Before 1868 the prominences and the corona could be studied only during a total eclipse, but in that year Norman Lockyer in England and Jules Janssen in France independently discovered that by using a spectroscope, the prominences at least can be seen at any time. The importance of this can hardly be over-estimated. It had already been found that the Sun has a cycle of activity with a period of about 11 years. At solar maxima, sunspots are frequent; at minimum, the disc may be free of spots for protracted periods. The spots themselves are about 2000°C cooler than the surrounding photosphere, which is why they appear dark (if they could be seen shining on their own, they would appear brilliant). It was later found that sunspots are associated with strong magnetic fields.

During 1877 the planet Mars was exceptionally well placed for observation. It was carefully studied by the Milan astronomer, G.V.Schiaparelli; he compiled new charts of the surface, and drew the white polar caps which are now known to be made up of ice, together with some solid carbon dioxide. There are dark patches on the Martian surface, once thought to be seas. Schiaparelli believed them to be the result of vegetation – an idea which persisted until 1965, when the first space-probe to Mars showed that there are no vegetation-tracts there.

Planetary Distances

		Mean distance from Sun (miles)
1	Mercury	36,000,000
2	Venus	67,000,000
3.	Earth	93,000,000
4	Mars	142,000,000
5	Jupiter	484,000,000
6	Saturn	887,000,000
7	Uranus	1,784,000,000
8	Neptune	2,794,000,000
9	Pluto	3,674,000,000

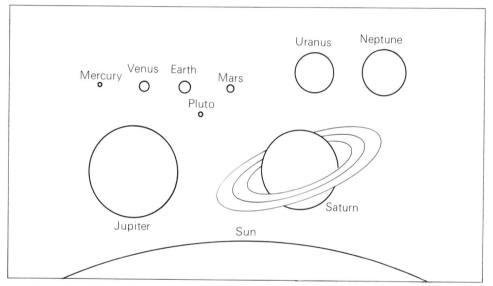

Relative sizes of the Sun and planets

	Distance from Sun (relative to Earth's distance)	Radius (relative to Earth's radius)	Mass (relative to Earth's mass)	Period of revolution, Earth years	Period of rotation or spin, Earth days	Orbital speed (miles per second)	Density (water = 1)
Mercury	0.39	0.4	0.056	0.24	59.0	30.0	5.0
Venus	0.72	1.0	0.8	0.62	243	22.0	5.3
Earth	1.0	1.0	1.0	1.0	1.0	18.0	5.5
Mars	1.52	0.5	0.11	1.88	1.03	15.0	4.0
Jupiter	5.2	11.0	318	12.0	0.41	8.0	1.3
Saturn	9.5	9.5	95.0	29.5	0.43	6.0	0.75
Uranus	19.2	3.5	14.5	84.0	0.45	4.5	1.5
Neptune	30.1	3.5	17.0	164	0.66	3.3	1.7
Pluto	40.0	0.5 (?)	0.1 (?)	247	0.27	3.0	?

Table of approximate planetary data

More surprisingly, Schiaparelli drew strange, straight lines crossing the reddish-ochre Martian 'deserts'. He called them *canali*, which is Italian for 'channels', but they became popularly known as canals. Schiaparelli himself kept an open mind as to their nature, but later in the nineteenth century Percival Lowell maintained that they were artificial, and had been built by intelligent beings to provide a vast irrigation system on a planet very short of water.

Other observers also drew the canals, and maps of Mars began to look very peculiar indeed. Lowell continued to believe in the 'Martians' until the time of his death, in 1916, but gradually it became clear that the atmosphere of the planet is very thin, and that conditions there were unsuited to higher life-forms of the type then known. The canal controversy was finally cleared up in our own time. In 1965 the automatic spacecraft Mariner 4 passed by the planet, and sent back pictures showing that it is cratered; the canals do not exist in any form, and were simply errors of observation.

One of the great dreams of mankind (going back to Lucian of Samosata) is the idea of interplanetary travel, but it was only in 1865 that the first really serious proposals were made. They were contained in a novel, *From the Earth to the Moon*, by the great French writer, Jules Verne. In it, Verne described how the projectile carrying his intrepid explorers was fired to the Moon at a speed of 7 miles per second from the mouth of a vast cannon. The speed is right; 7 miles per second is the Earth's escape velocity, so that a projectile starting off at this velocity will never return. Yet, sadly, Verne's scheme is impracticable, both because of the tremendous shock of departure and because friction against the lower atmosphere would burn up the projectile at once.

In 1881 the Russian inventor Kibaltchitch put forward different theories, but he was unwise enough to make a bomb which was used to assassinate the Czar, and – not unnaturally – was given no chance to continue his scientific research. Ten years later came proposals by an eccentric German, Hermann Ganswindt, who described a remarkable contrivance in which a series of explosions sent a piston up to the roof of a passenger-carrying vehicle, propelling it upwards by a series of jerks. One imagines that it would have been a bumpy ride, but Ganswindt had at least grasped the fundamental principle of 'reaction'.

The credit for putting forward the first practicable ideas for space-travel must go to a shy, deaf Russian teacher, Konstantin Tsiolkovskii, whose first really important papers appeared in 1903. Tsiolkovskii grasped the fact that a vehicle moving beyond the Earth's atmosphere must be powered by the principle of reaction; 'every action has an equal and opposite reaction'. In a gunpowder rocket, solid fuel is ignited; hot gases are sent out through the exhaust, and the rocket body is propelled in the opposite direction. In effect the rocket is 'pushing against itself', and does not depend upon surrounding atmosphere, as normal aircraft do. Tsiolkovskii also knew that solid fuels were not powerful enough or controllable enough to be used for space-travel, and he proposed to use liquid propellants; a fuel and an oxidant, which would be combined in a combustion chamber and would react together to produce the hot gases. He was purely a theorist, but in his lifetime, in 1926, R.H.Goddard in the United States fired the first liquid-propellant rocket. Today the same principles are used for the vehicles which have sent men to the Moon and probes to the planets. Tsiolkovskii died in 1934, by which time his pioneer work had been belatedly recognized.

Goddard's work was followed up by a German team, one of whose members was Wernher von Braun. Rockets were tested, and in the 1930s the Nazi Government took over the research, transferring the team to the Baltic island of Peenemünde. It was here that the Germans developed the V2 rockets which were used against England during 1944 and 1945. Subsequently von Braun and others went to America to take part in the development of rocketry there; it was von Braun who was principally responsible for the launching of America's first artificial satellite, Explorer 1, in 1958.

Modern Stellar Astronomy

The beginning of what may be termed the modern phase of stellar astronomy dates from 1908, with the work of the Danish astronomer Ejnar Hertzsprung. By then the spectra of many stars had been studied, and it was found that they were by no means all alike; hot, bluish or white stars had spectra quite different from those of the cooler, orange or red stars. Hertzsprung pointed out that orange and red stars were either very large and luminous (giants) or comparatively small and dim (dwarfs). There was a less clear-cut division for yellow stars, but not for the really hot stars with temperatures of over 10,000°C. Subsequently Hertzsprung and H.N.Russell, of the United States, developed what is called the Hertzsprung–Russell or H–R Diagram, in which stars are plotted according to their spectral types and their luminosities. Most of the stars fall along a band stretching from the upper left of the diagram to the lower right; this is termed the Main Sequence, and our Sun is a typical Main Sequence star. The various spectral types are denoted by letters of the alphabet: in order of decreasing surface temperature, O,B,A,F,G,K, and M. O and B stars are white or bluish; A, white; F, yellowish; G, yellow; K, orange, and M orange-red (other red stars are of types R, N and S). The Sun is of spectral type G, with a surface temperature of about 6000°C.

Giant stars, such as Betelgeux in Orion, fall to the upper right of the H–R Diagram. To the lower left are the curious White Dwarfs, which are very small (sometimes smaller than the Earth) but have hot surfaces. The best-known example is the faint companion of Sirius, the apparently brightest star in the sky. Sirius itself is twenty-six times as luminous as the Sun, while its companion has only 1/10,000 the power of its primary.

It was at first thought that the H–R Diagram might represent an evolutionary sequence, with a star beginning as a Red Giant and then passing down the Main Sequence to end up as a Red Dwarf, but this has been found to be wrong. Modern theories are based on the work of Hans Bethe and George Gamow, in 1938, who found that a star shines because of nuclear reactions taking place inside it. In a normal star the main constituent is hydrogen; near a star's core, where the temperature is very high (14,000,000°C in the case of the Sun), hydrogen is being changed into helium, with release of energy and loss of mass. Our Sun, which is a relatively mild star, is losing mass at the rate of 4,000,000 tons per second, though it is at least 5,000,000,000 years old and will not change much for 5,000,000,000 years in the future.

It now seems that a star begins by condensing out of interstellar material (dust and gas). As it contracts, under the influence of gravitation, its core heats up; eventually nuclear reactions are triggered off, and the star joins the Main Sequence. Massive stars, which evolve relatively quickly, join the Sequence near the upper left, while stars of lower mass join it to the lower right.

A star stays on the Main Sequence for the main part of its brilliant career. When the available hydrogen is exhausted, the star must change its structure. The core shrinks and the outer layers expand, so that the star becomes a Red Giant. What happens next depends upon the star's initial mass. If it is similar to that of the Sun, it will collapse into a small, super-dense White Dwarf when all its nuclear fuel is exhausted, ending its career as a dark, dead globe, but stars of greater mass die in much more spectacular fashion – either by exploding as supernovae, or by collapsing to form Black Holes.

Most stars shine steadily for year after year, century after century, but some change in brightness over shorter periods; these are the variable stars. The first variable to be identified was Mira in the constellation of Cetus, the Whale, in 1638; at its brightest it can attain the second magnitude, about as bright as the Pole Star, while at minimum it sinks to magnitude 9, and even binoculars will not show it. The period between successive maxima is, on average, 331 days.

Mira is a long-period variable, and, like most of its kind, is a Red Giant, well advanced in its evolutionary career. Other stars which fluctuate in magnitude are not true variables, but are what are termed eclipsing binaries, made up of two components revolving round their common centre of gravity, so that as the component passes in front of the other the magnitude drops. The prototype eclipsing binary, Algol in Perseus, was first interpreted in 1783 by a young deaf-mute astronomer, John Goodricke.

Genuine variables of short period (a few days to a few weeks) are known as Cepheids, because the best-known member of the class is Delta Cephei in the far north of the sky. They are as regular as clockwork, and are pulsating, so that their diameters and their luminosities change. In 1912 Miss Henrietta Leavitt, at Harvard University in the United States, was studying Cepheids in the system known as the Small Magellanic Cloud when she found something very remarkable. The Cepheids with the longer periods appeared to be brighter than those with shorter periods. The small Magellanic Cloud is made up of stars which may be assumed to be at the same distance from us (just as we can say that to all intents and purposes, London and Brighton are the same distance from New York). Therefore, the longer-period Cepheids were genuinely the more luminous. This led on to the 'Period-Luminosity Law', so that the real power of a Cepheid can be found merely by measuring its period. Obviously, the distance can then be calculated – just as the distance of a distant light can be estimated if we know whether it is genuinely powerful or very dim.

Cepheids act as 'standard candles' in space, and they are highly luminous, so that they can be seen across vast distances. Therefore, they are of tremendous importance to astronomers. There are also 'dwarf Cepheids' or RR Lyrae stars, all of which appear to be of about the same luminosity, and which can be used as standard candles in the same way, though they are much less powerful.

During the late nineteenth century very large refracting telescopes had been built. The largest of all, at the Yerkes Observatory in the USA, has an object-glass 40 inches in diameter. Yet reflectors have decided advantages, since large mirrors are much easier to make than large lenses. George Ellery Hale, an American pioneer of solar studies, planned giant reflectors and persuaded friendly millionaires to finance them – something which was much easier half a century ago that it is today! In 1908 he master-minded a 60-inch reflector on Mount Wilson in California, followed in 1917 by a 100-inch reflector. He next planned a telescope with a 200-inch mirror, but he died in 1938, well before the giant instrument was finished. For over thirty years the Mount Wilson 100-inch was the world's largest telescope.

The World's Largest Refractors

Location and diameter in inches

Yerkes Obs., Williams Bay, Wisconsin	40
Lick Obs., Mt. Hamilton, California	36
Astrophys. Obs., Potsdam, E. Germany	32
Paris Observatory, Meuden, France	32
Allegheny Obs., Pittsburgh, Pennsylvania	30
Univ. of Paris, Nice, France	30
Northern Hemisphere Obs., La Pala	28
Union Obs., Johannesburg	26.5
Universitäts-Sternwarte, Vienna	26.5
University of Virginia	26
Obs., Academy of Sciences, Pulkova, USSR	26
Astronomical Obs., Belgrade, Yugoslavia	26
Leander McCormick Obs., Charlottesville, Virginia	26
Obs., Mitaka, Tokyo-to, Japan	26
US Naval Obs., Washington, D.C.	26
Mt. Stromlo Obs., Canberra, Australia	26

The World's Largest Reflectors

Location and diameter in inches

Astrophysical Obs., Zelenchukskayá, USSR	236
Hale Obs., Palomar Mtn., California	200, 100, 60
Mt. Hopkins (SAO), Arizona	176, 60
Kitt Peak National Obs., Tucson, Arizona	158, 84, 60
Cerro Tololo, Chile	158, 60
Siding Spring, Australia	153
La Silla, Chile	141, 60
Lick Obs., Mt. Hamilton, California	120
McDonald Obs., Fort Davis, Texas	107, 82
Crimean Astrophys. Obs., Nauchny, USSR	104
Byurakan Obs., Armenia S.S.R.	102
Mt. Wilson Obs., Pasadena, California	100
Steward Obs., Tucson	90
Mauna Kea Obs., Univ. of Hawaii, Hawaii	88, 84
Shemakha Astroph. Obs., Azerbaijan S.S.R.	79
Saint Michel l'Observatoire (Basses Alpes), France	77
Haute Provence, France	76, 60
Tokyo Obs., Japan	74
Mt. Stromlo, Australia	74
David Dunlap Obs., Ontario, Canada	74
Helwan Obs., Helwan, Egypt	74
Astrophys. Obs., Kamogata, Okayama-ken, Japan	74
Sutherland, South Africa	74
Dominion Astrophys., Obs., Victoria, B.C.	73
Perkins Obs., Flagstaff, Arizona	72
Obs., Padua Univ., Asiago, Italy	72
Agassiz Station Harvard Obs., Cambridge, Mass.	61
National Obs., Bosque Alegre Sta., Argentina	61
U.S. Naval Obs., Flagstaff	61
Catalina Mtn., Arizona	61
Arizona Univ. Obs., Tucson	60
Boyden Obs., Bloemfontein, South Africa	60
Mt. Haleakala, Ha.	60
Figl Astroph. Obs., Vienna	60

When the Mount Wilson reflector came into operation it was already known that the Galaxy is a flattened system (as Herschel had believed, so long before) and the American astronomer Harlow Shapley even made a good estimate of its size; the overall diameter is of the order of 100,000 light-years, and the system contains about 100,000,000,000 stars. But what about the 'starry nebulae', including the spirals discovered by Lord Rosse? Using the Mount Wilson reflector, Edwin Hubble studied the starry nebulae, and in 1923 he was able to detect short-period variables in them. By measuring the periods of these stars he could find their distances, and he realized that they were much too remote to be members of our Galaxy. It followed that the systems in which they lay must be independent galaxies in their own right. This was possibly the most important astronomical discovery since the Copernican revolution over three and a half centuries earlier. Without the tremendous light-grasp of the 100-inch reflector, the distances of the galaxies could not have been measured.

The Andromeda Spiral, M.31, is one of the nearest of the galaxies (a few, such as the Clouds of Magellan, are closer). Hubble gave its distance as 750,000 light-years. Much later, in 1952, Walter Baade used the Palomar 200-inch reflector to show that there had been an error in the Cepheid scale. The variables were more luminous than had been thought, and therefore more distant; today we know that the Andromeda Spiral is 2,200,000 light-years from us. Here again we have an example of the great advances made possible with increased light-grasp. The Palomar reflector is still the largest in the world apart from the new Russian 236-inch, which has produced few valuable results as yet. Yet the Palomar telescope, completed in 1948, is now over a quarter of a century old.

The Great Spiral in Andromeda

Meanwhile, another astonishing fact had been discovered. The spectra of galaxies are made up of the combined spectra of millions of stars, but the main absorption lines can be identified, and their positions in the spectral band have showed that all the galaxies, except those of our own 'local group' (including the Andromeda Spiral and the Megellanic Clouds) are moving away from us. This has been proved by what is termed the Doppler Effect. If a light-source is

The Cooke Reversible Transit Circle, Royal Observatory, Herstmonceux

receding, its wavelength appears to be slightly lengthened; the spectral lines are moved over to the long-wave or red end of the band, and the amount of this 'red shift' is a key to the velocity of recession. There is a definite relationship between distance and velocity; the further away a galaxy is, the faster it is racing away, so that the entire universe is expanding. Today we know of systems which are receding at over 90 per cent of the velocity of light.

In 1931 Karl Jansky, an American radio engineer of Czech descent, was carrying out experiments into the nature of 'static', using an improvised aerial which was made up partly from a dismembered Ford car. To his surprise, he detected radio waves coming from the Milky Way. This was the beginning of the modern science of radio astronomy, though Jansky never followed up his great discovery as he might have been expected to do. The first intentional radio telescope was built in 1937 by another American, Grote Reber, but it was only after the end of the war that radio astronomy became a really important branch of scientific research.

The conventional picture of a radio telescope is that of a large metal 'dish'. The most famous instrument of this type is that set up in 1955 at Jodrell Bank in Cheshire, due to the energy and skill of Professor Sir Bernard Lovell. Yet not all radio telescopes are built upon this pattern; there are many forms of design.

Celestial bodies send out radiations at all wavelengths, and visible light makes up only a tiny fraction of the whole range of wavelengths or 'electromagnetic spectrum'. Beyond the short-wave end of the visible band we have ultra-violet radiation, then X-rays and finally the ultra-short gamma-rays; beyond the long-wave end we have infra-red, then microwaves, and then the long radio waves. A radio telescope collects and focuses the radio waves, just as an optical telescope collects and focuses light, but no actual picture is produced, and the general result is a trace on a graph; one certainly cannot look through a radio telescope! Neither can we hear 'noise' from space. Noise is carried by atmosphere, and there is no atmosphere above a few hundreds of miles, so that the 'radio noise' so often heard on BBC radio and television programmes is created inside the receiving apparatus.

It was soon found that there were various discrete radio sources. The Sun is a radio emitter, and so is the planet Jupiter. However, most sources lie well beyond the Solar System. Some are supernova remnants, such as the Crab Nebula; others are independent galaxies. By now many thousands of separate radio sources in the sky have been catalogued.

As radio astronomy techniques were perfected, it became possible to pinpoint the positions of the source very precisely. In 1963 it was discovered that radio waves were coming from what looked like a faint bluish star. When the optical spectrum was studied by Maarten Schmidt, at Palomar, it was found that the object was not a star at all – it was infinitely more dramatic. The lines in its spectrum were strongly red-shifted, from which it was clear that the object was extremely remote and almost incredibly luminous. This was the first quasar – a convenient abbreviation of the original designation of 'quasi-stellar radio source'.

Many other quasars have since been found, though not all are strong radio emitters. They are presumably the most luminous objects known, and also the most remote; they are far more powerful than normal galaxies. Their exact nature is still a matter for debate. They may be the nuclei of exceptionally active galaxies, but it is fair to say that as yet we do not really know.

Yet another unexpected discovery was made in 1967 – more or less by accident! During a survey of radio sources being carried out from Cambridge, Miss Jocelyn Bell (now Dr Jocelyn Bell-Burnell) detected a source which was pulsing rapidly and regularly at immense speed. For a brief period it was even thought that the source might be artificial – an idea known popularly as the Little Green Men theory – but it soon became clear that the strange 'ticking' source was natural. A systematic hunt was organized and other similar objects were tracked down; they were named pulsars. Two have so far been identified with optical objects. One is in the Crab Nebula, and the other in the remnant of a supernova in the southern constellation of Vela, the Sails of the old Ship Argo.

When a star comes to the end of its brilliant career, it develops according to its initial mass. As we have seen, a modest star such as the Sun will collapse into the White Dwarf state, and fade gradually away, though it takes an immensely long time to lose the last of its energy. With a more massive star, the end comes much more abruptly. Reactions 'run wild', so to speak, and the star explodes as a supernova, blowing most of its material away into space. For a few days or weeks it may shine with at least fifteen million times the luminosity of the Sun, but its glory is brief, and all that is left is a cloud of expanding gas together with the actual remnant of the old star – tiny, and thousands of millions of times denser than water. It is made up of neutrons, which are particles carrying no electrical charge, and it is spinning rapidly round. It has become a pulsar.

If the mass is still greater, the dying star will become neither a supernova nor a pulsar. Once the final collapse starts, nothing can stop it; the star becomes smaller and smaller, denser and denser, until its escape velocity has become greater than the velocity of light. The old star is then surrounded by a region from which light is unable to escape – and if light cannot do so, then certainly nothing else can. We are left with what is termed a Black Hole, virtually cut off from the surrounding universe, and detectable only by its effects upon objects which we can see.

Black Holes are indeed bizarre objects. Inside the 'forbidden zone' conditions are totally alien, and all the ordinary laws of science break down, though obviously we can do little more than speculate. It has been suggested, with good reason, that there may be massive Black Holes in the nuclei of galaxies which are very powerful radio emitters, and it is even possible that a Black Hole exists at the centre of our own Galaxy.

The Space Age

The Space Age officially began on 4 October 1957, with the launch of the first artificial satellite, Russia's Sputnik I. It was a tiny thing, about the size of a football, and it carried little apart from a radio transmitter, but it marked the opening of a new era. Obviously it has become impossible to separate 'astronautics' from astronomy, but some of the most important dates in the first decades of space research are:

1958: Explorer I   This was the first American artificial satellite, sent up by a team led by Wernher von Braun. Instruments in it detected zones of intense radiation round the Earth, now known as the Van Allen zones.

1959: Rockets to the Moon   Again these were of Russian origin, and were known as Luniks (or Lunas). Three were sent up during 1959. The first by-passed the Moon, and sent back useful information, such as confirmation that the Moon has no appreciable magnetic field. The second crash-landed on the lunar surface, and the third, in October, went round the Moon and sent back the first pictures of the far side – which can never be seen from Earth, because it is always turned away from us. Predictably, the far side of the Moon proved to be just as crater-scarred, barren and lifeless as the side which we already knew.

1961: The first space-man On 12 April 1961 Yuri Gagarin, of the Soviet Air Force, became the first man to go into space. He completed a full journey round the Earth in his miniature vehicle, Vostok 1, and made a safe landing. It is ironical that he was later killed in an ordinary aircraft crash.

1962: Telstar and television Telstar, a tiny unmanned American satellite, became the first long-range television relay; it provided direct television contact between Europe and America.

1962: Mariner 2 to Venus The first successful planetary probe. It passed within 21,000 miles of Venus, and sent back the first reliable information about that decidedly peculiar planet. Since then there have been many Venus probes, some of which have soft-landed there; in 1974 the Russian vehicles Venera 9 and Venera 10 actually sent back one picture each, direct from the surface, before being put permanently out of action by the intensely hostile conditions. Radar maps of much of the surface were obtained by America's Pioneer Venus, which went into orbit round the planet in 1978 and was still operating in 1981. We now know that the atmosphere is mainly carbon dioxide, with a ground pressure about ninety times that of the Earth's air at sea-level; the surface temperature – the hottest of all the known planets – is almost 500°C and the inviting-looking clouds contain large quantities of sulphuric acid. There are two highland areas, Ishtar and Aphrodite, with tall mountains and large, rather shallow craters. Venus has been aptly nicknamed 'the hell-planet', and manned flight there seems to be out of the question.

1965: Mariner 4 to Mars Mars was successfully by-passed for the first time by Mariner 4, which showed that the surface is cratered rather than smooth. Mariners 6 and 7 followed in 1969; then, in 1971–2, Mariner 9 went into a closed orbit, and provided maps of most of the surface. Mars is a world of craters, valleys and towering volcanoes, one of which (Olympus Mons) is a shield volcano far higher and more massive than any on Earth. In 1976 two Viking probes made soft landings on the Martian surface, and soil analyses were carried out; no signs of life were found, and it is now thought likely that Mars is sterile. Yet there is abundant evidence of past water activity, and it may be that the planet goes through violent changes of climate over periods of thousands of years.

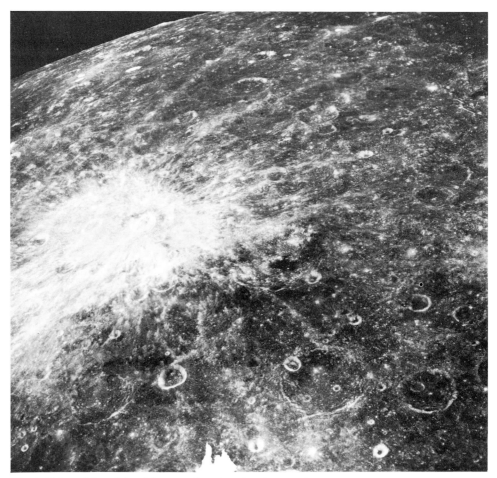

The hidden side of the Moon, taken by the Apollo 8 spacecraft in December 1968

1969: Men on the Moon   The Apollo programme of manned lunar flight had been initiated by President John F. Kennedy in the early 1960s. Much had to be done; the lunar surface was thoroughly mapped by the automatic Orbiter probes (1966–7), and there were two preliminary manned flights round the Moon, by Apollo 8 (1968) and Apollo 10 (early 1969). The final touch-down was achieved on 21 July 1969 by Neil Armstrong and Edwin Aldrin, in the lunar module of Apollo 11. Other flights followed; the programme ended in 1972 with the successful mission of Apollo 17.

Obviously our knowledge of the Moon has been dramatically increased by these space-flights. The age of the Moon is the same as that of the Earth; lunar rocks have been analysed, and it has been confirmed that there has never been any lunar life. There is a hot core, and there are small but persistent 'moonquakes'; there is to all intents and purposes no atmosphere.

1973–4; Skylab   During these years three successive crews, each of three astronauts, manned the Skylab space-station. Much scientific work of all kinds was carried out – and it is important to remember that from space, investigations become possible which can never be undertaken from beneath the Earth's atmosphere. (For instance, X-rays from space cannot penetrate to ground level, and X-ray astronomy could not begin before the Space Age; the first X-ray source was detected from an unmanned rocket sent up in 1962.)

Skylab was the first full-scale American space-station, and it remained in orbit until spiralling down to destruction in the lower atmosphere. Since then the Russians have been very active in this research, and their Salyut stations have been highly successful.

1973: Pioneer 10 to Jupiter   The first Jupiter probe made its pass in December 1973, sending back valuable information; it confirmed, for instance, that Jupiter is surrounded by zones of lethal radiation, and has an extremely powerful magnetic field. The surface is in a state of constant turmoil, and the famous Great Red Spot is simply a vast whirling storm – a phenomenon of Jovian meteorology: the colour is now believed to be due to red phosphorus. The temperature at the core of Jupiter is thought to be about 53000°F, more than six times hotter than the Earth's core, whereas the temperature at Jupiter's surface of −240°F is more than twice as cold as Earth's. Pioneer 11 followed in December 1974, after which it went on to a rendezvous with Saturn in 1979.

But the Voyagers of 1979 surpassed even the Pioneers. Spectacular pictures were obtained not only of the planet itself, but of its satellites. Of these, Callisto and Ganymede are icy and cratered; Europa icy and smooth, while Io, the innermost of the main satellites, has a red, sulphury surface which has been likened to a pizza, with active volcanoes. A Jovian ring has also been detected, though it cannot compare with the rings of Saturn.

1980: Voyager to Saturn   Following its successful pass of Jupiter, Voyager 1, travelling at over ten times the speed of a rifle bullet, achieved a rendezvous with Saturn in November 1980. Here, too, the results were as spectacular as they were unexpected. Saturn's rings, long known to be made up of tiny orbiting particles, were found to be far more complex than had been believed. They are 38,000 miles wide and less than a mile thick, and made up of billions of independently orbiting chunks of ice. Even the main gap in the rings, Cassini's Division, was found to be occupied by several thin rings. The surface of the planet was more bland than that of Jupiter, but there, too, were darkish belts and bright zones, and at least one red spot. Of Saturn's satellites or moons, the largest, Titan, was found to be hidden behind a layer of orange 'smog' and red clouds and to be composed mainly of nitrogen; it is thought that there may be oceans of liquid nitrogen upon the bitterly cold surface. Titan's atmosphere is thicker than Earth's. Most of the other satellites were icy and crater-scarred.

A computer mosaic picture of the rings of Saturn, taken 6 November 1980 by the Voyager 1 spacecraft at a range of about 5,000,000 miles

New small satellites were discovered; the total number of known attendants is now fifteen – one less than in the case of Jupiter.

Like the Pioneers which preceded it, Voyager 1 has already started its never-ending journey into space. It carries an identification plaque in case it should ever be recovered by some far-off civilization (the chances of which appear decidedly slim). It should be tracked until well into the 1990s, but then contact with it will be lost, and its final fate will never be known.

Meanwhile, Voyager 2 was travelling toward a rendezvous with Saturn in the late summer of 1981. If all goes well, it will then by-pass the outer giants, Uranus in 1986 and Neptune in 1989, after which it too will leave the Solar System for ever.

This sketch of the history of astronomy is very brief, and much has had to be left out. Some major questions still remain unanswered by astronomers. How, if ever, did the universe begin? Will it ever end? And can we hope to find life beyond the Earth?

Nobody can say much about the actual origin of the universe, which remains a complete mystery, but at least we can speculate about its evolution. According to the most widely accepted modern theory, the story began with the creation of all matter in a 'big bang', some 15,000,000,000 or more years ago; the universe started to expand, and this expansion has continued until the present day. In 1965–6 the American scientists, Penzias and Wilson, even detected microwaves coming from all directions which may indicate the remnants of the 'big bang'. It is not certain whether the expansion will continue indefinitely; it may well be that the present phase will be followed by a period of contraction, ending in another 'big bang' in about 60,000,000,000 years' time. Long before that, though, the Earth will have been destroyed by changes in the Sun, when it leaves the Main Sequence and becomes a giant star.

So far as extraterrestrial life is concerned, we can only say that we have found no trace of it. Yet we can know nothing about the planets of other stars, which must surely exist, and it would be rash to assume that man is unique. Now that the 'shuttle' seems a success, it is likely that the exploitation of space will in future be at least as important as its exploration, so whether we do ever establish contact with other civilizations remains to be seen.

At all events, discoveries about space during the last few years have been quite remarkable. We know more about the universe than would have seemed possible a few decades ago. Provided that we do not indulge in a third world war, which would destroy all life upon our world, there is every reason to hope that this progress will continue. The story of astronomy is not over. It may only be just beginning.

The Earth receives only 1/2,000,000,000th of the sun's energy.

The Earth travels over 1,500,000 miles every day.

It is only possible to see the Sun directly above your head if you are south of the Tropic of Cancer and north of the Tropic of Capricorn.

The power of modern telescopes enables us to look at galaxies 10,000,000,000 light years away.

The surface gravity on the star Sirius B is almost 250,000 times greater than gravity on earth.

A sunspot sighted in April 1947 covered almost 7,000,000,000 square miles of the Sun's surface.

Light travels 186,300 miles per second, or 5,878,499,814,000 miles in one year. This unit is called a light year. The light that reaches earth from outer space can take thousands of years to arrive. This is how long it takes from five familiar points in the heavens: From the moon – 1.25 seconds; From the sun – 8 minutes 27.3 seconds; From the nearest star (excluding the sun) – 4.28 years; From the most distant star in the Milky Way – 75,000 years; From the Andromeda Spiral (the most distant point visible with the naked eye) – 2,200,000 years.

If a small body from outer space, no larger than those that have already collided with planet Earth, made a direct hit on Columbus, Ohio, home of the humourist, James Thurber, the results would be truly devastating. A crater measuring 50 miles in diameter would replace the city. Débris from the impact would be hurled halfway across North America, almost a third of the people in the continent would be killed, and the only civilized life would take place west of the Rocky Mountains.

The Earth makes one complete turn on its axis every 23 hours 56 minutes 4.0996 seconds. Every 365 days 5 hours 48 minutes and 46 seconds it makes one complete revolution round the Sun.

The diameter of the Earth's orbit is almost exactly 1,000 times the distance travelled by light in one second.

There is still a body of people even today who believe that the earth is flat.

10

Transport

Travel is part of our everyday existence. There are many millions of people who commute many miles daily between their homes and their offices; it is possible to cross the Atlantic on a luxury liner in a few days, and to fly it in a few hours, so that it is quite practicable to have one's lunch in London and one's dinner in New York. In theory, travel has become easy. It is not easy, therefore, for us to appreciate the state of affairs less than two centuries ago, when a journey from, say, London to Edinburgh was much more troublesome than a flight to Australia would be now. The coming of mechanical transport has altered the situation beyond all recognition. It is probably fair to say that the new era began with the official opening of the world's first railway – the Stockton and Darlington railway – in 1825. Before that, transport depended upon human muscle, animal power, or the force of the wind. First, then, let us look back to very early times, and trace the story of transport from the Stone Age through to the present day.

Travel in Olden Times

Even before the start of what we usually term civilization there was often a need for transporting heavy loads from one place to another. The obvious course was to carry them – a duty which was presumably carried out mainly by women; the era of Women's Lib lay a long way in the future. But gradually, ways and means were found to ease the burden. Tree-trunk rollers probably date back to the Ice Age, and there is excellent evidence that snow sleds were used in Finland, so that they were presumably common in other countries where climates were cold. In the Near East, dust sleds were developed before 4000 BC. But the most important development – indeed, the most important in the whole history of transport – was the invention of the wheel.

It is impossible to say just when this happened. Whether it came about as a result of a sudden idea in the mind of some prehistoric genius, or whether wheels were developed gradually and fortuitously, is something we can never know; the latter seems much more probable. At any rate, those mysterious people, the Sumerians, certainly used wheels in the Tigris-Euphrates basin by 6300 BC, and by 2000 BC wheeled carts had spread to the Indus Valley, the Mediterranean coast and the island of Crete, then the site of one of the most advanced civilizations of the world – the Minoan, which was fated to be destroyed about 1500 BC by the catastrophic eruption of the volcanic island Thera. Strangely, wheels were not used in Egypt before 1600 BC, but by 1000 BC they were known in much of the civilized world, from China to Scandinavia. (It is all the more remarkable that they were never used by the brilliant Incas of so many centuries later – which may be one reason why the Inca civilization fell so easily to the invading Spaniards.)

Animals, of course, were used in transport from very early times. Before 3000 BC the ass was used in Egypt as a pack animal, and the method soon spread to Mesopotamia, but for most purposes the horse has overwhelming advantages – for one thing, it is much more amenable. A carving of a horse-rider found at Susa, Elam, has been dated back as far as 3000 BC, and riding soon became commonplace. There was also the camel, which was pressed into service in desert lands about the same time, though anybody who has tried to ride a camel will be profoundly grateful that alternative methods of travel have now been developed.

With the advent of the wheel and the cart, animals became more and more important in transport. Even before 4000 BC the Sumerians seem to have hitched up oxen by means of a yoke, but when they tried to develop a useful harness they fell far short of their usual brilliance, and the result was that the luckless animals were in constant danger of choking to death. The Sumerians never solved this particular problem, and in fact the first proper horse-collar dates only from about the ninth century AD, when it was developed in Europe. Meantime, water travel had made great progress.

The simplest forms of water transport are the log dugout canoes, still used in parts of Africa and south-east Asia, and the skin kayaks of the Eskimos. But as early as 7000 BC more sophisticated boats were built by the people of Greece and the valley of the Nile, and Greek seafarers often sailed across to the Ægean island of Milos in the quest for the coveted mineral, obsidian. Since Milos is well over seventy miles from the Greek mainland, the boats had at least to be reasonably strong.

By 4000 BC many of the Middle Eastern peoples had learned the art of using oar-powered ships, and by 2000 BC both the Cretans and the Phœnicians were using square sails on two or even three masts – thereby becoming the first to make attempts to harness the forces of nature. The Phœnicians managed to sail round Africa, and even penetrated to Europe, reaching the area of the Rhine. To the Egyptians must go the credit of building the first major canal; in 1380 BC the Pharaoh Amenhotep III linked the Nile with the Red Sea. And by 600 BC the Phœnicians had established sea routes to and from India.

As the supremacy of Egypt and China faded, so first Greece and then Rome rose to greatness. As ocean explorers the Greeks were supreme; Pytheas, about 325 BC, actually explored the coasts of Western Europe as far as Britain and perhaps even Norway, and in the same period Alexander the Great established a major navy. Under his authority Nearchus, the Admiral of the Fleet, used Indian shipbuilders to make 800 vessels, some of as much as 300 tons displacement; he also used Indian navigators to guide the fleet through the Persian Gulf. Meanwhile, ships were being developed for use in warfare. Carthage had risen to the status of a great power, and at first the Carthaginians were masters of the seas as well as being the most energetic traders in the Mediterranean. Their ships had five banks of oars, manned by well-drilled galley-slaves. When the first Punic War broke out, in 264 BC, the Romans were quick to realize that the Carthaginians had to be challenged on the water as well as on land. They built a fleet at breakneck speed, and in 260 BC sailed bravely out to fight. The resulting Battle of Mylae was a shock to Carthaginian pride; they were taken by surprise by the Roman *corvus*, which consisted of a wooden bridge with a large spike at its end. Normally the *corvus* was kept upright, but when a Carthaginian ship came close the bridge was dropped, sticking its spike into the enemy deck and allowing the Roman soldiers to swarm across. The first Punic War was really brought to an end in 242 BC by another Roman naval success, this time at the Battle of Ægates Insulæ. Later, during the second Punic War, the great Carthaginian general, Hannibal, had to transport his troops by sea from Africa to carry out his invasion of Italy – and eventually to bring them home again, to his only but final defeat at the land battle of Zama.

Navigation, of course, was still in its infancy, but it is worth noting that in 250 BC the Pharos lighthouse, one of the Seven Wonders of the World, was used to beam the light of a fire out to sea, making it visible over a range of at least a hundred miles – and that the lighthouse remained in operation for a further 1500 years.

The Greeks were not great road-builders, partly because of their belief that trees, gorges and valleys were sacred to gods and demigods; to interfere with them in any violent way was to risk offending the Olympians, who were not noted for their tolerance. The Romans were much more practical. In 312 BC Appius Cæcus ordered the construction of the Appian Way; by 220 BC the Flaminian Way had been completed between Rome and Rimini; in 179 BC the world's first stone bridge was constructed across the Tiber and named the Pons Æmilius; and streets in Rome were paved, which admittedly increased the noise of traffic, but made them passable throughout the year. By the third century AD, roads were so good that travellers could average at least a hundred miles per day. Roman roads were not confined to Italy; they can be traced in England even now.

The eclipse of the Roman Empire ushered in the so-called Dark Ages in Europe, but we must not forget the Chinese, who were then energetic in matters of transport. By the year 605 a force of a million labourers had completed the Chinese Grand Canal; by 1000 the Bridge of Ten Thousand Ages had been built at Foochow, and in 1086 a waterworks director, Shen Kua, demonstrated a crude form of magnetic compass, soon carried both by caravan leaders and by sailors. It may not have been very reliable, but it was a great deal better than nothing at all. Incidentally, Chinese roads of this period were remarkably good, and far superior to those in most of Europe.

As the Dark Ages drew towards their end in the West, voyages of exploration were undertaken; by 800 AD the Vikings were regularly sailing to France and England, using 80-foot vessels with 16 oars on each side, square sails, and paddle-steered, and before the year 1000 there is good evidence that some Vikings had crossed the Atlantic. So far as Britain was concerned, the credit for building the first true navy must go to Alfred the Great, one of the few leaders whose character and motives really stand up to close examination. Alfred challenged the Danish invaders on sea as well as on land; his galleys had from forty to sixty oars on each side, and proved to be highly manoeuvrable. However, the obsession with oars held back the development of sailing ships, and long voyages became infrequent until the time of the Crusades, when Richard I sailed to the Holy Land with a fleet of nine large sailing-ships, 150 smaller ones and a mere 38 galleys.

The situation changed again during the thirteenth and fourteenth centuries. Rudders were developed to replace oars, and bowsprits, allowing the forward corner of the mainsail to be hauled below the bows, enabled ships to sail much closer to the wind than had been previously possible. By 1338 many English ships were equipped with light cannon, and Henry V's fleet included ships of up to 1000 tons displacement, 165 feet long and 46 feet in beam. In the first part of the fifteenth century that great armchair explorer, Henry the Navigator of Portugal, sent out his ships to far lands; in 1492 Christopher Columbus sailed across the Atlantic; and the opening-up of the world had begun in earnest. The leading canal-builders were the French. In 1600 they linked the Seine with the Rhone, and their project for joining the Mediterranean to the Atlantic dates back as far as 1603 in its planning stage. But all long-distance voyages were emperilled by one all-important factor: inability to determine one's position.

The ocean navigator needs to know two things: his latitude, and his longitude. Latitude is easy enough, at least in the northern hemisphere. All one has to do is to measure the apparent altitude of Polaris, the Pole Star, above the horizon. If the altitude of the celestial pole is, say, 50 degrees, the latitude of the observer is also 50 degrees; and Polaris is within one degree of the polar point. Longitude, or one's distance east or west of the prime meridian, is much more of a problem, and there were numerous cases of ships turning east instead of west, or vice versa – often with disastrous results. Britain has always been a seafaring nation, and in 1714 a Board of Longitude was established to see what could be done.

Astronomical methods had already been suggested, and in fact Greenwich Observatory was founded by express order of King Charles II, so that a new star-catalogue could be drawn up for navigational purposes. But the main need was for a good timekeeper. If one knew the Greenwich time, longitude could be calculated by comparing Greenwich time with the local time. Accordingly, the Board offered a reward of £20,000 to be given to the first man who could produce a timekeeper which could be carried on board ship, and could be trusted to tell the navigator the Greenwich time at any moment.

As we saw in the chapter on Time, the challenge was taken up by John Harrison, and it was his invention of the chronometer that revolutionized all marine navigation. Other instruments, too, had been developed; the reflecting quadrant by Hadley in 1731, enabling the navigator to determine his latitude either by day or night, and the sextant by John Campbell in 1757. Meanwhile, the old tiller had been superseded in 1705 by the ship's wheel, and conditions had been improved in 1744 by Serson's invention of the gyroscope stabilizer, with its rotor supported on a pivot to prevent it from rolling or pitching. Less practical was the first submarine experiment by David Bushnell in 1776. The submarine was shaped like a pear, and was seven feet long; it was made of oak staves, with ballast tanks operated by foot-pumps, and two tubes for air intake. It was propelled horizontally by a hand-cranked propeller. In its way it worked, but clearly it was extremely limited, and no submarine could possibly be effective without some method of propulsion other than human muscle. But a change was at hand. In 1788 William Symington devised the first practical steamboat, using a direct-action steam engine to drive a paddle; and the end of the Age of Sail loomed ahead.

At least the land navigator had no need of a sextant or a Harrison chronometer, but it was not until about 1270 that roads in England and Europe began to be developed. However, there were few major developments in overland transport until the eighteenth century, apart from improvements in the design of carts and carriages, and the building of bridges. (London's first wooden bridge was built over the Thames during the tenth century, and a 900-feet stone bridge was completed in 1209.) But although specialized strains of horses were gradually developed for transport use, time was always a limiting factor. Before the steam-engine was invented, no man could travel faster than a horse could carry him.

In 1712 Thomas Newcomen built the first true steam-engine. In 1765 Nicholas Cugnot produced the first steam-driven road vehicle, a three-wheeled tractor which averaged $2\frac{1}{2}$ mph and had to stop every hundred feet to build up more steam, and five years later his 'steam carriage' was the first to travel as fast as $2\frac{1}{2}$ mph without the aid of man or animal to propel it. Mechanical travel had begun.

Powered Transport: The Railway

There are still people living who can cast their minds back to the time of Queen Victoria, when there were no cars, and all road transport was horse-powered; but there is certainly no one whose memory can go back before the Railway Age. Indeed, the modern British traveller sometimes wonders ruefully whether matters have improved during the present century insofar as railways are concerned. (According to an old timetable, there was a train running in 1898 which left London at noon and arrived at Chichester, in Sussex, at 1.35 p.m.

Today the same journey by train never takes less than 1 hour 50 minutes in theory, and generally over two hours in practice.)

The idea of using wheels on rails is, of course, very old. The Greeks made use of grooves six inches deep and three to five feet apart to transport heavy loads, and much later – in 1630 – a Northumbrian miner named Beaumont connected the two beams used by sleepers, while in 1767 Reynolds cast the first rails in iron instead of wood, placing flanges on the sides of the wheels to keep the cart on the tracks.

The most famous of the early railway pioneers were the Stephensons, George and his son Robert. Not that they met with universal support; one Parliamentary committee condemned their proposed train as 'the most absurd scheme ever to enter the head of a man . . . ladies will have miscarriages, cows cease to give milk. The passengers will go mad, because no human being can stand a speed of more than 10 mph . . . so we are to gallop at the rate of 12 mph with the aid of a devil in the form of a locomotive, sitting as postilion on the fore horse, with an Honourable Member sitting behind him to stir up the fire.' (No doubt there were prehistoric pessimists who similarly opposed the development of the wheel.) But George Stephenson was appointed engineer for the construction of the Stockton to Darlington railway, which was opened in 1825, and carried passengers who showed no obvious symptoms of insanity. In 1829 the *Rocket*, built mainly by Robert Stephenson, won the famous trials to choose a locomotive for the new Liverpool to Manchester railway, and Robert then turned his attention to the proposed railway between London and Birmingham. After solving considerable problems, he presided over the opening of the 112-mile long track in 1838.

Railway travel soon became an integral part of everyday life. The sleeping-car was developed by Pullman in 1859, and safety was much improved ten years later when George Westinghouse developed a braking system powered by compressed air. One minor annoyance was that trains became fast enough to cause difficulties with local time. Previously, towns and cities had kept their own local time, which may differ from Greenwich time by more than a quarter of an hour even over a country as small as England. There was a famous legal case in 1858. A trial was due to be held at Dorchester Assizes, but

> . . . The time appointed for the sitting of the Court was 10 o'clock am, and the learned Judge took his seat on the bench punctually at 10 by the clock in Court. The case was then called on and the plaintiff's counsel commenced his address to the jury, but as the defendant was not present and no one appeared for him, the learned Judge directed a verdict for the plaintiff. The defendant's counsel then entered the Court and claimed to have the case tried, on the ground that it had been disposed of before 10 o'clock. At that time it wanted one minute and a half to 10 by the town clock. The clock in Court was regulated by Greenwich time, which was some minutes before the time at Dorchester.

George Stephenson (1781–1848), inventor of 'The Rocket'

Obviously this sort of thing could lead to chaos, and something had to be done. A Parliamentary Bill, receiving Royal Assent on 2 August 1880, stated that 'railway time' – that is to say, Greenwich time – should henceforth apply to the whole country.

The longest railway tunnels in the world

Tunnel	Date	Miles	Yds	Operating railway	Country
Dai-shimizu	1979	13	1,384	Japanese National	Japan
Simplon No 1	1906	12	546	Swiss Fed. & Italian St.	Switz.-Italy
and No 2	1922				
Kanmon	1975	11	1,093	Japanese National	Japan
Apennine	1934	11	881	Italian State	Italy
Rokko	1972	10	158	Japanese National	Japan
Gotthard	1882	9	552	Swiss Federal	Switzerland
Lotschberg	1913	9	130	Bern-Lotschberg-Simplon	Switzerland
Hokuriku	1962	8	1,079	Japanese National	Japan
Mont Cenis (Frejus)	1871	8	847	Italian State	France-Italy
Shin-Shimizu	1961	8	675	Japanese National	Japan
Aki	1975	8	161	Japanese National	Japan
Cascade	1929	7	1,388	Burlington Northern	U.S.
Flathead	1970	7	1,319	Great Northern	U.S.
Keijo	1970	7	88	Japanese National	Japan
Lierasen	1973	6	1,135	Norwegian State	Norway
Santa Lucia	1977	6	656	Italian State	Italy
Arlberg	1884	6	643	Austrian Federal	Austria
Moffat	1928	6	366	Denver & Rio Grande Western	U.S.
Shimizu	1931	6	44	Japanese National	Japan
Kvineshei	1943	5	1,107	Norwegian State	Norway
Bigo	1975	5	927	Japanese National	Japan
Rimutaka	1955	5	816	New Zealand Gov.	New Zealand
Ricken	1910	5	603	Swiss Federal	Switzerland
Kaimai	1978	5	873	New Zealand Gov.	New Zealand
Grenchenberg	1915	5	575	Swiss Federal	Switzerland
Otira	1923	5	559	New Zealand Gov.	New Zealand
Tauem	1909	5	546	Austrian Federal	Austria
Haegebostad	1943	5	462	Norwegian State	Norway
Ronco	1889	5	272	Italian State	Italy
Hauenstein (Lower)	1916	5	90	Swiss Federal	Switzerland
Connaught	1916	5	34	Canadian Pacific	Canada
Karawanken	1906	4	1,677	Austrian Federal	Austria-Yugo.
Kobe	1972	4	1,671	Japanese National	Japan
New Tunna	1964	4	1,658	Japanese National	Japan

Source: Railway Directory & Year Book 1980. Tunnels over 4.9 miles in length.

The first London Underground train, powered by steam, was completed in 1863. By the latter part of Queen Victoria's reign the railway network extended over almost the whole of Britain – and on the whole the safety record has been remarkably high, though there have been occasional disasters; one was the collapse of the Tay Bridge in 1879 as a crowded passenger train was crossing it (a tragedy suitably solemnized in an ode by William McGonagall, universally admitted to have been the worst poet of all time). Other countries also perfected their railway systems. Japan's, for instance, began in 1871. By 1883 the great

Australian cities of Sydney and Melbourne had been linked; the Calais–Nice–Rome Express completed its journey in a mere eighteen hours, while the Orient Express from Paris to Constantinople used new four-wheel bogies and springing, enabling it to reach a speed of 50 mph on some stretches. The construction of the Trans-Siberian Railway began in 1891; the Paris Metro was opened in 1900; and the Trans-Siberian railway from Moscow to Vladivostok was completed in 1904 (with its total length of 3200 miles, it is still the longest in the world). Moscow's Metropol subway was completed in 1935 – a $5\frac{1}{2}$-mile track suitably decorated with murals, pillars and chandeliers, though admittedly it looks very different today. A year later came the London-to-Paris train ferry, with carriages loaded on to the ferry and disembarked at Dunkirk.

Today the once-familiar British steam engines have vanished, to be replaced by faster if less romantic Diesels. Sadly, the scope of the British railway system was destroyed during the 1960s by the economy axe wielded by Dr (now Lord) Beeching, but much remains, and no civilized country could now run efficiently without the aid of its railway for the transport of people and goods.

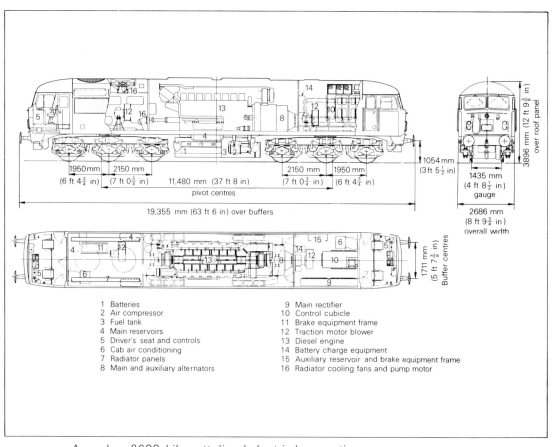

1 Batteries
2 Air compressor
3 Fuel tank
4 Main reservoirs
5 Driver's seat and controls
6 Cab air conditioning
7 Radiator panels
8 Main and auxiliary alternators
9 Main rectifier
10 Control cubicle
11 Brake equipment frame
12 Traction motor blower
13 Diesel engine
14 Battery charge equipment
15 Auxiliary reservoir and brake equipment frame
16 Radiator cooling fans and pump motor

A modern 2600-kilowatt diesel electric locomotive

Powered Transport: The Roads

Before discussing the motor-car – surely even more important today than the train – something must be said about the only remaining man-powered land vehicle: the bicycle. In its primitive form it began in 1813, in Germany, when the Baron Drais built a strange contraption in which the rider sat on a saddle between two wheels and 'ran' with his feet. Not unnaturally his invention never became popular, and was regarded with considerable amusement, but in 1852 another German, Fischer, provided fixed pedals, and may therefore claim to be the true pioneer of today's bicycle. In 1870 Pierre Lallement designed the 'penny-farthing', using a large front wheel and a small back wheel, and adding rotary pedals. Many of these early vehicles still exist – the present writer [PM] once rode one, admittedly with disastrous results.

The 'penny-farthing', designed originally in 1870

In 1876 H.J.Lawson designed the safety bicycle, which was rear-driven, with the cranks and pedals in the middle. Chains, wire-spoked wheels, padded spring saddles, and ball-bearings were added during the next few years, and then came the free-wheeling mechanism, the creation of an extraordinary man named Hermann Ganswindt. Ganswindt, born in 1856 in East Prussia, was the archetypal crazy inventor. First he devised a mechanism worked by a treadle, and installed it in a carriage; he tried out his 'tretmotor' in Berlin, causing so much interest that the authorities requested him to desist. He adapted the same principle for use in a fire-engine, and then invented a helicopter, driven by falling weights and capable of rising no more than a few feet above the ground. In 1891 he gave a lecture on the possibilities of space-travel, and described a proposed vehicle using dynamite as its propellent. But at least his free-wheeling mechanism for a bicycle actually worked!

Subsequently, the comfort of cycling was improved beyond all recognition by John Dunlop's invention of air-filled pneumatic tyres in 1888. Until cars became really practicable, the bicycle reigned supreme for short-distance journeys; even today there are countless people who would feel lost without it.

A car travelling at 30 mph loses the following percentages of its energy in converting petrol to mechanical energy:

Cooling water	−35.8%
exhaust gases	−35.6%
exhaust pipe	−1.0%
silencer	−1.2%
engine friction	−5.6%

Source: *Energy Resources*, Andrew Simon (Pergamon Press Inc, 1975)

This leaves a remaining 20.8% of the energy to move the car. But the motion itself loses energy through resistance:

rear tyres	−3.7%
front tyres	−1.1%
front wheels	−0.6%
wind resistance	−7.1%

This leaves the car with only 5.4% of its potential power to accelerate and climb.

The first mechanical road vehicles were steam-cars. In 1801 the -'Cornish giant', Richard Trevithick – another man who was a strange mixture of genius and crank – drove the 90-mile journey from Camborne to Plymouth; in 1831 Gurney devised a steam carriage which ran regularly between Cheltenham and Gloucester, attaining a speed of 12 mph; and in 1833 Ogle and Summers built a steam-car which could reach a top speed of 35 mph and could climb a steep hill at 24 mph. It ran for 800 miles without a single breakdown. By 1843 Hill's steam-coach was running regularly between Deptford and Hastings. Then, in 1860 Lenoir developed the first internal combustion engine, consisting of a single-cylinder horizontal engine; slide valves controlled the admission and expulsion of petrol and air, and the cylinder was cooled by a water jacket. Lenoir's design was not fully practicable, partly because it used vast amounts of

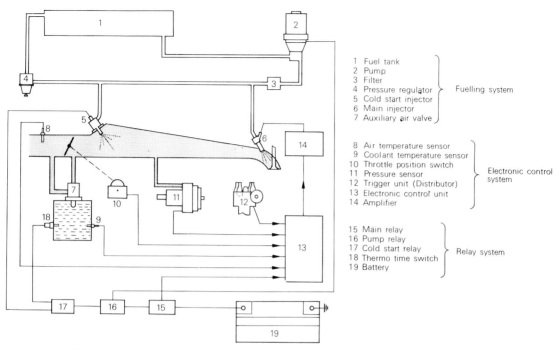

1 Fuel tank
2 Pump
3 Filter
4 Pressure regulator   } Fuelling system
5 Cold start injector
6 Main injector
7 Auxiliary air valve

8 Air temperature sensor
9 Coolant temperature sensor
10 Throttle position switch
11 Pressure sensor   } Electronic control
12 Trigger unit (Distributor)   system
13 Electronic control unit
14 Amplifier

15 Main relay
16 Pump relay
17 Cold start relay   } Relay system
18 Thermo time switch
19 Battery

Basic system of petrol injection in motor cars (source: Lucas Industries). Petrol engines in ordinary motor cars run at speeds of up to 5000–6000 revolutions per minute

petrol and was very low-powered, but an 1867 design by Otto and Langen was much better; the piston rod was geared so that it drove the shaft only on the downstroke, so that efficiency was improved and petrol consumption halved. By 1876 Otto had perfected the engine even further, with the introduction of one very important innovation – the compression of explosive mixture in the cylinder before ignition. The engine was horizontal, and required four strokes to complete the cycle. Otto also introduced the centrifugal governer into the combustion engine, to cut off the petrol supply if the engine speed became too great.

Petrol or steam? That question was not resolved as easily as might be thought. Originally, steam-cars more than held their own, and those of the Serpollet firm in particular were strong challengers. It has even been said that had equal attention been given to the steam-car, it might now be in general use. In view of the current shortage of oil, it would seem worth while to re-open the matter.

But there was never any doubt that the petrol engine would be fitted to road vehicles. In 1885 Daimler patented a single-cylinder engine and fitted it to a bicycle, using a carburettor and spark ignition; in the same year Karl Benz produced a three-wheeled motor-driven vehicle, capable of attaining 9 mph, and in 1892 René Panhard Levasser introduced the first car with pneumatic tyres. In the following year came the first Ford car, with tiller steering. Then, in 1896, Britain's Parliament repealed the 1865 act according to which any motor-driven vehicle on the public highway had to be preceded by a man carrying a red flag. The Age of the Car had dawned.

So far as the design and performance of the car are concerned, it has been a story of rapid and continuous progress. The first passenger buses appeared in Norfolk in 1900; taxis came to Paris in 1905, and in 1906 the firm of Rolls Royce manufactured a car using an almost silent six-cylinder engine developing 40 to 50 horsepower. The first Model T Ford – the 'Tin Lizzie' – dates from 1908; the first electric self-starter, designed by C. Fettering, from 1911. Roads were improved to cope with the flow of traffic, and in 1921 the Germans opened the first autobahn, with a length of $6\frac{3}{4}$ miles. (The longest motorable road in the world today is the Pan-American highway, stretching over 17,000 miles from Alaska to Chile.) Power-steering units were introduced by Francis Davis in 1927, and in 1938 the 'people's car', the Volkswagen, was assembled in Germany. It had an air-cooled engine, and today the Volkswagen is still one of the most popular of all 'family cars'. Of course there have been other types of engine, notably the Diesel, which runs on oil and needs neither sparking plugs, battery nor carburettor; it was invented in 1893 by Rudolf Diesel (later to

Progressive world land speed records

Speed (mph)	Date	Driver	Motive power
39.24	1898	Comte Gaston de Chasseloup-Laubat	Electric engine
65.79	1899	Camille Jenatzy	Electric engine
103.56	1904	Louis Rigolly	Petrol engine
150.87	1925	Captain Malcolm Campbell	Petrol engine
203.79	1927	Sir Henry Segrave	Petrol engine
253.968	1932	Sir Malcolm Campbell	Petrol engine (supercharged)
301.13	1935	Sir Malcolm Campbell	Petrol engine (aeroplane)
350.20	1938	John Cobb	Petrol engine (2 super-charged aero-engines)
394.196	1947	John Cobb	Petrol engine

(including one run of over 400 mph)

622.287	1970	Gary Gabelich	Rocket powered

(In 1979 Stan Barrett attained the highest speed ever reached in any wheeled vehicle when he drove a rocket-powered car at 739.666 mph)

Source: The Guinness Book of Car Facts and Feats 1977
The Guinness Book of Records 1981

disappear mysteriously crossing the Channel). There is also the gas-turbine powered car, of which the Rovers in 1952 were the first. In 1980 a specially designed car of this type reached a speed of something like 600 mph. The days of the walker carrying a red flag to warn of an approaching vehicle seem very far away.

'The Bulldog' – Aston Martin's twin turbo-charged V8-engined 'ultimate supercar', with gull-wing doors, costing £130,000 to develop and build

Yet there are disquieting facts. The steady toll of deaths by road accident is unacceptable; in many countries the roads are becoming hopelessly crowded (at least 200,000 vehicles flow round Hyde Park Corner every day), and the motor-car cannot be regarded as an unmitigated blessing. What can be done to solve these problems remains to be seen. They are pressing now, but they will be far more pressing before the twentieth century comes to its end.

Powered Transport: The Ocean

'Men might as well project a voyage to the Moon as attempt to employ steam navigation across the stormy North Atlantic Ocean.' So commented Dr Dionysius Lardner in 1838, in an address to the British Association. Dr Lardner proved to be a poor prophet. True, a trip to the Moon was deferred for another 131 years after his speech, but steamships already existed; as early as 1807 a Watt and Boulton four-stroke engine had been installed in the 133-foot vessel *Clermont*, which was driven by paddle-wheels. Wooden ships were superseded by vessels made of iron; and, presumably unknown to Dr Lardner, the steamship *Royal William* actually crossed the Atlantic in 1833, taking seventeen days to do so. Five years later Brunel's *Great Western*, of 1340 tons displacement and fitted with a 440 horsepower engine, cut this time by two days. An important development was the work of Pettit Smith in 1839, who designed the *Archimedes* and drove it by means of a screw instead of paddle-wheels. The new Bessemer process meant that steel could be produced at an economical price, and, soon, steel ships were built, initially in 1863. Meantime, efforts were being made to cut the times of long voyages, and the Suez Canal was opened in 1870.

The steam turbine was the result of the work of Sir Charles Parsons, whose *Turbinia*, capable of $34\frac{1}{2}$ knots, was displayed at Spithead in 1897, on the occasion of Queen Victoria's Diamond Jubilee, and made its Admiralty critics look very foolish indeed. The first passenger turbine ship was the *King Edward* of 1902, and about the same time John Holland invented a submarine which was propelled by electric motors under the water and an internal combustion engine above. Submarines became practicable, as was all too evident during World War One, 1914–18, when Allied losses at sea were alarmingly great. By then the Panama canal had been opened, and sea-travel had become common.

The inter-war years marked the zenith of the luxury passenger liners; the *Queen Mary*, the *Queen Elizabeth*, the *Mauritania*, the *Normandie* and others whose names have passed into legend. And during the Second World War, control of the sea was all-important. Subsequently, nuclear-powered submarines were built, beginning with the *Nautilus* in 1955 – the same *Nautilus* which ventured under the north pole in 1958. By 1960 the United States submarine, *Triton*, made the first undersea round-the-world voyage, taking 84 days, and today the nuclear submarines of both Russia and America, with their capability of launching devastating attacks, are a threat to the whole of civilization.

Nowadays there are few luxury liners left; the *Queen Elizabeth II*, completed in 1969, is the best-known of them. Air travel has almost completely superseded the more leisurely sea voyages between one continent and another, while sailing-ships are used for pleasure only. How many readers of this book have crossed the Atlantic by sea? Probably very few; but only half a century ago, it was to all intents and purposes the only way.

Travel in the Air

The idea of flying goes back to the very start of recorded history. Legends about it abound – one of the most famous being that of Dædalus and his son Icarus, who equipped themselves with wings and soared upwards; Dædalus completed his trip safely, but Icarus flew too close to the Sun, so that the wax glueing his wings together melted, and he fell to his death in the sea.

World air speed records

Speed over a straight course
3,529.56 kph. (2,193.16 mph) – Capt. Elden W. Joersz, USAF, Lockheed SR-71; Beale AFB, Cal., July 28, 1976
Speed over a closed circuit
3,367.221 kph. (2,092.294 mph) – Maj. Adolphus H. Bledsoe Jr., USAF, Lockheed SR-71; Beale AFB, Cal., July 27, 1976.
Distance in a straight line
20,168.78 kms (12,532.28 mi.) – Maj., Clyde P. Evely, USAF, Boeing B52-H; Kadena, Okinawa to Madrid, Spain, Jan. 11, 1962.
Distance over a closed circuit
18,245.05 kms (11,336.92 mi.) – Capt. William Stevenson, USAF, Boeing B52-H; Seymour-Johnson, N.C., June 6–7, 1962.
Altitude
37,650 meters (123,523.58 feet) – Alexander Fedotov, USSR, E-266M; Podmoskovnoye, USSR, Aug. 31, 1977.
Altitude in horizontal flight
25,929.031 meters (85,068.997 ft.) – Capt. Robert C. Helt, USAF, Lockheed SR-71; Beale AFB, Cal., July 28, 1976

Another legend concerns Bladud, King of England, who is said to have attempted a flight over London with the aid of artificial wings, with the usual disastrous result. But the first attempt which has any real historical foundation was made by an English monk, Oliver of Malmesbury, about 1020. Oliver equipped himself with wings, climbed a high tower and jumped bravely off. If the reports are to be trusted, he glided for some 200 yards, though his enthusiasm may have been somewhat tempered by the fact that on landing he broke both his legs.

The next figure of note is that of Roger Bacon, a Franciscan friar, who lived from 1214 to 1292. Bacon knew that the Earth's air is limited in extent, but he thought – wrongly – that it must have a definite upper surface, so that it might be possible to 'row' a flying machine much as a boat is rowed upon the surface of the sea. He proposed to build a globe, made of thin copper, and fill it with some lighter-than-air substance, after which it could be launched to the top of the atmosphere from a high mountain. Essentially, then, Bacon's proposed vehicle was more in the nature of a balloon than an aeroplane.

Next came a Jesuit, Francesco de Lana, who planned a vehicle on much the same lines, and did some sound scientific research in the process, though evidently he made no practical trials. The first hot-air balloon which actually flew was made by a Portuguese, Bartholomeu de Gusmão, in 1709. According to Russian claims, an inventor named Kryakutny went up in a balloon in 1731. Frankly, this seems improbable, and pride of place must go to the Montgolfier brothers, who took off on 21 November 1783 and rose to a height of some 6000 feet. Shortly afterwards another Frenchman, Jacques Charles, ascended to 10,000 feet in a balloon which was filled with hydrogen instead of hot air, and in 1785 Blanchard and Jeffries made the first cross-Channel flight.

The troubles with ballooning were twofold. First, hydrogen – the lightest and therefore most effective gas – is highly inflammable. Secondly, balloons are very difficult to steer. It has even been said that every balloon flight is a prolonged emergency. All the same, the French engineer, Henri Giffard, made and flew a 143-foot dirigible in 1852, equipping it with a 3-horsepower steam-engine; and in 1870 the astronomer, Jules Janssen, made a balloon escape from the besieged city of Paris, because he was anxious to observe an eclipse of the Sun. (It was sheer bad luck that after this hazardous but successful flight, his observations of the eclipse were frustrated by a layer of cloud.)

Giffard's vehicle might well be classed as an airship rather than a balloon, but it was not until 1897 that the first structured airship was designed – the work of the German Count von Zeppelin. During the war Zeppelin airships carried out air-raids over England, though they were never really effective. For a while it seemed that airships might prove to be the main vehicles of the twentieth century, but their tendency to explode proved an insuperable handicap, and the loss of the *Hindenburg* in 1937 brought airship development to a halt. Today there is more than a hint of revival. Helium, which is an inert gas, can be produced cheaply enough to replace the explosive hydrogen, and it is true that a voyage in an airship must be both comfortable and attractive – even though by modern standards it is bound to be slow. Perhaps the airship will eventually return. But meanwhile, all the emphasis is upon heavier-than-air machines.

Early ideas were proposed by the 'Forerunner' – Leonardo da Vinci, the 'universal genius' who lived from 1452 to 1519. Leonardo made various important aeronautical advances – particularly his description of a workable parachute and some sound theories about propellers. Unfortunately he concentrated mainly on 'ornithopters' (wing-flappers), and he was handi-capped by some faulty ideas about how a bird actually flies. He attempted to design a helicopter, but without an engine it could never have flown. Moreover, we are now quite certain that a man's muscles are quite inadequate to support him by the ornithopter principle, even though enthusiastic amateurs continue to experiment from time to time, and have even managed short, rather breathless 'hops'. So for once in a way, Leonardo was on the wrong track. (Of course, theorists can be wrong. Acording to all the principles of aerodynamics, the humble bumble-bee is far too heavy and cumbersome to leave the ground at all. But bees continue to fly – presumably because nobody has ever told them that they can't.)

The real 'father of aeronautics' was Sir George Cayley, who lived near Scarborough. First he considered that age-old toy, the kite. If you hold a kite by the end of its string and walk along, the kite will remain aloft – provided that you are giving it a thrust which is greater than the wind thrust plus air resistance. Much the same principle applies to the feathered or vaned arrow. After being launched, the arrow will continue in flight until gravity, together with air resistance, overcomes the thrust given by the initial speed. Make a 'powered arrow', then, and why should it not fly?

In effect, this is what Cayley did. Having made careful studies of 'lift', 'thrust' and 'drag', terms familiar to anyone who takes an interest in aircraft design, he produced a five-foot long model glider, complete with a tail unit to act as a rudder. The wings were set near the head instead of the tail, as with an arrow. Five years later, Cayley made a full-sized glider with a wing area of 200 square feet. Not long before his death, in 1857, he successfully experimented with man-carrying gliders, and at least two people are known to have flown in them.

The inspiration provided by Cayley led others also to make gliders, and then, in 1857–8, a French naval officer, Félix du Temple, made a steam-powered model which actually flew. Naturally, he went on to make what he hoped would be a man-carrying vehicle. It was a machine with wings swept forward, a tailplane and rudder, and a retractable undercarriage, with a steam-driven propeller. About 1874 it was tested, but unfortunately without success, and never rose more than a few inches.

In 1884, a Russian, Alexander Mozhaisky, tested a powered machine of the same basic type. Piloted by I.N.Golubev, it seems to have risen briefly, but, like du Temple's, it was not a real success. Neither was the *Eole*, made by Clement Ader in France, even though it flew (unpiloted) for over three hundred yards. The main troubles, of course, were faulty design plus the feeble power of available engines. But a major breakthrough lay close ahead. It was due to the combined work of Samuel Pierpont Langley, Otto Lilienthal, Octave Chanute, and above all Orville and Wilbur Wright.

Langley, a famous American astronomer, became interested in mechanical flight about 1886, and built various successful models, after which he turned his attention to manned vehicles. He constructed a full-sized vehicle, the *Aerodrome*, and carried out tests in 1903, but with no success; each time the machine was launched, it plunged down into the waters of the Potomac River. Yet he had made notable advances, and deserves more credit than he is usually accorded.

Otto Lilienthal concentrated upon gliders, and improved them beyond all recognition. It was his work which inspired the Wright brothers, but unhappily

Lilienthal was killed during a glider flight in 1896. Octave Chanute, an American of French descent, designed gliders and wrote a classic book, *Progress in Flying Machines*, published in 1894. He did not take up aeronautics until middle-aged, and he was too old to fly gliders himself, but he supervised their tests. He gave all possible help to the Wrights; without him, it is quite likely that the first manned flight would have been delayed for years.

Orville and Wilbur Wright were mechanically-minded, and became bicycle manufacturers, but after reading books upon aeronautics – notably Chanute's – they began experimenting. By 1903 they had completed the *Flyer*, which was just over 21 feet long, with a wing-span of 40 feet and a total weight of 750 pounds. It was a biplane, with two propellers. And on 17 December 1903, Orville few for twelve seconds, covering a distance of over a hundred feet at a speed of 28 knots. It was the world's first powered, sustained and controlled flight by man. Three more flights were made during the same day, two by Wilbur and one by Orville, before an inconvenient burst of wind rolled the *Flyer* over and put it temporarily out of action.

The Wright brothers' aeroplane in flight in France, 1908

The essential problem had been overcome; the Wrights lost no time in building better machines, despite initial scepticism from people who should certainly have known better (notably Professor Simon Newcomb, the famous astronomer, who had maintained that no heavier-than-air machine could possibly fly, and persisted in this view even after the Wrights had demonstrated their skill). By 1908 Wilbur was able to stay aloft for over an hour, carrying a passenger, and the newly-founded Wright Company started to produce aeroplanes. Wilbur died of typhoid fever in 1912, but Orville lived on until 1948, though for the last thirty years of his life he virtually gave up flying. It is interesting to remember that his life-span overlapped those of Yuri Gagarin, the first cosmonaut, and Neil Armstrong, the first man on the Moon . . .

By 1909 other designers had entered the field of aeronautics; the French pilot, Louis Blériot, crossed the Channel in a monoplane, and Farman covered 140 miles in only four hours. Even before the outbreak of the first world war, in 1914, impressive new records had been set. Using an Albatros biplane, Boehm stayed aloft for 24 hours 10 minutes; Oelrech, in a DFW biplane, reached an altitude of 25,750 feet; and Prévost, in a Deperdussin monoplane, achieved a speed of 126 mph. During the war, air warfare became a grim reality. The first air-raids and aerial 'dogfights' showed, yet again, that every great invention is capable of being misused.

In 1919, a year after the end of hostilities, Alcock and Whitten-Brown achieved the first transatlantic crossing; they flew a Vickers machine, covering 1880 miles in 16 hours 12 minutes. Donald Douglas made a round-the world flight in 1924 in a *World Cruiser* powered by Liberty engines; he could stay up for 18 hours before having to land for refuelling, and the whole journey took only 15 flying days. During the next decade record after record was broken; for instance Amy Johnson flew her tiny *Gypsy Moth* from London to India, and Kingsford-Smith and Ulm completed a trans-Pacific journey from California to Melbourne, in the triple-motor Fokker monoplane *Southern Cross*.

In England, Frank Whittle began to experiment with the principle of jet propulsion. He met with no official encouragement. In 1934 the British Under-Secretary of State for Air wrote that 'we follow with interest any work that is being done in other countries on jet propulsion, but scientific investigation into its possibilities has given no indication that the method can be a serious competitor to the airscrew-engine combination. We do not consider that we should be justified in spending any time or money on it ourselves.' (Shades of Dr Dionysius Lardner.) But the first jet-aircraft flew in May 1941, during Hitler's war, and by now the jet-engine has taken over for all long commercial flights. In 1950 the regular *Comet* passenger flights began, to be followed in 1969 by *Concorde* – capable of flying at more than twice the speed of sound, and a magnificent technical triumph, even if a financial liability. The Jumbo Jets that now fly the Atlantic weigh a thousand times more than the Wright Brothers' *Flyer*.

The greatest journey of all time must surely have been the transport of man to the moon. Buzz Aldrin stands on the lunar surface in 1969, with Neil Armstrong reflected in his visor

Then, in April 1981, came an entirely new type of vehicle – the Space Shuttle, which was launched like a rocket, flew like a spacecraft and landed like a glider. After seemingly endless delays, the Shuttle, *Columbia*, blasted away from Cape Canaveral in Florida, carrying two men: John Young, who could be classed as a 'space veteran' and had been to the Moon, and Robert Crippen. They completed 36 orbits of the Earth, and landed smoothly on the dirt runway of Rogers Dry Lake in California. Their success in the pioneer 'recoverable spacecraft' was of immense significance. It showed that men will be able to travel freely to and from the great orbital space-stations which will certainly be set up within the next couple of decades.

Transport and travel have, especially in the last two hundred years, opened up the world. Discoveries and developments in engineering and technology have made it possible to take people on journeys, and to transport freight, farther and faster than ever before. Tankers use the sea lanes to carry oil around the world; railway systems and roads abound in most countries; barges ply the rivers and canals of Europe; planes criss-cross the air above continents and oceans; and man still rides the bicycle. In space, men have flown beyond the Earth, and walked upon the Moon. (Let us not forget, incidentally, that there has also been one woman cosmonaut, Valentina Tereshkova.) Unmanned vehicles have penetrated close to the Sun, by-passing Venus and Mercury, and also out to Saturn in the remoter part of the Solar System. Few parts of the Earth remain untravelled and uncharted by man, but, given a peaceful world, the possibilities of further space travel are endless.

Differential gearing was known in China before the birth of Christ.

In 1615 a Dutch inventor, Cornelius van Drebbel, demonstrated a submarine in England. The vessel consisted of a rowing boat covered with leather that was then rowed along underwater.

Several years after the Wright brothers had flown successfully for the first time the US Congress passed a bill to prevent the army from wasting funds experimenting with flying machines.

In 1868 the first traffic signals were installed outside the Houses of Parliament. They were fitted with red and green gas lamps, though the design was modified after the first set blew up and killed a policeman.

It was not until 1920 that brakes on all four wheels became standard features of motor cars.

When Charles Lindbergh made his historic crossing of the Atlantic in 1927 the fuel tanks fitted to the *Spirit of St Louis* were so large that he had to look through a periscope to see where he was going.

During peak production in World War Two one jeep was rolling off the production line every eighty seconds. A total of nearly 649,000 jeeps was manufactured during the war.

The first time that cars were generally started by ignition keys was in 1949.

The train journey from Vladivostok across the USSR to Moscow lasts nine days and covers 6,000 miles.

Birmingham has 22 more miles of canal than Venice.

You can sail all the way round the earth on latitude 60° South.

11

Communication

What is the particular ability which singles out man from all other mammals? Obviously there are outward differences, but we must accept the fact that a modern astronomer, an orang-outan and a lemur have common ancestry in the small, tree-living primates of the Eocene Period, some 70,000,000 years ago. Perhaps the one vital difference between man and any other animal is our ability to use language – in fact, to communicate with each other.

Animals (perhaps lower forms of life also) can communicate to some extent. Recently there has been a great deal of talk about the language of dolphins, which would be extremely interesting if we could understand it, and may be more complicated than we think. Neither are dolphins alone in possessing this ability. But a complicated *language* in the true sense of the term is another matter. Mr Dolphin might be able to convey to Mrs Dolphin the news that 'It is dangerous to go over there'. He would certainly not be able to say 'Good-morning, my dear. You are looking remarkably well. Shall we go for a morning swim and call in upon our friends by West Beach?'

Admittedly this is a somewhat ridiculous example, but it does stress that only man can hold what we normally call a conversation. Just when true language started is a matter for debate. Gradually the 'Ug' and 'Og' of the cave-dwellers of the Stone Age evolved into a language that was no doubt simple at first. More accurately one should say 'languages', because the many differences in tongue must have become apparent at a very early stage. This is shown, for instance, by the tremendous variety of languages among primitive tribes today. It is thought that there were 500 different Aborigine dialects alone, even though the total number of Aborigines probably never exceeded 250,000. But language was bound to develop, partly because the human physiology makes it possible, and partly because a greater proportion of our brains is devoted to ear and tongue co-ordination than is the case with any other creature.

Our knowledge of the 'earliest men' is still limited, but of one thing we may be sure: the spoken language of early men was already complicated before the first attempts were made to write it down. At first, too, 'words' took the form of pictures. Our earliest-known pictograms are Sumerian; they date from about 3200 BC, and are really rough drawings of the objects which are to be described. The next step was to formalize these pictograms into wedge-shaped impressions on clay; we have come to the famous cuneiform script. Symbols were invented to describe ideas as well as objects. 'Ideograms' replaced pictograms..

The earliest surviving cuneiform script comprises about 2000 ideograms. By about 3000 BC the number required had been reduced to 800 or thereabouts, which made the writings not only clearer but much more economical. Five hundred years later the necessary ideograms had been reduced to a mere 600. There has been immense difficulty in translating some of the cuneiform writings, and even now we cannot claim to have an exact knowledge of them, but we can state, without much fear of contradiction, that the Sumerian script was the root of all Western alphabets.

Then, of course, there were Egyptian hieroglyphics. The word means, literally, 'sacred writing'. The earliest known examples are those found in the tombs of the Pharaohs at Abydos, and date from about 3200 BC. As time went by, the hieroglyphics were joined by a cursive script which may have been based on them; both forms of writing became distinctly phonetic as they evolved – but for a long time they, too, defied translation. The situation was largely saved by the famous Rosetta stone, dating from 196 BC, which contains an inscription in hieroglyphics and also a translation into Greek. Obviously it gave the all-important clue – and but for the near-miracle of this stone's survival, our knowledge of the writing that was current in Ancient Egypt would be very much more meagre than it actually is.

The Phœnicians were of Semitic origin, and were traders based on the north coast of Africa; their greatest city was, of course, Carthage, the rival of Rome, eventually destroyed more completely and permanently than any major city has been before or since. (Had the Carthaginians conquered Rome, as under Hannibal they very nearly did, the whole story of civilization – and also the story of language – would have been different.) The Phœnicians adopted the Sumerian script and used it in keeping their records and accounts. In so doing, they invented the first true alphabet. It is difficult to set a date to this vitally important development, but it was long before Carthage's rise to greatness.

What we do know is that around 1500 BC, a 29-character phonetic alphabet came into use among the Phœnicians, and a little later another alphabet, this time of only 22 characters, came into use. It was the forerunner of the Greek alphabet – and hence the forerunner also of the Etruscan, Roman and all modern Western alphabets; and through the South Arabian and Aramaic scripts it was to give rise to the alphabets of Arabia and India – the earliest Hebrew script (the Moabite Stone inscription) dates back to 890 BC.

Subsequent developments were more rapid. By 700 BC the Greeks were borrowing elements from the Phœnician alphabet – it is interesting to note that early Greek writing was read from right to left, though this did not persist for long. The eighth century BC was the time of Hesiod, one of the earliest of the 'great' writers. By 675 the classical Greek alphabet was in being, and the earliest Latin inscription dates from about 650 BC. Actually, the difference between these two alphabets is much more superficial than real. (It takes an Englishman only an hour or so to learn the Greek alphabet, and a very small amount of practice will enable him to read Greek aloud in a recognizable form even if he cannot understand it – and of course the converse is also true.)

This was all very well for the Mediterranean area, but it was quite different for the Orient. In China, writing began similarly with pictograms and ideograms, but the ideograms were never replaced by phonetic symbols. Therefore, the ideograms went on increasing in number as the script developed. The first known pictograms are on the so-called 'oracle bones' of about 1400 BC, but by the sixth century BC the famous Confucius was complaining about

NORTH SEMITIC					GREEK					RUSSIAN		ETRUSCAN	LATIN		MODERN ROMAN
Phoenecian	Early Hebrew	Classical and Modern Hebrew	Name	Modern Transliteration	Early		Name	Transliteration Classical	Transliteration Modern	Cyrillic	Transliteration		Early	Classic	English
𐤀	𐤀	א	alef	’	Α	Α α	alpha	a	a	А а	a	𐌀	A Λ	A	A a
𐤁	𐤁	ב	bet	b,v	B	Β β	beta	b	v	Б б	b	𐌁	B	B	B b
										В в	v				
𐤂	𐤂	ג	gimel	g	Γ	Γ γ	gamma	g	gh,y	Г г	g	𐌂	C	C	C c
𐤃	𐤃	ד	dalet	d	Δ	Δ δ	delta	d	dh	Д д	d	𐌃	D	D	D d
𐤄	𐤄	ה	he	h	Ε	Ε ε	epsilon	e	e	Е е	e,ye,yo	𐌄	E	E	E e
𐤅	𐤅	ו	waw, vav	w,v	Ϝ	(see letter V)						𐌅	F	F	F f
	(see letter C)													G	G g
										Ж ж	zh				
𐤆	𐤆	ז	zayin	z	Ι	Ζ ζ	zeta	z	z	З з	z	𐌆			
𐤇	𐤇	ח	ḥet	ḥ,ch	Η	Η η	eta	ē	i			𐌇	H	H	H h
𐤈	𐤈	ט	ṭet	ṭ,t	⊗	Θ θ	theta	th	th			𐌈			
𐤉	𐤉	י	yod	y	Ι	Ι ι	iota	i	i	И и	i	𐌉	I	I	I i
	(see letter I)														J j
										Й й	y,i				
𐤊	𐤊	כך	kaf, khaf	k, kh	Κ	Κ κ	kappa	k	k	К к	k	𐌊	K K	K	K k
𐤋	𐤋	ל	lamed	l	Λ	Λ λ	lambda	l	l	Л л	l	𐌋	L	L	L l
𐤌	𐤌	מם	mem	m	Μ	Μ μ	mu	m	m	М м	m	𐌌	M	M	M m
𐤍	𐤍	נן	nun	n	Ν	Ν ν	nu	n	n	Н н	n	𐌍	N	N	N n
𐤎	𐤎	ס	samekh	s	Ξ	Ξ ξ	xi	x	x,ks						
𐤏	𐤏	ע	‘ayin	‘	Ο	Ο ο	omicron	o	o	О о	o	𐌏	O	O	O o
𐤐	𐤐	פף	pe, fe	p,f	Π	Π π	pi	p	p	П п	p	𐌐	Γ Γ	P	P p
𐤑	𐤑	צץ	tsade	ts,tz											
𐤒	𐤒	ק	qof	q									Q	Q	Q q
𐤓	𐤓	ר	resh	r	Ρ	Ρ ρ	rho	r,rh	r	Р р	r	𐌓	R	R	R r
𐤔	𐤔	ש	shin, sin	sh,s	Σ	Σ σ,s	sigma	s	s	С с	s	𐌔	S S	S	S s
𐤕	𐤕	ת	taw	t	Τ	Τ τ	tau	t	t	Т т	t	𐌕	T	T	T t
															U u
					Υ	Υ υ	upsilon	y,u	i	У у	u	𐌖	V	V	V v
															W w
						Φ φ	phi	ph	f	Ф ф	f				
					Χ	Χ χ	chi	ch	h,kh	Х х	kh, h		X	X	X x
														Y	Y y
														Z	Z z
					Ψ	Ψ ψ	psi	ps	ps						
					⊙	Ω ω	omega	ō	o						
										Ц ц	ts				
										Ч ч	ch,č				
										Ш ш	sh,š				
										Щ щ	shch,šč				
										Ъ ъ	” (hard sign)				
										Ы ы	ȳ				
										Ь ь	(soft sign)				
										Э э	e,è				
										Ю ю	yu				
										Я я	ya				

What most sharply distinguishes man from other creatures is his ability to talk. This table shows the development of the modern alphabet, from Phoenician to English

many troublesome variations in the ideographic script, which by then had become well-established. It was sheer bad luck that, later on, when writing was introduced into Japan, it was in the Chinese form rather than the Mediterranean; and this has persisted until the present day. This is something that many modern Japanese regret, since they are the first to admit that the European form is vastly more convenient. Originally the reason for retaining the ideograms may have been that they could be read by people who spoke in different dialects and therefore had completely different pronunciation, but the eventual result was unfortunate. Periodical attempts have been made to improve the situation, and a fully phonetic script has now been introduced even though it has not yet replaced the ideograms. It is quite likely that in the foreseeable future the Japanese, at least, will change over to the European alphabet, though there is naturally a wide range of disagreement upon so important an issue. It is significant that the European visitor to modern Tokyo or any other major Japanese city will find the information signs generally written in European as well as in Japanese characters.

But if the Chinese produced inconvenient writing, they were pioneers in many ways, notably in paper-making and printing. It seems that as early as 105 BC, Ts'ai-lun invented paper to replace bamboo slips – it is said that he was driven to do so by the unwelcome attentions of paper-wasps! In 751 the Arabs captured some Chinese paper-makers, and the use of paper spread through the Arab world, reaching Europe in the late thirteenth century to replace vellum, which is merely sheepskin. Moreover, by 700 the Chinese were using wooden blocks to stamp 'charms' on to paper or silk, which is, after all, a very elementary form of printing; and in 1041 Pi Sheng made moveable type in the form of hundreds of ideogram-bearing clay blocks. Wood-blocks for printing highly elaborate capital letters in manuscripts were cut in 1174 – not in China, but in Switzerland, at a monastery near Engelberg. By the late thirteenth century illustration blocks were being produced in Italy. Movable type followed in France, Holland and elsewhere, but the man traditionally credited with the invention of 'real' printing was a German goldsmith, Johannes Gutenberg, who joined with his partner Johann Fust to set up the first large printing-house. By 1448 his 'factory' at Mainz had cast enough type to set a whole Bible, and a Bible was in fact printed in 1456 – possibly by Gutenberg himself. So far as England was concerned, pride of place goes to William Caxton, who set up his printing press at Westminster in 1476 – having previously established a press at Bruges in Belgium. Examples of Caxton's work still survive.

(Even in the early days of printing, there were occasional embarrassing mistakes. In an edition of the Holy Bible printed in 1631 by Robert Barker, the seventh commandment is given as 'Thou shalt commit adultery'. Whether any of its readers obeyed this command is not known, but the printer was fined £300 and the entire edition of one thousand copies was ordered to be destroyed,

A wooden hand printing press of the kind used over 400 years ago

though fortunately for posterity two copies still survive!)

The impact of printing upon civilization can hardly be overestimated. Previously, all books had had to be hand-copied, and it is easy to see how laborious this process was. Moreover, in most countries (including England) the illiteracy rate approached 100 per cent. Anyone who could read and write was regarded as exceptionally learned. But when books became available the entire position changed, and it is fair to say that printing ushered in 'the age of education'. Of course, there are still some countries where books are extremely scarce; and here we find a situation comparable with that in pre-Caxtonian England.

Paris had its first print-shop in 1470. And in 1605, the year of the Gunpowder Plot in England, there came the world's first newspaper. It was produced in Antwerp by a man named Abraham Verkoevan, whose right to immortality is somewhat prejudiced by the fact that he was hardly of sober habits – indeed, it is said that he was drunk almost all the time, which presumably influenced the quality of his work. The first regular newspapers followed in 1609; the *Aviso Relation oder Zeitung* in Lower Saxony, and *Aller Furnemmen und Gedenckwurdigen Historien* in Strasbourg. It was not until 1702 that London had its first daily newspaper – the *Daily Courant*; the oldest periodicals still extant were both due to Richard Steele and Joseph Addison – *The Tatler* in 1709 and *The Spectator* two years later.

The development of printing since those far-off days has been steady and continuous. Among important developments were the 1725 invention by William Ged of Edinburgh, who used plaster of Paris impressions to cast an unlimited number of metal printing plates; the 1798 machine designed by Louise Robert in France which made it possible to produce paper from wood pulp in a continuous roll; the invention of lithography by the Bavarian printer Aloys Senefelder in the same year; and the first rotary press, due to Richard Hoe of New York, in 1846, which printed by means of a central cylinder rather than a flat bed and could produce more than 10,000 sheets per hour. Subsequent advances in printing technology have brought about the widespread use of other processes such as offset litho and photocomposition, and today computers are becoming widely used.

As for the appearance of the printed page, the last major modification to the printed word was the dropping of the old-fashioned *s*, which had been written f unless it came at the end of a word. (There are still some European languages which retain letters not in use in England. The Icelandic alphabet includes two letters, ð and þ, both of which are – somewhat confusingly – pronounced as *th*; Icelandic is, of course, related to Anglo-Saxon, and these letters linger on while Sweden has its å, Denmark its ø, Germany its ß and so on.)

Despite the spread of printed books, much work had still to be done by hand – until the arrival of the typewriter. Strictly speaking, the prototype was produced in 1843 by Charles Thurber, and was known as a 'hand-printing chirographer', using a cylinder which moved horizontally and included a device for letter-spacing, but the first true typewriter was that of Christopher Sholes in 1868; it had a keyboard, with the letters arranged so as to prevent consistent jamming, and the original Remington came out in 1873, though it was not until the late 1880s that typewriters became convenient enough for everyday use (apparently the first European author to use one was Leo Tolstoy, in 1885). The familiar keyboard arrangement, with the top letter line making up the never-to-be-forgotten 'qwertyuiop', has its disadvantages, but is so well-established that even today manufacturers are reluctant to change it.

Modern typewriters can do amazing things, and most of them are electric, though diehards still prefer the old mechanical machines. (The writer of the present chapter [PM] admits that he is using his 1908 Woodstock typewriter which he has had for the past fifty years, and which he would hate to change!)

One of the earliest commercial typewriters

It goes without saying that different languages have to have completely different typewriters; Cyrillic and Greek are cases in point, and here the disadvantage of the Chinese and Japanese systems is manifest. It may even be one powerful argument in favour of a change-over to the Western alphabet, though this still lies in the future.

Mention must also be made of shorthand, the aim of which is to write quickly and legibly. The Pitman system was devised in 1834, by Isaac Pitman, and was (and still is) purely phonetic; secretaries would be very much at a loss without it. The Gregg system is different, but based on the same general principle, and today there are methods such as 'speedwriting'. However, it is fair to say that Pitman shorthand has always remained the most popular.

Another problem is the diversity of languages. There are some people who are naturally good at languages; others who are not, and smaller nations are at something of a disadvantage. Finnish, for instance, is notoriously difficult, and it is of little use outside Finland. Attempts have been made to compile an 'international' language; of these the best known is Esperanto, invented by Lazarus Zamenhof, of Poland, in 1886. It draws its vocabulary from many established languages, and is made deliberately easy; one can learn Esperanto grammar in an hour or two. There are many Esperantists spread over the world, but the idea has never really 'caught on', which is probably a pity. Incidentally, if it were decided to adopt as a standard the most commonly-spoken language in the world it would presumably be Chinese – an idea which would hardly be calculated to appeal to Europeans.

The world's top twenty languages

		Number of speakers
1	Mandarin (Chinese)	701,000,000
2	English	386,000,000
3	Great Russian	265,000,000
4	Spanish	245,000,000
5	Hindi	237,000,000
6	Arabic	147,000,000
7	Portuguese	145,000,000
8	Bengali	144,000,000
9	German	119,000,000
10	Japanese	117,000,000
11	Malay-Indonesian	109,000,000
12	French	103,000,000
13	Urdu	68,000,000
14	Punjabi	63,000,000
15	Italian	61,000,000
16	Korean	58,000,000
=17	Tamil	57,000,000
=17	Telugu	57,000,000
19	Marathi	55,000,000
20	Cantonese	52,000,000

Source: (Based on) *The World Almanac and Book of Facts 1981*

Turning now to long-range communication, we go back first to the Persia of 500 BC, when the Great King, Darius, placed loud-voiced subjects on tops of mountains to shout orders to people below. This must have been decidedly tiring, and a better scheme was used by the Greeks, who used torch-signals from hilltop to hilltop – a method also used by the Romans. One historical case of a message sent over a long distance dates from AD 43, when the Roman legions had begun their invasion of Britain, and were by no means having matters all their own way. The Army commander considered that he should send for the Emperor, that strange, stammering ruler Claudius, who was awaiting news in Rome itself. Fires were lit on hilltops, and a 'chain message' was sent across Europe. Claudius received it, and knew that his presence was called for. Accordingly he set out, arrived in England, and master-minded an extremely quick campaign which put the issue beyond doubt. (At least, this is one version. Opinions about Claudius differ, but at any rate there is no doubt that he was summoned to Britain in this way.)

Visual signalling, by semaphore, was developed in France by 1792, and is still used in very much its original form. It is obviously limited, but operators using telescopes were able to pass on the messages they received, and it is said that soon after the system was invented a signal was received in Paris only three minutes after it had been sent out from Lille.

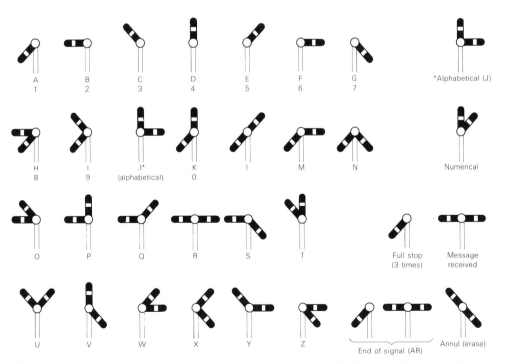

The position of the two arms, human or mechanical, to indicate different letters or numerals in the Semaphore Code

The next great step forward in communication evolution was that of the electric telegraph, offered to the British Admiralty in 1823 by Francis Ronalds. This made use of wires whose ends were attached to a battery at the starting-point, with two electrodes in acidified water at the receiving end. In 1831 Joseph Henry used an electromagnet to send messages over considerable distances by using a pattern of clocks as a code (presumably the ancestor of Morse), and in 1844 the Cooke-Wheatstone telegraph was used over the nineteen miles separating Paddington from Slough. One interesting development followed a year later. A message was sent out over the telegraph: 'Suspected murderer has taken first-class ticket on the 7.42 from Slough to Paddington. He is wearing a brown greatcoat down to his feet and he is in a second-class carriage.' The murderer was duly caught as soon as he stepped off the train. Meantime, in 1838, the Morse code had been worked out, and the name of Samuel Morse became immortal.

The Morse Code, with its dot-dash system of telegraphy, came into use after 1843

At that period everything depended on cables; one was laid between Dover and Calais in 1851 (no doubt the British thought that it was unfair to cut the mainland of Europe off from the nerve-centre of civilization), and in 1858 came the first transatlantic cable, though not without a series of misfortunes and delays. In 1860 Philip Reis, of Frankfurt-am-Main, invented a system whereby sounds could be converted into visible signs, and he called it the 'telephone', but true telephones were due largely to Alexander Graham Bell, of Edinburgh, who discovered that an iron diaphragm will vibrate when close to a permanent magnet with a wire coil around it; a weak current is set up, varying with the rhythm of vibrations, so that Bell could convert sounds into electrical impulses at the transmitter, and turn the impulses back to sound at the receiver. In 1878 Hughes made a microphone using carbon bars, so amplifying the sound signals at the receiver, and the first automatic telephone exchange was opened in 1889

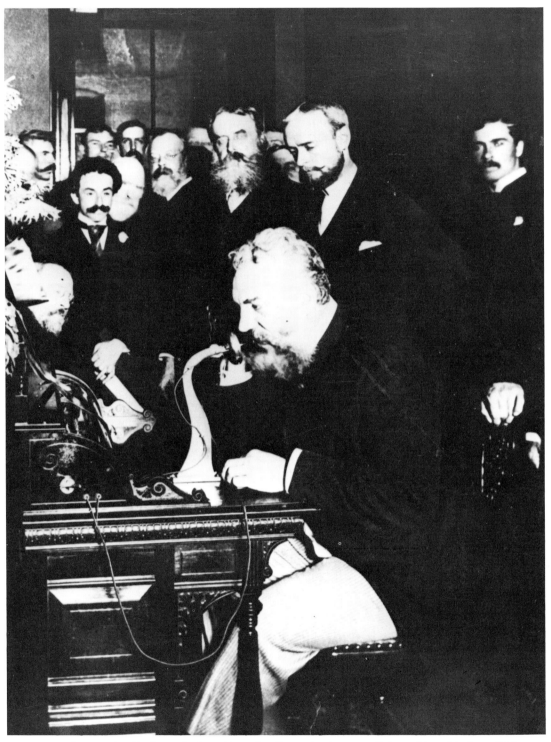

Alexander Graham Bell making the first telephone call from New York to Chicago, 1892

by Alman Strowger, who also devised the system of dial and numbers. In some ways the system was easier than that of today. A sheet of notepaper was recently found bearing the address of a London businessman, and also his telephone number – London 3 . . .

Radio waves were first studied in 1885 by Heinrich Hertz, and 'wireless' was born. By 1899 Guglielmo Marconi had established wireless communication between France and England. The first news transmission was made in Ireland, when the results of the Kingstown Regatta were sent to Dublin. Then, in 1901, Marconi was able to send a message from Poldhee in Cornwall across the Atlantic to Newfoundland. It had been widely supposed that radio contact over such immense distances would be impossible; radio waves, it was pointed out, move in straight lines, so that presumably they would simply go out into space. What nobody (not even Marconi) had realized was that there are high-altitude layers in the atmosphere which reflect radio waves and 'bounce' them back to earth. The mystery was solved by the English physicist, Oliver Heaviside, who correctly predicted the existence of such a layer in the lofty region now called the ionosphere. In America, Arthur Kenelly had come to the same conclusion, and the reflecting layer is now known as the Kenelly-Heaviside layer. (Note that there really will be a problem when we set up bases on the Moon, which has no atmosphere. Messages from one part of the lunar surface to another will have to be relayed either via the Earth or by way of artificial satellites.)

Guglielmo Marconi with receiving and transmitter apparatus, c. 1901.

The breakthrough had been made, and radio communication was developed quickly. There were some famous episodes; for instance in 1912 David Sarnoff in New York picked up an ominous message – 'S.S. *Titanic* ran into iceberg. Sinking fast', after which the letters SOS in Morse were adopted as an international distress signal. In 1922 the Sykes Committee established the BBC, under (Sir) John Reith, and the era of broadcasting began. Television followed. The early stages of it are always associated with the name of John Logie Baird, of Scotland, who was yet another curious mixture of genius and eccentric. In 1922 Baird began research into a system involving the scanning of a scene with a rapidly-moving spot of light, and four years later he gave the first demonstration of a television picture. The Baird system was adopted by the BBC for its first television programme, in 1929, though it had marked disadvantages, and in 1937 was replaced by an electronic scanning system. The first motion pictures from BBC television date from 1936 – it seems strange now to consider a world without television. Yet it was only after World War Two that television became an integral part of everyday life, and it was not until the mid-1960s that the BBC started to transmit in colour.

By then, of course, the cinema had been long established. Photography dates back as far as 1829, when Joseph Niepce and Louis Daguerre began their pioneer experiments. In 1895 came the first pocket camera (fittingly, a Kodak)

The first Kodak camera, 1888

and in the same year the first motion pictures were shown in France – due to Luis Lumière; his original 'movie' showed workers leaving his factory for their lunch break, and passed 16 frames per second. In 1903 the Edison studios produced the first film containing a complete story, 'The Great Train Robbery' (no connection, let it be said, with Mr Biggs, who had not then been born). Gramophones had been invented; in 1923 the first sound-and-film demonstration was given in New York, and the old silent films gave way to the 'talkies'. The greatest period of the film industry was probably between 1930 and 1950. Then television took control, and today there are many towns which do not boast of even one cinema.

All in all, it must be said that the coming of television has changed the civilized world beyond all recognition, and there are grounds for suggesting that its influence may be too great. Certainly it has affected world governments. No politician has much chance of achieving the highest office unless he (or she) is a good television performer, and as a propaganda system television has no rival. For that matter, it had been claimed that the present ease of communication all over the globe has been responsible for much unrest. It cannot be long now before 'pocket TV sets' become as common as transistor radios, and before the end of the century it will be a matter of custom to use such equipment to call up a friend who may be in a different continent. Already, in the early 1980s, we are girding ourselves for the promised 'video revolution' – that is, information brought to – and, above all, repeatable on – our television screens by means of special discs and cassettes purchased as one would a book or record.

Finally, there is communication by way of outer space. The pioneer scheme was proposed in 1945 by the British scientist and author, Arthur C. Clarke, in an article in the periodical *Wireless World* which aroused little interest at the time, but which is now regarded with some reverence. Clarke's plan was to use what are called geostationary satellites. If an artificial satellite is set up at the correct distance above the equator (roughly 26,000 miles), it will keep pace with the rotating Earth, and will remain directly above the same point. Clarke proposed to use three geostationary satellites. If equally spaced, at least one of them would be above the horizon from any point on the Earth's surface further than $8°$ from the poles, so that they could act as global radio and television relays.

In 1945 artificial satellites lay in the future, and the whole idea of space-travel was still widely regarded as far-fetched, but events moved swiftly. Only seventeen years after the publication of Clarke's paper the first transatlantic television link by satellite actually took place, and was watched by 200,000,000 people. The satellite concerned – Telstar – was not geostationary; it moved in an orbit ranging from 600 to 3500 miles above the ground, and it took 158 minutes to complete one journey round the Earth. Since it was a mere $34\frac{1}{2}$ inches in diameter, it was well below naked-eye visibility. On 23 July 1962 the first full-scale transatlantic exchange took place, lasting for twenty minutes;

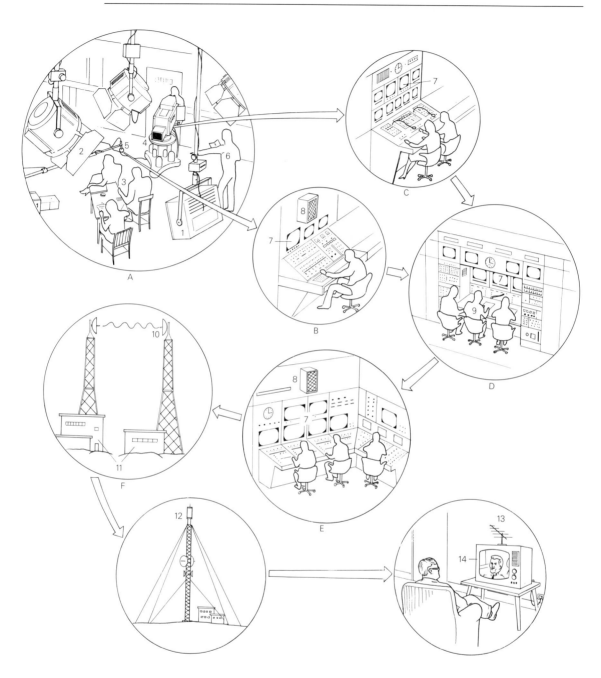

A Studio
B Sound control room
C Lighting and vision control
   room
D Production control room
E Central control room
F National network

1 2-kw lighting
2 Spotlight
3 Performers
4 Camera on hydraulic
   pedestal
5 Microphone

6 Studio director
7 Bank of monitor screens
8 Loudspeaker
9 Producer directing cameras and
   choosing picture to be transmitted

10 Directional aerial
11 Microwave relay station
12 Transmitting aerial
13 Receiving aerial
14 Television

The subject matter to be 'televised' is scanned electrically, the resulting signals being transmitted for subsequent reconstitution at the receiver into an image on the domestic television screen

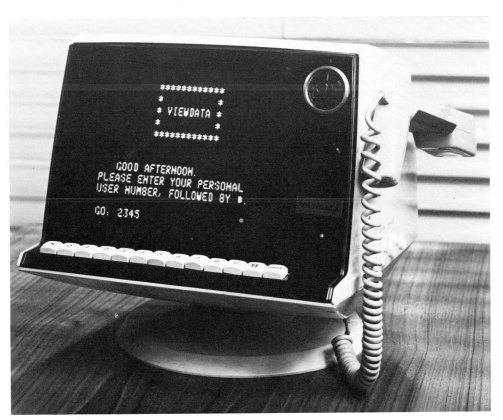

The Post Office's Viewdata is a radically new telephone service which can display a wide range of information on an ordinary TV set, or on this purpose-built terminal. It incorporates a telephone and a keying system to call up information on the screen

viewers in Britain were able to see a game of baseball being played in America (though to most Britons, baseball was probably rather more of a mystery than Telstar). Geostationary satellites followed, and by now the whole system has been perfected to a degree which even Arthur C. Clarke could hardly have foreseen when he wrote his classic paper.

Communication, in fact, is now world-wide. Nobody, wherever he lives, need be out of touch. We have done more; there has been perfect direct-voice communication with the astronauts who have walked on the Moon, almost 250,000 miles away, and communication has been maintained with the unmanned probes which have journeyed into the depths of the Solar System, beyond the giant planet Saturn – whose mean distance from the Sun is no less than 886,000,000 miles.

Will we ever be able to communicate with other intelligent races? This is something which we cannot yet decide. Most astronomers (though not all) believe that life is likely to be widespread in the universe, but there is no advanced life in the Solar System except on Earth, and probably none at all.

Therefore, the nearest alien civilizations must live on planets circling other suns – and even radio waves, moving at the speed of light (186,000 miles per second) would take years to cover such a distance. The two nearest stars which are reasonably like the Sun, and which might have inhabited planets in their systems, are about 11 light-years away. This means that if a message were transmitted from Earth to one of these systems, and was answered at once, the time-delay between sending the signal and receiving a reply would be 22 years, thereby making quick-fire repartee rather difficult.

Of course, this is speculation; but at least we can now say that so far as Earth is concerned, the communications problems have been largely solved. We have come a long way during the 2500 years that separate us from Darius' loud-voiced subjects perched on the tops of their mountains.

Typewriters were originally developed to help the blind.

There are 845 dialects spoken in India.

The most frequently used letter in the English language is 'E'. The one used least is 'Q'.

The only Semitic language spoken in Europe is Maltese.

There are seventy-two letters in the Cambodian alphabet.

53,000,000 ballpoint pens were sold during the first year of their appearance on the British market. This amounted to almost one ballpoint for every person in the country.

No evidence exists to suggest that either Jesus Christ or Muhammad knew how to write.

In 1941 a bottle containing a message was dropped over the side of an American ship sailing in the Pacific. After fifty-three days, and 1,250 miles, it landed on the beach of a remote island. However, the native who found it could not read any of the eight languages in which the message was written.

The telephone was developed out of research into the invention of a hearing aid.

12

Miscellanea

Meters and measuring instruments

acidimeter—acids
actinometer—heat of sun's rays
alcoholometer—alcohol contents
altimeter—altitudes
ammeter—electric currents
amperemeter (ammeter)—amperages
anemometer—wind speeds
araeometer—liquids
argentometer—strength of silver solutions
arithmometer—calculation
astrometer (astrophanometer)—apparent relative
    magnitude of stars
astrophotometer—intensity of star's light
atmometer—rates of exhalation of moisture
audiometer—hearing
auxanometer—plant growths

barometer—atmospheric pressures
bathometer—ocean depths
bathymeter—ocean depths
bolometer—heat

calorimeter—heat (quantity)
cathetometer—small vertical distances
chlorometer—bleaching powers
chondrometer—balance for weighing grain
chronometer—time (with high accuracy)
clinometer—angles of elevation
colorimeter—colour hues and brightnesses
comptometer—calculation
craniometer—skulls
cryometer—low temperatures
cyanometer—atmospheric tints
cyclometer—circles, cycles
cymometer—wavelengths (early)
cyrtometer—curves of a chart

dasymeter—density of gases
declinometer—declination of magnetic needles
dendrometer—trees
densimeter—specific gravities
diameter—straight line passing through centre of
    circle or sphere, each end terminating at
    circumference
diaphanometer—atmospheric transparency
dilatometer—expansions
dimeter—two measures
drosometer—dew
dynameter—magnifying power of telescopes
dynamometer—energy

echometer—duration of sounds
elaeometer—specific gravity of oils
electrometer—electrical forces
ergometer—quantity or power of ergs
eriometer—fibre diameters
eudiometer—oxygen
extensometer—ductility

fathometer—sea depth (fathoms)
floodometer—flood levels
fluviometer—river levels

galactometer—flow of milk
galvanometer—small electric currents
gasometer—gas storage container

geometer—a geometrician; a moth
glaciometer—motion of glaciers
goniometer—angles (esp. crystals)
gradiometer—gradients
graphometer—angles
gravimeter—gravity

halometer—form, angles, and planes of crystals
heliometer—delicate atronomical measurement
hodometer—distance covered by wheeled
    vehicles
hydrometer—density of liquids
hyetometer—rain
hygrometer—humidity of air or gas
hypsometer—altitude by boiling point

inclinometer—terrestrial magnetic force

konometer—dust
kryometer—low temperatures

labidometer—the foetal head
lactometer—specific gravity of milk
litrameter—specific gravities in liquid
logometer—chemical equivalents

macrometer—distance of inaccessible objects
magnetometer—magnetic forces
manometer—gas or vapour pressures
metageometer—non-Euclidean space
micrometer—thickness

nilometer—rise and fall of river (esp. Nile)
nitrometer—nitrogen content

odometer—distance over ground
ohmmeter—ohms (electrical resistance)
ombrometer—rain
oometer—birds' eggs
opisometer—curved lines
optometer—range of vision
orometer—height of mountains
oscillometer—roll of a ship or spacecraft
osmometer—accuracy of sense of smell

pachymeter—thickness
pantometer—angles, elevations, distances
pedometer—distance walked
perimeter—the outer boundary of a figure
photometer—relative intensity of light
piezometer—pressure or compressibility of liquids
planometer (planimeter)—plane surfaces
pluviometer—rain
pneumatometer—quantity of air inhaled or
    exhaled at one breath
polarimeter—polarization of light
porometer—leaf respiration
potentiometer—potential difference of electrical
    pressure
potometer—water intake
psychrometer—atmospheric humidity
pulmometer—lung capacity
pulsimeter—pulse rate
pulsometer—vacuum pump for raising water
pycnometer (pyknometer)—specific gravity of
    liquids
pyrheliometer—sun's heat
pyrometer—high temperatures

psychometer—duration and intensity of mental states

radiometer—radiation
reflectometer—smoke content
refractometer—refraction
rheometer—force of blood circulation
rotometer—map distances

saccharimeter—sugars by polarized light
saccharometer—amount of sugar solution by specific gravity
salinometer—brine (marine engine boilers)
salimeter—salinity
scintillometer—stellar scintillation
sclerometer—hardness of crystals
seisomometer—earthquakes
sensitometer—sensitivity of photographic plates
sillometer—speed of ships
sonometer—sounds
spectrometer—deflection of rays by prisms
speedometer—speed (of machinery)
spherometer—radii and curves of spheres
sphygmomanometer—blood pressure
spirometer—lung capacity
stactometer—pipette for counting drops of liquid
stadometer—theodolite
stereometer—volume of solid bodies; specific gravity of liquids
stethometer—chest movement during respiration

tachymeter (tacheometer)—rapid surveying

tachometer—speed
taseometer—structural strains
tasimeter—minute variations in pressure
taximeter—time and distance (taxis)
telemeter—distant objects
thermometer—temperature
thoracometer—movement of chest-wall in respiration
tintometer—tints
tonometer—a tuning-fork
torquemeter—speed ranges
trechometer—distance covered by a vehicle
tribometer—sliding friction

udometer—rain
urinometer—specific gravity of urine

vaporimeter—pressure of gases
variometer—variations of magnetic force
velocimeter—velocity
viameter—distance travelled
vibrometer—vibrations
vinometer—alcoholic strength of wine
viscometer—viscosity of liquids
volumeter—volume of gas
voltimeter—voltage

wattmeter—electric power in watts
weatherometer—weather resistance of paint

zymometer—fermentation

Major inventions and their innovators

Achievement	Date	Inventor/Discoverer
Adding Machine	1623	Wilhelm Schickard (Germany)
Aeroplane	1903	Orville and Wilbur Wright (USA)
Air Conditioning	1911	Willis H. Carrier (USA)
Airship (non-rigid)	1852	Henri Giffard (France)
Arc Lamp	1879	C. F. Brush (USA)
Aspirin	1893	Hermann Dreser
Bakelite	1907	Leo. H. Baekeland (Belgium/USA)
Balloon	1783	Jacques and Joseph Montgolfier (France)
Ball-Point Pen	1888	John Loud (USA)
Barbed Wire	1867	Lucien Smith
Barometer	1643	Evangelista Torricelli (Italy)
Bicycle	1839	Kirkpatrick Macmillan (Scotland)
Bifocal Lens	1780	Benjamin Franklin (USA)
Bunsen Burner	1855	Robert von Bunsen (Germany)
Car (Internal Combustion)	1860	Jean Joseph Etienne Lenoir (France)
Car (Petrol driven)	1886	Karl-Friedrich Benz (Germany)

Major inventions and their innovators (*cont.*)

Achievement	Date	Inventor/Discoverer
Cash Register	1879	James Ritty (USA)
Cathode Ray Tube	1897	Karl Ferdinand Braun (Germany)
Celluloid	1861	Alexander Parkes (Britain)
Cement (Portland)	1824	Joseph Aspdin (Britain
Chronometer	1735	John Harrison (Britain)
Clock (mechanical)	725	I-Hsing and Liang Ling-Tsan (China)
Clock (pendulum)	1657	Christian Huygens (Holland)
Combustion (theory of)	1775	Antoine Lavoisier (France)
DDT	1939	Paul Muller (Switzerland)
Dental Plate	1817	Anthony Plantson (USA)
Diesel Engine	1895	Rudolf Diesel (Germany)
Disc Brakes	1902	Dr. F. Lanchester (Britain)
Dyes (synthetic)	1857	William Perkins (Britain)
Dynamite	1867	Alfred Nobel (Sweden)
Dynamo	1860	Antonio Picinotti (Italy)
Electric Lamp	1879	Thomas Edison (USA)
Electric Motor (d.c.)	1873	Zenobe Gramme (Belgium)
(a.c.)	1888	Nikola Tesla (USA)
Electro magnet	1824	William Sturgeon (Britain)
Electrometer	1788	Alessandro Volta (Italy)
Electronic computer	1942	J. G. Brainerd, J. P. Eckert, J. W. Mauchly (USA)
Film (moving)	1885	Louis le Prince
(talking)	1926	Warner Bros. (USA)
Fluorine	1771	Wilhelm Scheele (Sweden)
Fountain Pen	1884	Lewis Waterman (USA)
Gas Turbine Engine	1791	John Barber (Britain)
Gear (Differential)	1828	Onésiphore Pecquer (France)
Glider	1853	Sir George Cayley (Britain)
Gramophone (phonograph)	1878	Thomas Edison (USA)
Gyro Compass	1911	Elmer Sperry (USA)
Helicopter	1924	Etienne Ochmichen (France)
Hovercraft	1955	Sir Christopher Cockerell (Britain)
Hydrogen	1766	Henry Cavendish (Britain)
Incubator	1666	Cornelius Drebbel (Holland)
Jet Engine	1929	Sir Frank Whittle
Laser	1960	Dr. Charles Towney (USA)
Light (Wave theory of)	1690	Christian Huygens (Holland)
Lightning Conductor	1752	Benjamin Franklin (USA)
Linoleum	1860	Frederick Walton (Britain)
Locomotive	1804	Richard Trevithick (Britain)
Logarithms	1614	John Napier (Scotland)
Long-playing Record	1948	Dr. Peter Goldmark (USA)
Machine Gun	1718	James Puckle (Britain)
Magnetic Recording	1898	Vlademar Poulsen (Denmark)
Margarine	1863	Hippolyte Mège-Mouriès (France)
Match (safety)	1855	J. E. Lundstrom (Sweden)

Major inventions and their innovators (*cont.*)

Achievement	Date	Inventor/Discoverer
Microphone	1876	Alexander Graham Bell (USA)
Microscope (electron)	1939	Vladimir Zworykin (Russia/USA)
Microscope	1590	Zacharias Jansen (Holland)
Motor Cycle	1885	Gottlieb Daimler (Germany)
Nylon	1930	Wallace Carothers (USA)
Oxygen	1774	Joseph Priestley (Britain) Wilhelm Scheele (Sweden)
Paper	105	Ts'ai-lun (China)
Parachute	1797	André-Jacques Garnerin (France)
Passenger Lift	1852	Elish G. Otis (USA)
Pendulum	1581	Galileo Galilei (Italy)
Piano	1709	Bartolommeo Cristofori (Italy)
Photography (on metal)	1826	J. Nicéphore Niepce (France)
Penicillin	1929	Alexander Fleming (Britain)
Radar	1922	Albert Taylor and Leo Young (Britain)
Radio telegraphy	1895	Guglielmo Marconi (Italy)
Radium	1898	Pierre and Marie Curie (France)
Rayon	1883	Joseph Swan (Britain)
Refrigerator	1850	James Harrison (Britain) and Alexander Twining (USA)
Rubber (vulcanized)	1839	Charles Goodyear (USA)
Safety pin	1849	Walter Hunt (USA)
Safety Razor	1847	William Samuel Henson (Britain)
Silicones	1904	F. S. Kipping (Britain)
Slide Rule	1621	William Oughtred (Britain)
Sewing Machine	1829	Barthélemy Thimmonnier (France)
Steel production	1856	Henry Bessemer (Britain)
Tank	1914	Sir Ernest Swinton (Britain)
Telegraph	1837	William Coke, Charles Wheatstone (Britain)
Telephone	1876	Alexander Graham Bell (USA)
Telescope	1608	Hans Lippershey (Holland)
Television	1926	John Logie Baird (Britain)
Terylene	1941	J. R. Whinfield, J. T. Dickson (Britain)
Thermometer	1593	Galileo Galilei (Italy)
Transistor	1948	Walter Brattain, John Barden (USA)
Typewriter	1829	William Burt (USA)
Watch	1462	Bartholomew Manfredi (Italy)
Water Closet	1589	Sir John Harrington (Britain)
X-rays	1895	Wilhelm von Roñtgen (Germany)
Zip Fastener	1891	Whitcomb Judson (USA)

Weights and measures – a comparative chart

Unit	Value	Metric Value
1 acre	43,560 sq. ft.	4047 sq. m.
	4840 sq. yds.	0.4047 ha.
	160 sq. rods	
	10 sq. chains (surveyor's)	
1 agate (typography)	$\frac{1}{14}$ in	
1 are	119.6 sq. yds.	100 sq. m.
	0.0247 acre	1 sq. dcm.
1 bale	500 lbs.	
1 barrel (bbl.)		
liquid	31–42 gals.	
	4.14–5.61 cu. ft.	
alcohol	50 gals.	189 litres
petroleum	42 gals.	159 litres
	5.61 cu. ft.	0.159 cu. m.
dry salt	280 lbs.	127 kg.
dry cement	376 lbs.	171 kg.
1 board foot (fbm)	144 cu. ins.	
1 bolt (of cloth)	40 yds.	36.58 m.
1 bushel (bu.)	4 pecks	35.238 litres
struck measure:	2150.42 cu. ins.	
	32 qts.	
heaped measure:	$1\frac{5}{18}$ struck measures	45.04 litres
	2747.7 cu. ins.	
1 cable length	720 ft.	219.456 m.
	120 fathoms	
1 carat (metric)	3.086 gr.	200 mg.
	0.007 oz. (avdp.)	0.2 g.
Celsius (C)	212°F (boiling pt. of water)	100°C
	32°F (freezing pt.)	0°C
centare see square metre		
1 centigram (cg.)	0.15 gr.	10 mg.
	0.0004 oz. (avdp.)	0.01 g.
1 centilitre (cl.)	0.6 cu. in.	10 ml.
	0.338 fluid oz.	0.01 litre
	0.018 pt. (dry)	
1 centimetre (cm.)	0.39 in.	10 mm.
1 century	100 yrs.	
1 chain (ch.)		
Gunter's or surveyor's	100 links	20.1168 m.
	66 ft.	
	$\frac{1}{10}$ furlong	
engineer's	100 links	30.48 m.
	100 ft.	
1 circle (revolution)	360°	
	4 quadrants	
1 cord (firewood)	128 cu. ft.	3.6 cu. m.
1 cubic centimetre (cu. cm.)	0.0610 cu. in.	1000 cu. mm.
	0·0003 gal.	
1 cubic decametre (cu. dem.)	1307.9 cu. yds.	1000 cu. m.
1 cubic decimetre (cu. dm.)	61.023 cu. ins.	1000 cu. cm.
	0.035 cu. ft.	
1 cubic foot (cu. ft.)	1728 cu. ins.	28.3 cu. dm.
	7.481 gals. (liq.)	0.0283 cu. m.
	0·0370 cu. yd.	
seawater	64 lbs.	
fresh water	62.43 lbs. at 39.2°F	
ice	56 lbs.	
1 cubic hectometre (cu. hm.)	1,307,950.6 cu. yds.	100 cu. dcm.

Weights and measures – a comparative chart (*cont.*)

Unit	Value	Metric Value
1 cubic inch (cu. in.)	4.43 fluid dr.	16.387 cu. cm.
	0.554 fluid oz.	0.016 litre
	0·00058 cu. ft.	
	0·000021 cu. yd.	
1 cubic metre (cu. m.)	264.2 gals.	1,000,000 cu. cm.
	35.3147 cu. ft.	1000 cu. dm.
	1.3079 cu. yds.	
1 cubic millimetre (cu. mm.)	0.00006 cu. in.	0.001 cu. cm.
1 cubic yard (cu. yd.)	46,656 cu. ins.	765.534 litres
	201.974 gals.	0.765 cu. m.
	27 cu. ft.	
1 cubit	18 ins.	45.72 cm.
1 cup (measuring)	16 tablespoons	236.6 ml.
	14.44 cu. ins.	
	8 fluid oz.	
	0.5 pt. (liq.)	
1 day	24 hrs.	
1 decagram (decg.)	0.35 oz. (avdp.)	10 g.
1 decalitre (dcl.)	18.16 pts. (dry)	10 litres
	2.6 gals.	
	1.14 pecks	
	0.284 bushel	
1 decametre (dem.)	393.7 ins.	10 m.
	32.81 ft.	
	10.93 yds.	
1 decastere (dcs.)	13.1 cu. yds.	
1 decigram (dg.)	1.5 gr.	10 cg.
	0.0035 oz. (avdp.)	0.1 g.
1 decilitre (dl.)	6.1 cu. ins.	100 ml.
	3·38 fluid oz.	10 cl.
	0·182 pt. (dry)	
	0.106 qt. (liq.)	
1 decimetre (dm.)	3.937 ins.	100 mm.
		10 cm.
1 decistere (ds)	3.53 cu. ft.	
1 degree (°)	60 minutes (′)	
dekagram *see* decagram		
dekalitre *see* decalitre		
dekametre *see* decametre		
dekastere *see* decastere		
1 dram (dr.)		
avoirdupois (dr. avdp.)	27.34 gr.	1.772 g.
	0.0625 oz.	
apothecaries' (dr. ap.)	60 gr.	3.887 g.
	3 scruples	
	0.14 oz. (avdp.)	
Fahrenheit (F)	212° (boiling pt. of water)	100°C
	32° (freezing pt.)	0°C
1 fathom (fm.)	72 ins.	1.83 m.
	8 spans	
	6 ft.	
1 fluid dram (fl. dr.)	60 minims	3.7 ml.
	0.23 cu. in.	3.7 cu. cm.
	0.125 fluid oz.	
1 fluid ounce (fl. oz.)	8 fluid dr.	29.57 ml.
	6 teaspoons	29.57 cu. cm.
	2 tablespoons	
	1.8 cu. ins.	
	$\frac{1}{16}$ pt. (liq.)	
1 foot (ft.)	12 ins.	30.48 cm.
	0.333 yd.	0.3048 m.

Weights and measures – a comparative chart (*cont*.)

Unit	Value	Metric Value
1 furlong (fur.)	660 ft.	201.2 m.
	220 yds.	
	40 rods	
	10 chains (surveyor's)	
	$\frac{1}{8}$ statute mi.	
1 gallon (gal.)	231 cu. ins.	3.785 cu. cm.
	128 fluid oz.	3.785 litres
	16 cups	0.0003785 cu. m.
	8 pts.	
	4 qts.	
1 gill (gi.)	7.22 cu. ins.	118.3 ml.
	4 fluid oz.	0.118 litre
1 grain (gr.)		
avoirdupois	0.036 dr.	65 mg.
	0.0023 oz.	0.065 g.
troy	0.042 dwt.	0.065 g.
apothecaries'	0.05 scruple	65 mg.
	0.0021 oz.	0.065 g.
1 gram (g.)	15.43 gr.	1000 mg.
	0.035 oz.	100 cg.
	(avdp.)	10 dg.
1 great gross	12 gross (1728)	
1 gross	144 items	
	12 dozen	
1 hand	4 ins.	10.16 cm.
1 hectare (ha.)	2.47 acres	10,000 sq. m.
		100 ares
1 hectogram (hg.)	3.5 oz. (avdp.)	100 g.
		10 dcg.
1 hectolitre (hl.)	26.42 gals.	100 litres
	3.53 cu. ft.	10 dcl.
	2.84 bushels (dry)	
1 hectometre (hm.)	328.08 ft.	100 m.
	109.36 yds.	10 dcm.
1 hogshead	14,553 cu. ins.	
	2 bbls.	
1 hour (hr.)	60 mins.	
	0·0417 day	
1 hundredweight (cwt.)		
long	112 lbs. (avdp.)	50.80 kg.
	0.05 long ton	
short	100 lbs. (avdp.)	45.36 kg.
	0.05 short ton	
1 inch (in.)	0.083 ft.	25.40 mm.
	0·027 yd.	2.540 cm.
1 kilogram (kg)	35.3 oz. (avdp.)	1000 g.
	32.1 oz. (troy)	10 hg.
	2.9 lbs. (troy)	
	2.2 lbs. (avdp.)	
1 kilolitre (kl.)	264.18 gals.	1000 litres
	35.3 cu. ft.	10 hl.
1 kilometre (km).	3280.8 ft.	1000 m.
	1093.6 yds.	100 dcm.
	0.621 mi. (stat.)	10 hm.
	0.540 mi. (Brit. naut.)	
1 kilowatt (kw.)	1.341 hp.	
1 league		
land	3 mi. (stat.)	4.827 km.
nautical	3.452 mi. (stat.)	5.556 km.
	3 mi. (Brit. naut.)	

Weights and measures – a comparative chart (*cont.*)

Unit	Value	Metric Value
1 light-year	5,880,000,000,000 mi.	
1 link (li.)		
Gunter's or surveyor's	7.92 ins.	0.2012 m.
engineer's	1 ft.	0.3048 m.
1 litre (l.)		
liquid	33.81 fl. oz.	1000 ml.
	2.113 pts.	100 cl.
	1,057 qts.	10 dl.
	0·264 gal.	
dry	61.02 cu. ins.	1000 cu. cm.
	0·908 qt.	
1 metre (m.)	39.37 ins.	1000 mm.
	3.2808 ft.	100 cm.
	1.0936 yds.	10 dm.
	0.547 fathom	
	0·0006215 mil. (stat.)	
	0·0005396 mi. (Brit. naut.)	
1 microgram (μg.)	0.000015 gr.	0·000001 g.
1 micron (μ)	0·00004 in.	1000 nm.
		0·001 mm.
1 microsecond	0·000001 sec.	
1 mil	0·001 in.	0·0254 mm.
1 mile (mi.)		
statute (stat.)	5280 ft.	1609 m.
	1760 yds.	1.609 km.
	320 rods	
	80 chains	
	8 furlongs	
	0·8684 mi. (Brit. naut.)	
nautical (Brit. naut.)	6080 ft.	1852 m.
	2026.67 yds.	1.852 km.
	1.151 mi. (stat.)	
1 millennium	1000 yrs.	
1 milligram (mg.)	0.015 gr.	1000 μg.
		0.001 g.
1 millilitre (ml.)		
liquid	16.23 min.	
	0.27 fl. dr.	
dry	0·06 cu. in.	
	0·002 pt.	
1 millimetre (mm.)	0.04 in.	1000 μ
millimicron *see* nanometre		
1 minim (min.)		
liquid	0.0167 fluid dr.	0.062 ml.
	0.0038 cu. in.	
	0.0021 fluid oz.	
1 minute (')	60 seconds (")	
1 month	28–31 solar days	
1 nanometre (nm.)	0.00000004 in.	0·001 μ
1 ounce (oz.)		
avoirdupois	437.5 gr.	28.349 g.
	16 dr.	
	0.9115 oz. (apoth. or troy)	
	0.0625 lb.	
apothecaries'	480 gr.	31.1 g.
	24 scruples	
	8 dr.	
	1.0971 oz. (avdp.)	
troy	480 gr.	31.1 g.
	20 dwt.	

Weights and measures – a comparative chart (*cont.*)

Unit	Value	Metric Value
1 parsec	3.26 light-years	
1 peck	537.6 cu. ins.	8809.7 cu. cm.
	16 pts. (dry)	8.81 litres
	8 qts. (dry)	
1 pennyweight (dwt.)		
troy	24 gr.	1.555 g.
	0.05 oz.	
1 pica	12 points	
	$\frac{1}{6}$ in.	
1 pint (pt.)		
liquid	128 fluid dr.	473.2 cu. cm.
	28.875 cu. ins.	0.473 litre
	16 fluid oz.	
	4 gills	
	2 cups	
dry	33.6 cu. ins.	0.550 litre
	0.5 qt.	
1 pipe	2 hogsheads	
1 point (typography)	$\frac{1}{12}$ pica	
	0.014 in.	
1 pound (lb.)		
avoirdupois	7000 gr.	453.6 g.
	256 dr.	0.4536 kg.
	16 oz. (avdp.)	
apothecaries'	5760 gr.	373.2 g.
	288 scruples	0.373 kg.
	96 dr.	
	13.17 oz. (avdp.)	
	12 oz. (troy)	
troy	5760 gr.	373.2 g.
	240 dwt.	0.373 kg.
	13.17 oz. (avdp.)	
	12 oz. (troy)	
	0·823 lb. (avdp.)	
	(avdp.)	
1 quadrant	90°	
	1 right angle	
1 quart (qt.)		
liquid	256 fluid dr.	0.946 litre
	57.75 cu. ins.	
	32 fluid oz.	
	4 cups	
	2 pts.	
dry	67.20 cu. ins.	1101 cu. cm.
		1.101 litres
1 quintal (q.)	220.46 lbs. (avdp.)	100,000 g.
		100 kg.
1 quire	25 sheets	
1 radian	57.296°	
1 ream	20 quires	
	500 sheets	
1 rod (rd.)	16.5 ft.	5.029 m.
	5.5 yds.	
1 scruple (apoth.)	20 gr.	1.30 g.
	0.33 dr.	
	0.0457 oz. (avdp.)	
section *see* square mile		
1 span	9 ins.	22.86 cm.
1 square (building)	100 sq. ft.	
1 square centimetre (sq. cm.)	0.16 sq. in.	100 sq. mm.
	0.0011 sq. ft.	

Weights and measures – a comparative chart (*cont.*)

Unit	Value	Metric Value
1 square chain (sq. ch.)	484 sq. yds.	404.7 sq. m.
	16 sq. rods	
1 square decametre (sq. dcm.)	119.6 sq. yds.	100 sq. m.
	0.025 acre	
1 square decimetre (sq. dm.)	15.5 sq. ins.	100 sq. cm.
	0.108 sq. ft.	
1 square foot (sq. ft.)	144 sq. ins.	929.03 sq. cm.
	0.111 sq. yd.	0.093 sq. m.
1 square hectometre (sq. hm.)	2.471 acres	100 sq. dcm.
1 square inch (sq. in.)	0.0069 sq. ft.	6.451 sq. cm.
	0.00077 sq. yd.	
1 square kilometre	247.1 acres	1,000,000 sq. m.
	0.3861 sq. mi. (stat.)	100 ha.
	0·2912 sq. mi. (Brit. naut.)	
1 square metre (sq. m.)	10.76 sq. ft.	1,000,000 sq. mm.
	1.1960 sq. yds.	10,000 sq. cm.
		100 sq. dm.
1 square mile (sq. mi.)	27,878,400 sq. ft.	258.89 ha.
	102,400 sq. rods	2.5889 sq. km.
	640 acres	
1 square millimetre (sq. mm.)	0.0016 sq. in.	
square pole *see* square rod		
1 square rod (sq. rd.)	625 sq. links	25.293 sq. m.
	272.25 sq. ft.	
	30.25 sq. yds.	
	0.00625 acre	
1 square yard (sq. yd.)	1296 sq. ins.	0.8361 sq. m.
	9 sq. ft.	
stere *see* cubic metre		
1 straight angle	180°	
	2 quadrants	
1 tablespoon	4 fluid dr.	14.79 ml.
	3 teaspoons	
	$\frac{1}{2}$ fluid oz.	
1 teaspoon	$1\frac{1}{3}$ fluid dr.	4.93 ml.
	$\frac{1}{3}$ tablespoon	
ton		
assay		29,167 mg.
		29.2 g.
freight or measurement	40 cu. ft.	
long or displacement	2240 lbs. (avdp.)	1.0160 metric tons
	20 long cwt.	
metric (mt.)	2204.6 lbs. (avdp.)	1000 kg.
		10 q.
	1.1023 short tons	
short or net	2000 lbs.	907,185 kg.
	20 short cwt.	0.9072 metric ton
1 township (tp.)	36 sq. mi.	93.2 sq. km.
1 week	7 days	
1 yard (yd.)	36 ins.	0.9144 m.
	3 ft.	
1 year		
common	365 solar days	
leap	366 solar days	

Discoveries and Innovations: Chemistry, Physics, Biology, Medicine

	Date	Discoverer	Nationality
Acetylene gas	1892	Wilson	U.S.
ACTH	1949	Armour & Co.	U.S.
Adrenalin	1901	Takamina	Japanese
Aluminium electro-lytic process	1886	Hall	U.S.
Aluminum isolated	1825	Oersted	Danish
Aniline dye	1856	Perkin	English
Anaesthesia, ether	1842	Long	U.S.
Anaesthesia, local	1885	Koller	Austrian
Anaesthesia, spinal	1898	Bier	German
Anti-rabies	1885	Pasteur	French
Antiseptic surgery	1867	Lister	English
Antitoxin, diphtheria	1891	Von Behring	German
Argyrol	1901	Barnes	U.S.
Aspirin	1889	Dresser	German
Atabrine	. . .	Mietzsch, et al.	German
Atomic numbers	1913	Moseley	English
Atomic theory	1803	Dalton	English
Atomic time clock	1947	Libby	U.S.
Atom-smashing theory	1919	Rutherford	N.Z.
Aureomycin	1948	Duggar	U.S.
Bacitracin	1945	Johnson, et al.	U.S.
Bacteria (described)	1676	Leeuwenhoek	Dutch
Barbital	1903	Fischer	German
Bleaching powder	1798	Tennant	English
Blood, circulation	1616	Harvey	English
Bromine from sea	1924	Edgar Kramer	U.S.
Calcium carbide	1886	Wilson	U.S.
Calculus	c. 1670	Newton/Leibniz	English/German
Camphor synthetic	1898	Haller	French
Canning (food)	1804	Appert	French
Carbomycin	1952	Tanner	U.S.
Carbon oxides	1925	Fisher	German
Chlorine	1810	Davy	English
Chloroform	1831	Guthrie, S.	U.S.
Chloromycetin	1947	Burkholder	U.S.
Classification of plants and animals	1735	Linnaeus	Swedish
Cocaine	1860	Niermann	German
Combustion explained	1777	Lavoisier	French
Conditioned reflex	1914	Pavlov	Russian
Conteben	1950	Belmisch, Mietzsch, Domagk	German
Cortisone	1936	Kendall	U.S.
Cortisone synthesis	1946	Sarett	U.S.
Cosmic rays	1910	Gockel	Swiss
Cyanimide	1905	Frank, Caro	German
Cyclotron	1930	Lawrence	U.S.
DDT	1943	Zeidler	German
Deuterium	1932	Urey, Brickwedde, Murphy	U.S.
DNA (structure)	1951	Crick	English
		Watson	U.S.
		Wilkins	English
Electric resistance (law)	1827	Ohm	German
Electric waves	1888	Hertz	German

Discoveries and Innovations: Chemistry, Physics, Biology, Medicine (*cont.*)

	Date	Discoverer	Nation
Electrolysis	1852	Faraday	English
Electromagnetism	1819	Oersted	Danish
Electron	1897	Thomson, J.	English
Electron diffraction	1936	Thomson, G.	English
		Davisson	U.S.
Electroshock treat-			
ment	1938	Cerletti, Bini	Italian
Erythromycin	1952	McGuire	U.S.
Evolution, natural			
selection	1858	Darwin	English
Falling bodies, law	1604	Galileo	Italian
Gases, law of			
combining volumes	1808	Gay-Lussac	French
Geometry, analytic	1619	Descartes	French
Gold (cyanide process		MacArthur,	
for extraction)	1887	Forrest	English
Gravitation, law	1687	Newton	English
Holograph	1948	Gabor	British
Human heart			
transplant	1967	Barnard	S. African
Indigo, synthesis of	1880	Baeyer	German
Induction, electric	1830	Henry	U.S.
Insulin	1922	Banting, Best	
		Macleod	Canadian
Intelligence testing	1905	Binet, Simon	French
Isinazid	1952	Hoffman-	
		La-Roche	U.S.
		Domagk	German
Isotopes, theory	1912	Soddy	English
Laser (light amplification			
by stimulated emission			
of radiation)	1958	Townes,	
		Schawlow	U.S.
Light, velocity	1675	Roemer	Danish
Light, wave theory	1690	Huygens	Dutch
Lithography	1796	Senefelder	Bohemian
Lobotomy	1935	Egas Moniz	Portuguese
LSD-25	1943	Hoffman	Swiss
Mendelian laws	1866	Mendel	Austrian
Mercator projection			
(map)	1568	Mercator (Kremer)	Flemish
Methanol	1925	Patard	French
Milk condensation	1853	Borden	U.S.
Molecular hypothesis	1811	Avogadro	Italian
Motion, laws of	1687	Newton	English
Neomycin	1949	Waksman,	
		Lechevalier	U.S.
Neutron	1932	Chadwick	English
Nitric acid	1648	Glauber	German
Nitric oxide	1772	Priestley	English
Nitroglycerine	1846	Sobrero	Italian
Oil cracking process	1891	Dewar	U.S.
Oxygen	1774	Priestley	English
Ozone	1840	Schonbein	German
Paper, sulfite process	1867	Tilghman	U.S.
Paper, wood pulp,			
sulfate process	1884	Dahl	German

Discoveries and Innovations: Chemistry, Physics, Biology, Medicine (*cont.*)

	Date	Discoverer	Nation
Penicillin	1929	Fleming	Scottish
practical use	1941	Florey, Chain	English
Periodic law and			
table of elements	1869	Mendeleyev	Russian
Planetary motion, laws	1609	Kepler	German
Plutonium fission	1940	Kennedy, Wahl,	
		Seaborg, Segre	U.S.
Polymixin	1947	Ainsworth	English
Positron	1932	Anderson	U.S.
Proton	1919	Rutherford	N.Z.
Psychoanalysis	1900	Freud	Austrian
Quantum theory	1900	Planck	German
Quasars	1963	Matthews,	
		Sandage	U.S.
Quinine synthetic	1918	Rabe	German
Radioactivity	1896	Becquerel	French
Radium	1898	Curie, Pierre	French
		Curie, Marie	Pol.-Fr.
Relativity theory	1905	Einstein	German
Reserpine	1949	Jal Vaikl	Indian
Salvarsan (606)	1910	Ehrlich	German
Schick test	1913	Schick	U.S.
Silicon	1823	Berzelius	Swedish
Streptomycin	1945	Waksman	U.S.
Sulfadiazine	1940	Robin	U.S.
Sulfanilamide	1934	Domagk	German
Sulfanilamide theory	1908	Gelmo	German
Sulfapyridine	1938	Ewins, Phelps	English
Sulfathiazole	. . .	Fosbinder, Walter	U.S.
Sulfuric acid	1831	Phillips	English
Sulfuric acid, lead	1746	Roebuck	English
Terramycin	1950	Finlay, et al.	U.S.
Tuberculin	1890	Koch	German
Uranium fission		Hahn, Meitner,	
(theory)	1939	Strassmann	German
		Bohr	Danish
		Fermi	Italian
		Einstein, Pegran,	
		Wheeler	U.S.
Uranium, fission,		Fermi,	
atomic reactor	1942	Szilard	U.S.
Vaccine, measles	1954	Enders, Peebles	U.S.
Vaccine, polio	1953	Salk	U.S.
Vaccine, polio, oral	1955	Sabin	U.S.
Vaccine, rabies	1885	Pasteur	French
Vaccine, smallpox	1796	Jenner	English
Vaccine, typhus	1909	Nicolle	French
Van Allan belts,			
radiation	1958	Van Allen	U.S.
Vitamin A	1913	McCollum, Davis	U.S.
Vitamin B	1916	McCollum	U.S.
Vitamin C	1912	Holst, Froelich	Norwegian
Vitamin D	1922	McCollum	U.S.
Wassermann test	1906	Wassermann	German
Xerography	1938	Carlson	U.S.
X-ray	1895	Roentgen	German

Some Physical Constants

Time measurement

1 h = 60 min = 3600 s
Mean solar day = 24 h = 86,400 s = return of Sun to meridian
Solar (tropical) year = 365·2422 days
Average civil year = 365·2425 days
= Julian sequence of 3 years of 365 days, followed by a leap year of 366 days (n years whose number is divisible by 4) subject to the Gregorian correction that century years are not leap years unless divisible by 400.
Sidereal day = 86164·09 s
Sidereal year = 366·2564 sidereal days
= 365·2564 mean solar days
= Circuit of the Earth round the Sun with reference to a fixed star. The difference between the sidereal and solar years is due to precession of the Earth's axis. It was the invention of the pendulum clock (*Huygens*, 1657) and its regulation by reference to star observations that enabled the second to become an accurately measurable time interval. See also ATOMIC CLOCK

Circular measure

Radian : 1 rad = angle subtended at centre of circle
    by arc of length equal to the radius
Degree: 1° = $(\pi/180)$rad
Minute: 60' = 1°
Second: 60'' = 1'

1 rad = 57·295 78°
Circle = 2π rad = 360° = 1,296,000''
Circumference of circle = $2\pi r$ (where r = radius)
Area of circle = πr^2

The Earth

Radii: sphere of equal volume = 6371 km
    polar = 6356·6 km
    equatorial = 6378·1 km
Quadrant: meridian = 10,002 km actual (10,000 km nominal)
    equator = 10,019 km nominal
Surface area = $5·101 \times 10^{14}$ m²
Land area = $1·49 \times 10^{14}$ m²
Ocean area = $3·61 \times 10^{14}$ m²
Volume = $1·083 \times 10^{21}$ m³
Mass = $5·976 \times 10^{24}$ kg
Mean density = 5517 kg/m³
Density at 5000 km = 11,500 kg/m³

Atmosphere

On weather charts atmospheric pressure is recorded in millibars (mb).
100 mb = 1 bar
= 750·062 standard millimetre of mercury (mm Hg)
= 100 000 Pa
The standard millimetre of mercury is based on mercury density 13,595·1 kg/m³, g = 9·806 65 m/s². Standard atmospheric pressure (1 atm) = 101,325 Pa. Density of half-saturated air at 20 °C and 760 mm Hg = 1·199 kg/m³. The density increases in proportion to increased pressure and decreases in inverse proportion to absolute temperature; at 20 °C it decreases with humidity roughly by 0·000 1 kg/m³ for each 1 per cent increase in relative humidity, and decreases with altitude roughly as follows:

Altitude (thousands of metres)	0·9	1·8	3·0	4·3	5·5
Relative density	0·9	0·8	0·7	0·6	0·5

Beaufort wind scale: 0 = calm, 5 = fresh breeze, 10 = whole gale, 12 = hurricane.
Velocity of sound in air = 1100 ft/s approx. = 34 km/s approx.

Gravity

Gravity varies with latitude, and (slightly) with altitude; equator, 9·78 m/s²; London, 9·81 m/s²; poles, 9·83 m/s². These values are due to both the Earth's attraction (due to G, the gravitational constant) and the centrifugal force due to the Earth's rotation (equivalent to about 0·03 m/s² at the equator). Standard acceleration (standard gravity) = 9·816 65 m/s², by convention; rounded equivalent = 32·1740 ft/s².

Thermometry

To convert Fahrenheit temperatures to Celsius, T °F = $\{5(T-32)/9\}$ °C
Colours of hot bodies: red, 550 to 700 °C; cherry, 900 °C; orange, 1100 °C; white, 1400 °C+.
Blood heat (normal) 98·4 °F = 36·9 °C, 10 °C = 50 °F, 15 °C = 59 °F, 20 °C = 68 °F, 25 °C = 77 °F.
The thermometer scales are based on the Kelvin thermodynamic scale of temperature which is hard to realise so that in practice the International Practical Scale of Temperature 1948 (IPST) is used. It is based on various fixed points, viz., boiling point (b.p.) of oxygen, −182·970 °C; melting (m.p.) of ice, 0 °C; b.p. water, 100 °C; b.p. sulphur, 444·600 °C; freezing point (f.p.) of silver, 960·8 °C; f.p. gold, 1063·0 °C. Interpolation between these fixed points is by defined instruments and formulae, and above 1063·0 °C temperatures are defined in terms of Planck's law of radiation.
    On the thermodynamic scale of temperature which starts from 0 K at absolute zero of temperature, m.p. ice, 0 °C, = 273·15 K and triple point of (ice, water and water vapour all in equilibrium) = 273·16 K.

Some Physical Constants (*cont.*)

Sound

Musical scale:
International concert pitch: *A* above middle *C* = 440 Hz
Natural scale: notes of octave have relative frequencies 24, 27, 30, 32, 36, 40, 45, 48
Tempered scale: 12 semitones with frequencies in equal ratios

Frequency (Hz)	*C*	*D*	*E*	*F*	*G*	*A*	*B*	*c*
Natural scale	264	297	330	352	396	440	495	528
Tempered scale	261·7	293·7	329·7	349·2	392	440	493·9	523·3

Velocity (m s^{-1}):
Water (20° C)	1484	Glass	3500–6000
Dry air (0° C)	331·46	Iron	c 5500

Magnetism

North magnetic pole	76° N, 101° W
South magnetic pole	67° S, 144° E

Earth's magnetic field at Hartland Magnetic Station, North Devon (1963):
Declination	9°41′ W
Inclination	66°38′
Horizontal intensity	14·97 A m^{-1}
Vertical intensity	34·64 A m^{-1}

Atomic physics

Avogadro's number	$6·02252 \times 10^{23}$ atoms mol^{-1}
Loschmidt's number	$2·68713 \times 10^{19}$ atoms m^{-3} at STP
Faraday's constant of electrolysis	96,487 C mol^{-1}
Charge of electron	$1·60207 \times 10^{-19}$ C
Mass of electron	$9·1085 \times 10^{-31}$ kg
Ratio of charge to mass of electron	$1·7589 \times 10^{11}$ C kg^{-1}
Planck's constant	$6·6252 \times 10^{-34}$ J s
Rydberg constant for hydrogen	10,967·758 mm^{-1}
Mass of proton	1836·12 × mass of electron
Mass of neutron	1838·6 × mass of electron
Electron volt (eV)	$1·60219 \times 10^{-19}$ J
Unified atomic mass unit	$1·66053 \times 10^{-27}$ kg

Substance	Melting point (°C)	Boiling point (°C)	Specific heat kJ kg^{-1} K^{-1}	Latent heat of fusion kJ kg^{-1}	Latent heat of vaporisation kJ kg^{-1}	Thermal conductivity W m^{-1} K^{-1} at 0°C
Alcohol	−117	78·5	2·18 (20 °C)	—	858	0·176
Aluminium	660·1	2330	0·915	402	—	240
Carbon	Sublimes	4347	0·854	—	—	1·16
Copper	1083	2582	0·394	205	—	385
Gold	1063	2660	0·130 (20 °C)	63	—	310
Helium	—	−268·9		—	25	0·139 (20 °C)
Hydrogen	−259·2	−252·8	25·1 (−253 °C)	—	452	0·170 (20 °C)
Iron	1535	2800	0·473 (20 °C)	268	—	76·2
Lead	327·3	1750	0·128 (20 °C)	25	—	35·2
Mercury	−38·87	356·58	0·134	12	272	9·00
Nitrogen	−209·9	−195·8	0·117 (−200 °C)	25	200	0·025 (20 °C)
Oxygen	−218·8	−182·970	1·47	14	214	0·025 (20 °C)
Silver	960·8	2193	0·233	105	—	418·7
Sodium	97·7	883	1·18 (0 °C)	113	—	135
Brass	c. 950	—	0·395	—	—	96–109
Glass	800–1000	—	0·50–0·67	—	—	0·42–0·84
Steel	ca 1400	—	ca. 0·448	—	—	c. 46
Water	0·000	100·00	4·1686 (20 °C)	334	2135	0·419 (10 °C)

Absolute zero temperature	= −273·16 °C		Boltzmann's constant	= $1·38042 \times 10^{-23}$ J K^{-1}
Mechanical equivalent of heat	= 4·1855 joule cal^{-1}		Stefan–Boltzmann constant	= $5·69 \times 10^{-8}$ W m^{-2} K^{-4}
			Wien's constant	= 0·00289 m K

Mathematical constants

$\pi = 3·1415927$ $\log_{10} \pi = 0·4971499$ $e = 2·7182818$ $\log_e 10 = 2·3025851$

Index